Backyard Antennas

Peter Dodd, G3LDO

Radio Society of Great Britain

Published by the Radio Society of Great Britain, Cranborne Road, Potters Bar, Herts
EN6 3JE.

First published 2000. Reprinted 2002.

ISBN 1 872309 59 3

Cover design: TYGA, Potters Bar.
Illustrations: Ray Eckersley, Roy Pettit and Bob Ryan.
Typography: Ray Eckersley, Seven Stars Publishing, Marlow.
Production: Mark Allgar.

Disclaimer
The opinions expressed in this book are those of the author, and not necessarily
those of the RSGB. While the information presented is believed to be correct, the
author, publisher and their agents cannot accept responsibility for consequences
arising from any inaccuracies or omissions.

Printed in Great Britain by Black Bear Press, Cambridge.

There is a web page for this book at: www.rsgb.org/books/extra/backyard.htm

Contents

Chapter 10: Estimating and measuring antenna performance 174

Glossary of terms 186

Appendix 193

Index 199

Preface

THE objective of this book is to provide practical amateur radio antenna designs to overcome site (usually size) restrictions. It also discusses methods of obtaining the good antenna efficiency and effectiveness from restricted site and restricted size antennas. For the purpose of this book I have defined a restricted site as one in which it is not practicable to erect a 12m high lattice tower with a multi-band three-element beam. Site size may not be the only criterion – planning restrictions also play their part.

This book is not a comprehensive book about antennas. The number of different antennas described is limited to those whose performance is well known and whose construction is relatively easy.

Chapter 1 deals with long-term HF propagation prediction because it may influence the type of antenna you may wish to erect. The limitations of your location and ways of circumventing them are also discussed.

Chapters 2 and 3 are descriptions of various HF wire antenna designs with their advantages and disadvantages. My classification of single-element antennas for HF may be regarded as unconventional. The usual method is to classify them as horizontal or vertical. I have classified these antennas as fed with transmission line or end-fed. The reason for this is that although a dipole may be regarded as a horizontal antenna it can also be used as a sloping or even a vertical antenna. Many of these antennas require an ATU and to reduce repetition ATUs are described in a separate chapter.

Chapter 4 covers the various types of ATUs that can be used, which in these days of solid-state, fixed-impedance, power amplifiers are essential to the overall efficiency of an antenna system. In the case of some end-fed antennas the ATU is described in Chapter 3 because it forms an integral part of the antenna.

If you are into plumbing then the antennas in Chapter 5 (compact loops) and Chapter 6 (small beams) will interest you.

The VHF enthusiasts are not forgotten. Chapter 7 covers antenna designs from 50 to 430MHz with some practical designs for high-gain Yagis.

Chapter 8 gives some practical advice on where to find and how to use material for antenna construction and the all-important subject of fixing the antenna to your house.

Transmission lines are described in Chapter 9. Although antenna theory has generally been avoided in this book a small amount of transmission line theory has been included to explain SWR etc.

Chapter 10 deals with estimating antenna performance and checking the performance of an antenna during or after installation.

It has to be said from the start that if you are restricted to living in semi-detached houses with 'postage-stamp' gardens, or apartments with no gardens at all, then you are not going to put out a signal as strong as someone with a large site and a six- or eight-element beam on a mast 20 or 25m high.

However, how you deal with the restrictions of a small site is a matter of attitude; for example, mobile operation has even greater space restrictions but this doesn't deter keen mobile operators. QRP operators impose even greater restrictions on themselves but enjoy the hobby.

Peter Dodd, G3LDO

Acknowledgements

Much of the material used in this book in this is taken from RSGB publications. All this material has been edited for the purposes of integration. The source of a publication is referenced at the appropriate point within the text but the scope of the referenced material is given below.

Articles

'Fitting coaxial connections', Roger Blackwell, G4PMK, *Radio Communication* May 1988.
'Balanced to unbalanced transformers', Ian White, G3SEK, *Radio Communication* December 1989.
'Taming the end-fed antenna', Alan Chester, G3CCB, *Radio Communication* September 1994.
'A remote controlled ATU', L B Uphill, G3UCE, *Radio Communication* February 1989.
'A general-purpose antenna tuning unit', M J Grierson, G3TSO, *Radio Communication* January 1987.
'An improved Z-match ATU', Louis Varney, CEng, MIEE, AIL, G5RV, *RadCom* October 1998.
'High performance long Yagis', Ian White, G3SEK, *Radio Communication* April 1987.
'A balanced line ASTU', Ted Garrott, G0OUJ, *RadCom* July/August 1998.
'Electrically tunable loop', Roberto Craighero, I1ARZ, *Radio Communication* February 1989.
'Experimental magnetic loop antenna', C R Reynolds, GW3JPT, *RadCom* February 1994.
'Skeleton slot aerials', B Sykes, *RSGB Bulletin* (forerunner of the RSGB's *RadCom*) January 1953.
'The HF skeleton slot antenna', Bill Capstick, *Radio Communication* June 1996.

Columns

Erwin David, G4LQI, has over the years provided us with a window on the rest of Europe in his column 'Eurotek' in *RadCom*. 'Eurotek' provides translations of articles from European amateur radio magazines and is the source of much useful antenna information, particularly on VHF/UHF. All the material from Erwin's columns is referenced where appropriate in the text.

For those of you who have not seen it, the column 'In Practice' in *RadCom* by Ian White, G3SEK, is written in the form of answers to readers' questions. It is very practical advice written in an informal style, but with a sound theoretical basis. Much of Ian's material is ideally suited to practical problems of backyard antenna engineering and is referenced in the text where appropriate.

'Technical Topics' by Pat Hawker, G3VA, is now an institution in *RadCom* and needs no introduction from me. The following two items from 'TT' are used in this book.

'Roof-space dual band magnetic loop', Eric Sandys, GI2FHN, February, 1993.
'The T-network antenna tuner', April 1995.

Publications

Material from the following RSGB publications has been used in the text and is referenced there where appropriate.

Practical Wire Antennas, John D Heys, G3BDQ.
The Radio Amateur's Guide to EMC, Robin Page-Jones, CEng, MIEE, G3JWI.
HF Antennas for all Locations, L A Moxon, G6XN.
The LF Experimenter's Source Book, Peter Dodd, G3LDO.
The Antenna Experimenter's Guide, 2nd edn, Peter Dodd, G3LDO.
RSGB Planning Application Booklet.

The Glossary is a slightly edited edition of the Glossary from the *ARRL Antenna Book*. It is used in this book with the permission of the ARRL.

Internet

The following material has been included with permission of the author:
'Link Coupled Antenna Tuners: A Tutorial', L B Cebik, W4RNL. URL is http://funnelweb.utcc.utc.edu/.

Addendum to first printing

THE MOXON RECTANGLE

The Moxon Rectangle antenna shown on p99 created a lot of interest due to the fact that it is simple to build, lightweight, compact and appears to perform well. It has been built by several readers who report good results.

The configuration of this antenna originated from W4RNL's website, although I devised the multiband arrangement shown in Fig 6.18. However, although this antenna works well as a single-band antenna, tests done subsequent to publication indicate that it does not appear to function as a multiband antenna as shown. This is probably due to the coupling between parasitic and driven elements being more critical than in the VK2ABQ, or the Double-D antenna shown in Fig 6.21, where a multiband configuration appears to work when tuned for optimum performance.

The original VK2ABQ antenna is a square structure – see Fig 1. The driven element and the reflector are a quarter-wavelength apart, although the tips of the elements support each other using insulators. These insulators are constructed so that the tips of the elements are 6mm (¼in) apart and, according to the original description [1], capacitive end (voltage) couples the driven element to the reflector, as opposed to the coupling that occurs on a Yagi. The gap between the tips of the elements is described as "not critical".

Multiband editions of this antenna were constructed without any known difficulty.

G6XN changed the structure from a square to a rectangle, thereby reducing the centre-section spacing of the elements from 0.25 wavelength to 0.17 wavelength, which resulted in improved gain and directivity [2].

C B Cebik, W4RNL, reduced the element spacing further to 0.14 wavelength and obtained yet more gain and improved directivity [3]. This antenna he called the *Moxon Rectangle* and is the one described on p101. The downside of this higher performance is the multibanding problem.

Tony Box, G0HAD, built a G6XN antenna back in 1993. The overall size of this structure was 6.1m × 3.8m (20ft × 12ft 6in) as recommended by G6XN; this antenna outperformed his previous commercial mini beam. I used a computer model (EZNEC) to check these dimensions, and this produced the dimensions 6.92m × 3.8m (22ft 10in × 12ft 6in). The reason for this

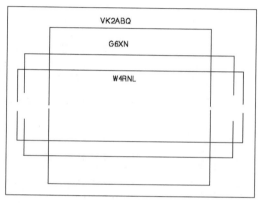

Fig 1. The original VK2ABQ antenna structure compared with the G6XN and the W4RNL. The G6XN has a centre-section spacing of the elements of around 0.17 wavelength, while the W4RNL has element spacing further reduced to 0.14 wavelength

discrepancy is that G6XN used loops in the elements at the element support points. This makes for a more compact antenna but increases the mechanical complexity slightly.

Shown below are the formulae to calculate dimensions for the G6XN antenna (without loops at the element support points).

$$\text{Reflector: } \frac{155}{f} = \text{length(m)}$$

$$\text{Driven element: } \frac{149.4}{f} = \text{length(m)}$$

$$\text{Reflector: } \frac{508}{f} = \text{length(ft)}$$

$$\text{Driven element: } \frac{490}{f} = \text{length(ft)}$$

The size of the antenna, using dimensions A and E from Fig 6.18, can be found by:

$$A(m) = \frac{98.26}{f}$$

$$E(m) = \frac{53.96}{f}$$

$$A(ft) = \frac{322}{f}$$

$$E(ft) = \frac{177}{f}$$

G0HAD found by experiment that the gaps between the tips of the elements needed to be larger than published [2], being 560mm (22in) for 20m, 380mm (15in) for 15m and 250mm (10in) for 10m (values for C in Fig 6.18). This is confirmed by computer modelling, which shows an improvement in the front-to-back ratio when these gaps are increased.

The formula to calculate the length of each support (cane or glassfibre rod) structure required is:

$$\frac{56.09}{f} = \text{length of diagonal(m)}$$

$$\frac{184}{f} = \text{length of diagonal(ft)}$$

The units in feet are a decimal number. To convert 12.5ft to feet and inches multiply the part after the decimal by 12, eg $0.5 \times 12 = 6$ so this is 12ft 6in.

PARALLEL DIPOLES

If you wish to operate on several of the HF bands and you don't have an ATU then parallel dipoles may be the answer. An example of such an antenna is described on pp20 and 21.

However, if more than three parallel dipoles are used with the construction method shown in Fig 2.8, the structure becomes complicated and difficult to manage.

Stewart, GM4UTP, uses a parallel-dipole design that tidies up all the wires of the multiple dipole. This arrangement uses the lowest-frequency dipole to support the higher-frequency dipoles using spacing insulators made from 11mm plastic electrical conduit. The construction is shown in Fig 2.

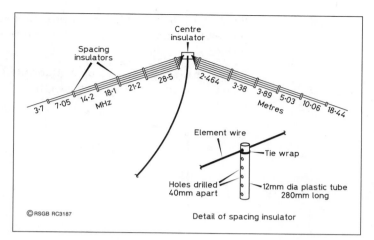

The antenna is configured as an inverted-V with the weight of the centre insulator and the 1:1 balun mounted on a 10m high aluminium scaffold pole. Low centre-band SWRs are possible if some time is spent tuning each dipole. This can be achieved by arranging the ends of the elements so that they are clear of their support insulators by about 200mm. The dipole lengths can be reduced or increased by folding back the end and securing with plastic tape.

The resonance of these dipoles can be interactive – when you adjust one it affects the resonance of the other so be prepared to have to re-resonate elements.

A similar arrangement is described by K0GPD [4]. In this design all the spacer insulators are made the same length and a nylon cord is run from the end of the highest-frequency dipole to the end of the multiwire sections of the antenna to improve mechanical stability.

Fig 2. The GM4UTP multiband antenna. The detail shows the larger spacers to accommodate six wires. The outer spacers are progressively shorter with holes drilled for five, four, three and two wires respectively. The 24MHz dipole is not shown but the lengths are 2.84m (9ft 4in)

REFERENCES

[1] 'VK2ABQ Antenna', Fred Caton, VK2ABQ, *Electronics Australia* October 1973.
[2] *HF Antennas for all Locations*, L A Moxon, G6XN, RSGB.
[3] http://www.cebik.com/. Note that this site replaces that shown in the reference on p107.
[4] 'A great 10 through 40 portable antenna', Edward L Henry, K0GPD, *The ARRL Compendium*, Vol 1, ARRL.

GENERAL ERRATA

Heading to Table 4, p63. 'G3OLB' should be 'G0LMJ'.

References, p67. 'G0OUJ' should be 'G0LMJ'.

Table 7.1, p115. The dimensions are for one side of the quad rather than the whole element length as shown in the UHF 'circular' quad in Fig 7.16 on the same page.

Fig 7.22, p120. This drawing implies that Yagis 2 and 4 are fed 180° out of phase with Yagis 1 and 3. The driven elements of all Yagis must be fed in phase.

Fig 9.7, p151. The first value of transmission loss should be 0.5dB rather than 0.05 as shown. '10m' in the caption should read '30m'.

1 Overcoming the limitations

I N this chapter we will look at the problems you can face when operating an amateur radio station from a location that is far from ideal. Operating an amateur radio station from a backyard type of location imposes many limitations that can be best overcome when you understand them. These limitations are:

- Your location and its restrictions
- Planning restrictions and property covenants
- Your available operating times

TYPES OF BACKYARD LOCATIONS

A number of different types of restricted locations will now be considered, with possible solutions to erecting a suitable antenna. Where a solution is general a reference will be made to suitable antennas described in following chapters. If the solution is specific then it will be described under the location heading. A detached house with plenty of space has not been considered because it falls outside the category of a 'backyard' location.

Rather than describing a 'dwelling' as a location for an antenna, I have considered the type of location. For example, a long narrow garden could be associated with older terraced houses or two-storey flats where the gardens are partitioned off into thin strips. Likewise, a suitable loft may be found in any house, bungalow or multi-storey flat.

A map of your house and the garden can be useful when trying to consider which antenna or antennas you use. Mark out the size and location of the house and any trees. It is useful to make the drawing on graph or quadrille paper with the squares being related to whatever units of measurement you are comfortable with.

Overhead AC supply cables are rare in backyard antenna locations. However, if you are unfortunate enough to have these obstructions then it is very important that antennas are positioned so that they cannot possibly come in contact with them.

Wire antennas and dipoles can be bent into all sorts of shapes. Although this may affect the resonant frequency of a resonant antenna (such as a dipole) it will not seriously affect the performance provided the bends are not too extreme.

Long narrow garden

For the HF bands any of the wire antennas described in Chapters 2 and 3 are suitable. Most of these houses have a chimney so a short mast, fixed using a chimney bracket as described in Chapter 8, will make a good support of one end. A length of scaffolding pole can be used at the opposite end, although a small version of the self-supporting fold-over mast, also described in Chapter 8, would be suitable. The gardens of these types of dwelling are usually too narrow for a guyed mast. VHF/UHF antennas can be fixed to the chimney or to the wall on a small mast (but check the condition of the brickwork if the house is old) as described in Chapter 8.

Small garden

A small garden associated with either a semi-detached house or bungalow is usually rectangular. It may be large enough to erect a fold-over mast as shown in Chapter 8 and fit a small HF beam with a rotator. If your interest is VHF or UHF then a fold-over mast will support a fairly ambitious VHF/UHF DX antenna; otherwise a more modest array can be fixed to a chimney or wall-mounting bracket.

An HF wire antenna will probably have to bent in more than one place. If the dwelling has a chimney then it should be pressed into service as an antenna support as described in Chapter 8.

If any of the HF antennas described cannot be erected then consider the large multi-band delta loop described in Chapter 5. This type of antenna works very well as a transmitting antenna but is prone to electrical interference. In this case the antenna can be used with a receiver loop antenna located some distance from the house.

Lofts

Most dwellings in the UK have a loft. Normally the loft is an unused part of the house and is used for storing junk. All modern houses have a layer of roofing felt under the roofing tiles and the area is relatively dry and weatherproof. The advantage of loft antennas is that they do not need weatherproofing. In addition there are numerous wooden beams that can be used to support the antenna using cheap TV antenna fittings.

The disadvantage is that they may be located close to electrical wiring with the possibility of mutual interference. There may be another disadvantage.

I once lived in an old town house in Harrogate that was in the centre of a row. It had no garden but it had four floors so the roof was quite high. Not long after moving in I ventured into the loft, which was festooned with black cobwebs, and was overjoyed to find that there was no wall in the loft between my house and my neighbours either side. There was enough room up there for a real antenna farm. I started, modestly enough, with a 14MHz dipole. I fired up the rig expecting to work the world and found my antenna to be almost useless. I felt that there must be some fault with the construction and replaced the dipole and the feeder. The antenna performance was still just as poor. I then draped the antenna out through the top bedroom window and its performance improved dramatically.

I am not sure why the antenna did not work inside the loft space. The tiles on this old house were of Welsh slate and I felt that this might have been the problem.

I then constructed a ground-plane antenna as shown in Chapter 3 and had it fixed to outside to the chimney (using a suitable clamp as described in Chapter 8) by a television antenna erection company. This antenna performed very well on the 14MHz band.

Nevertheless, I have used a loft antenna in a modern house with moderate success, which implies the roofing material does play a part in antenna effectiveness with this type of installation.

I would suggest that anyone contemplating an indoor or loft antenna make an electrically short loaded antenna (Chapter 3) or a loop (Chapter 5) and try the antenna inside and outside the building. Note any changes in performance on transmit and the signal-to-noise ratio on receive in these different locations. This test is particularly important for VHF/UHF, where the roofing material attenuation may be more significant than on HF.

A HF multi-band loop, designed specifically for lofts, is described in Chapter 5.

The high-rise apartment

The high-rise apartment block is usually constructed using a steel girder frame, which can have a significant effect on antenna performance. If the apartment has a large balcony and/or you have access to the roof the high-rise apartment can be an effective location for an antenna.

I lived in such an apartment in the Netherlands some years ago and initially felt that amateur radio was not possible. The apartment had three windows and a door, which led on to a small balcony, but there was no access to the roof. The usual solution for this type of location is to use a small loaded vertical, such as a mobile antenna, fed against the metalwork of the balcony railings.

My eventual solution was to use a dipole for 14MHz. The centre of the dipole was located at the centre window. The ends of the dipole were connected to the window frame on one side and to the balcony at the other. The centre of the dipole was held away from the wall of the apartment using a cane as shown in Fig 1.1.

My apartment was located on the fifth floor, about 18m high, so this arrangement really worked well as a DX antenna. The whole metal structure of the apartment block worked as a massive reflector for the dipole so, although it only radiated in one direction, it was better to get out well in one direction than not at all.

This antenna could have been easily made into an upper HF multi-band doublet as described in Chapter 2. If you can obtain access to the roof then there are greater possibilities. The Commupole antenna, described in Chapter 2, is a Dutch solution to feeding a multi-band antenna located on the roof of an apartment block.

I have heard some really good DX signals from radio amateurs using a beam antenna on the roof of a high-rise apartment, particularly from Japan.

When working on antenna or antenna support systems on a high-rise block balcony or rooftop, pay attention to safety details. Not only should you not put yourself in danger; if you drop the smallest of tools or antenna fittings they can have a dangerous velocity by the time they reach the ground. Tie all tools and fittings loosely together with strong thin nylon cord, so that movement is not impeded but to ensure they don't fall far if dropped.

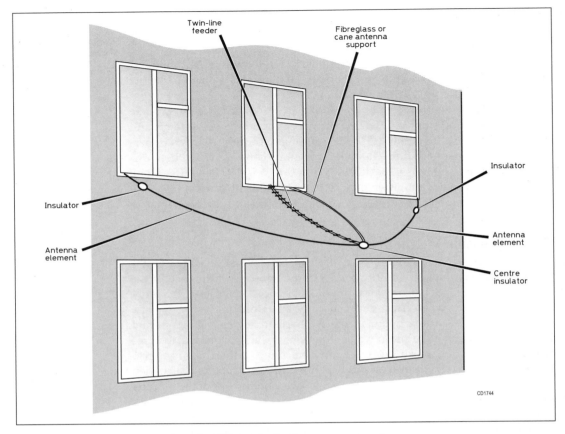

Labels on figure:
- Twin-line feeder
- Fibreglass or cane antenna support
- Insulator
- Insulator
- Antenna element
- Antenna element
- Centre insulator
- CD1744

Fig 1.1. Construction of a multi-band dipole for the apartment dweller

Locations with restrictive covenants

Many houses, flats and apartments now have covenants imposed on them by their deeds or tenancies which prohibit the fixing of antennas of any kind to the structure of the building or in the garden. The first thing to do is to find out if such covenants are legally enforceable. If they are, don't give up – there are a few tricks that can be used to circumvent the situation.

Firstly, find out what is allowed. Are you allowed a flagpole? Are you allowed trees? For HF you can make either of these items into a vertical antenna as described in Chapter 3.

If you have an existing tree or similar support then an end-fed antenna (Chapter 3) made from 1.5mm enamelled copper wire is almost invisible. Instead of using insulators use lightweight strimmer cord, which is clear and has excellent insulating properties, so a noticeable insulator is not required. If you do not have an additional support other than the building then the large delta loop (Chapter 5), constructed from 1.5mm wire and supported by strimmer cord, may be a solution. You could also use lightweight nylon cord as a support but the insulating properties are not as good as strimmer cord. However, clear nylon toothbrush handles make excellent insulators, even at LF where the voltages on a transmitting antenna are very high.

A loft antenna is the ultimate invisible antenna.

PLANNING PERMISSION

Regulations governing the erection of antennas vary enormously from country to country. In this country the best advice is contained in a booklet from the RSGB [1]. The following is given as a very rough guide and should not be regarded in any way as being definitive [2].

Basically, in town and country planning we have to consider whether the combined structure of antenna and support is such that its erection is a 'building operation'. Unfortunately 'building' has a very wide definition as 'any structure or erection' but we have some judicial interpretation which limits this definition as otherwise every piece of wire or cord may be a 'building'. The judicial interpretation appears to indicate that there must be something sufficiently substantial or permanent in nature to affect the physical character of the house and garden.

By letter (1969) to the RSGB, the Minister of Housing & Local Government agreed that an antenna system similar to a domestic TV or FM broadcast antenna does not require planning permission because it does not materially affect the external appearance of the building. Put another way, it is expected to be found on most houses and is part of the general residential scene. It is doubtful whether we are entitled to use this pronouncement where UHF TV antennas are in use; however, the amateur antenna is not unlike a multi-element VHF FM Yagi. This is just an example of the multitude of uncertainties with which we are faced. Nevertheless the 'local type' of TV antenna would always be a useful support for a wire antenna attached to a tree at the other end. One cannot imagine any planning authority seriously suggesting that a long wire tied to the chimney at one end and a tree at the other requires planning permission. It cannot be a 'building' even within the very wide definition indicated above.

Another Court decision on the definition of 'building' is that the subject must be built of constructed things of substantial size. It is thought that a trap or balun in a long wire or wire dipole could in no way be described as 'of substantial size'.

It should be explained that there are vast areas of uncertainty simply because antennas have not been the subject of many Court decisions, presumably because no amateur feels that it is worth spending a considerable sum in pursuing an appeal through the Courts. The Planning Appeal Decisions of the Department of the Environment are of great interest and afford some guidance but they do not set binding precedents in the same way as do Appeal Court Decisions on points of law.

Whether in any given circumstance planning permission is required is a point of law; whether when planning permission is necessary it ought to be granted on the merits of the application is not a point of law.

If you are considering erecting a mast and/or an antenna, should you automatically apply for planning permission or just put the antenna up and apply for planning permission if some one complains to the local council?

There are pros and cons for either choice of action. When you apply for planning permission for a mast and antenna it focuses people's minds on the proposed structure and gives them an opportunity to oppose it. You can also be unfortunate enough to have a local busybody who orchestrates action against your application. On the other hand, when you do get planning permission then there is nothing anyone can do in the future to get you to remove the installation.

My approach is to put up a small antenna, such as a wire dipole, and at some later stage put up larger ones – a process of gradual encroachment. This ploy worked for me for over 35 years at many different locations without any problems. The disadvantage of this method is that a new neighbour may arrive who complains about your antenna. Then you have to go through the whole planning procedure. This happened to me at this present location.

There is a time factor. If the antenna has been up for a given length of time (at the time of writing over four years) then planning permission is not required; however, you will have to prove that the planning requirement has timed out. Other than getting some friendly neighbour to write a letter confirming the rough date the antenna was installed some documentary evidence is required. The best that I can suggest is to take a photo of the antenna installation using one of these cameras that prints out the time and date the photo was taken. My antenna had been up more than four years but I was unable to prove it.

My experience of planning applications is that if you have a fold-over mast, and you only propose to raise the antenna at certain times, then the chances of success of the planning application is much improved. Some commercial towers are unsuitable for regular raising and lowering because of the time and effort required and the wear on the cables. The home-made fold-over masts, described in Chapter 8, are more suitable for this purpose. I now have planning permission for a counter-weighted fold-over mast, which I can raise or lower in 10 seconds.

It is very important that you DO NOT invest in expensive antennas and towers until the planning issue has been resolved.

OPERATING TIMES

A further consideration (or even perhaps the primary consideration) is your life style and main interest within amateur radio.

Each of the HF bands have different characteristics, depending on sunspot activity, season and time of the day. If you work for a living and can only operate in the evenings or weekends then the upper HF bands may have limited value and wider multi-band operation is often necessary. Also, there are often contests on at weekends on the main frequency bands but not the WARC bands. If you can only operate during weekends then this may influence which bands you use. You cannot create a contest-grade station from a backyard location but you can still have fun participating if that is your interest.

Retirement gives the opportunity for operating at any time. Some operators in this category concentrate on a single band using a beam antenna.

It is often the case that the situation creates the interest – a persistent case of TVI or BCI causes the operator to try QRP operation, or the difficulty in finding space for an HF antenna causes the operator to discover VHF/UHF satellite operation. You can even get involved in moonbounce operating from a backyard site on the 70cm band, but this is a specialised mode – not to be undertaken lightly.

SITING AN ANTENNA
Minimising interference on receive

The following advice is from *The Radio Amateurs's Guide to EMC* [1].

Interference reaches the receiver either by direct radiation or by a combination of conduction and radiation. This means that interference generated at any particular location is likely to travel at least part of the way by a path involving a conductor of some sort. As previously discussed, signals can travel considerable distances using electrical wiring as a transmission line. In effect the electromagnetic energy is propagated between the wire and earth, though the situation is so indeterminate that it would be unrewarding to attempt to analyse it in any depth. Depending on the conditions, the wiring will also radiate energy; in this aspect the wire usually acts as a grounded antenna. In engineering terms the situation is an untidy collection of unknown factors, but so far as the present problem is concerned the message is simple. Keep your receiving antennas as far away as possible from house wiring.

The rules for minimising interference are the same as for reducing breakthrough and the reasons are much the same. Good receiving antennas for the HF bands should, wherever possible, be:

(a) horizontally polarised, as interference radiated from house wiring is predominantly vertically polarised;

(b) balanced, because just as poorly balanced antennas give rise to radiation from feeders, they will also allow signals to be picked up by the feeders; and

(c) compact, so that neither end comes close to house wiring.

If it is not possible to locate the antenna away from electrical wiring and interference is a problem, then the compact resonant loop described in Chapter 5 gives an improved performance on receive in the presence of electrical noise.

Minimising the EMC problems caused by a transmitting antenna

Electrical wiring, such as mains supply, telephone or other utilities, will clutter the vicinity of any amateur station. The general plumbing and central heating system can also cause an unpredictable effect to nearby antennas. A poorly sited antenna will couple RF into the electrical wiring, causing EMC problems.

Try not to be persuaded by social pressures into using low, poorly sited antennas. This can cause breakthrough problems that sour local relations far more than fears of obtrusive antennas might have done. It may be possible to improve transmitter antenna effectiveness without substantially increasing the visual impact of the antenna. An example of a real situation, where increasing the transmitting antenna effectiveness also cured a TVI problem, is described below.

Improving transmitting antenna effectiveness

A recently licensed acquaintance decided to put up a simple horizontal dipole so that he could make a start. He connected the one end of the dipole to

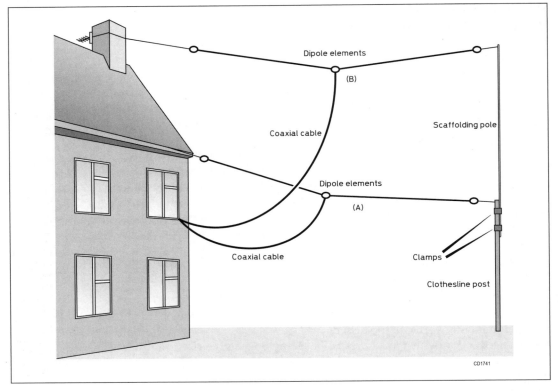

Dipole elements
(B)
Coaxial cable
Scaffolding pole
Dipole elements
(A)
Coaxial cable
Clamps
Clothesline post
CD1741

Fig 1.2. Antenna A shows a quick-fix installation for a 21MHz dipole. With the minimal effort the dipole height can be raised substantially (B). See Chapter 8 for details of a suitable clamp for extending the height of the mast

the eaves of the house and the other to an extension of the washing line post at the bottom of the small garden as shown in Fig 1.2.

This gave the antenna an average height of around 4m (15ft). The antenna performed to his satisfaction with good reports from all over Europe, the Middle East, North Africa and the USA; and soon he was working towards a DXCC. However, the signals from greater distances were proving more difficult because they were weak and because of the QRM from the very strong nearby European stations. He also experienced interference from domestic electrical devices and caused interference to his neighbour's bedroom television.

I suggested fixing one end of the dipole to the chimney and the other end to a taller pole at the bottom of the garden, raising the average height to, say, 8m (23ft) – see Fig 1.2.

The reason for this suggested increase in height is to lower the angle of radiation. The interaction of the antenna with ground at different heights above ground is described in Chapter 10. The improvement in performance achieved by repositioning the dipole is illustrated in the computer model shown in Fig 1.3.

In the 'HF propagation' section that follows, you can see that the long-distance signals arrive at the antenna at an angle of less than 20°. From Fig 1.3 it would seem that the modest increase in height would give an increase in gain to DX stations of 2dB while at the same time reducing the short-skip signals levels by the same amount.

HF PROPAGATION

If you are an HF operator then a basic knowledge of HF propagation pays dividends. Very basic HF propagation has been included here because conditions on the upper HF bands are very much affected by the activity in the Sun. This activity has, over the years, followed a predictable pattern and should be considered when planning which antenna to use.

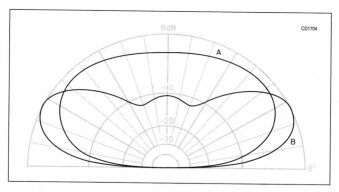

Fig 1.3. Elevation patterns for two dipoles at different heights above the ground as shown in Fig 1.2. The pattern for dipole A gives more gain in the direction of the high-angle signals shown in Fig 1.4 and less gain for low-angle DX signals. Dipole B gives at least 2dB increase in gain for DX signals, while at the same time giving 6 to 8dB reduction in short-skip signals

All signals outside of ground range are propagated over large distances by being refracted via ionised layers of the ionosphere. The most important of these layers is the outer one, known as the *F layer*. This layer, located around 300 to 400km high, is responsible for most of the long-distance HF communications.

When a signal is transmitted over a certain path there is a maximum frequency which can be used. As the transmission frequency is increased the signal penetrates further into the ionospheric layers until it passes straight through, as shown in Fig 1.4. The frequency at which communications just start to fail is known as the *MUF* (maximum usable frequency).

The density of the ionosphere, and hence the MUF, depends on the amount of ultra-violet radiation being received from the Sun. This radiation is greater during periods when sunspots are visible on the latter. The areas of the sunspots vary and have cyclical variation with a period of about 11 years as shown in Fig 1.5.

At one time solar activity was measured by a complex method of measuring the 'sunspot number'. A more reliable method has been devised by measuring the level of solar noise. This is normally measured at 2800MHz (a wavelength of 10.7cm) and is called the *solar flux*. It is closely related to the daily sunspot number.

At the low point of the cycle, the high-frequency bands above 20MHz or so may not support ionospheric refraction, whereas at the peak of the cycle frequencies at 50MHz and higher may be propagated.

A more representative (but still simplified diagram) of the ionosphere, see Fig 1.6, shows the ionosphere to be far more complex than shown in Fig 1.1. These layers are designated 'D', 'E', 'F1' and 'F2'.

The D layer is the lowest of the layers of the ionosphere. It is ineffective in bending HF signals back to the Earth and only attenuates signals passing through it. This attenuation is low at the higher HF frequencies but very high at the lower HF frequencies. At night the D layer disappears; this explains why the lower HF frequencies give the best propagation at night.

The role of the E layer is more complex; it partly absorbs and partly propagates radio signals.

These lower-level ionised layers mean there is a lower limit to the range of frequencies that allow radio propagation between two distant locations. The point where the signal becomes unreadable is known as the *lowest usable frequency* (LUF). The LUF increases in periods of high solar activity because

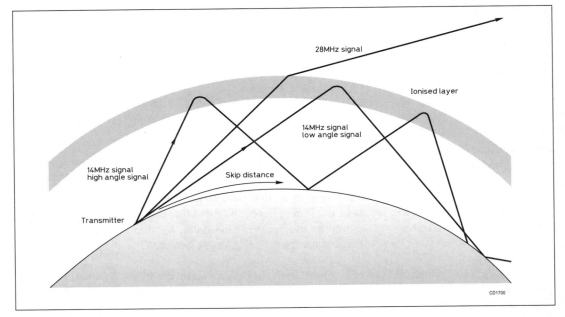

28MHz signal

Ionised layer

14MHz signal
low angle signal

14MHz signal
high angle signal

Skip distance

Transmitter

CD1700

Fig 1.4. A very simpli-
fied diagram of the
ionosphere and radio
propagation. Signals
on 14MHz radiated
from a transmitter are
propagated by refrac-
tion from the F layer.
In practice the signal
may make several
skips before arriving at
a distant receiver. The
28MHz signals are
higher in frequency
than the MUF and pass
through the ionised
layer

increased radiation from the Sun increases the D layer ionisation and hence its absorption. Sometimes the LUF is higher than the MUF; under these circumstances there is no propagation at all and the band(s) are dead.

In general higher frequencies give the best results. This is because the effect of attenuation by the D layer is reduced. Although signals may pass through the D layer they still suffer some attenuation as already mentioned. As losses are incurred at each reflection hop, either at the ionosphere or at the Earth, the minimum number of reflection hops is desirable.

The best time to contact DX stations on the other side of the world is when the D layer is non-existent or relatively weak and the F layer is dense enough, see Fig 1.6, to sustain radio propagation. This phenomenon nor-mally occurs around sunrise and several hours after, and in the evening, depending on the solar flux and the frequency in use. If you are interested in this type of DX operation it is useful to know the paths on which this propagation occurs at your location. An example of this twilight grey-line path is shown in Fig 1.7.

The angle at which the signal leaves the antenna and travels towards the ionosphere is defined as the *angle of radiation*, the angle between the main lobe of the signal and the ground. The low-angle signals shown in Fig 1.4 travel much further in a single hop than the high-angle ones. Even a rela-tively small increase in the angle of radiation can considerably reduce the distance covered in one hop. The maximum distance, which can generally be achieved using reflection from the F layer, is considered to be 5000km. This is reduced to just 1000km if the angle of radiation is 20°. The angle of radiation depends on where the antenna is placed and how it is orientated.

Translating basic propagation forecasts

Although solar flux and sunspot activity may be used to predict the HF bands you might use, the short-term conditions are much more complex.

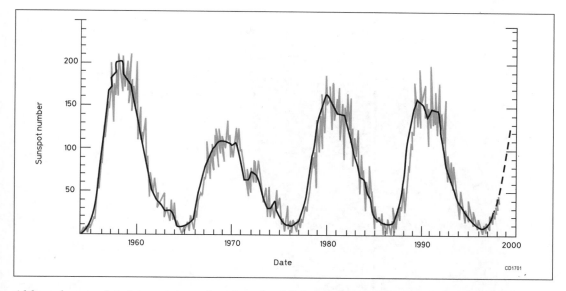

Although not related to antenna planning, the following simplified G3ENI [4] method of translating basic propagation forecasts has been included to complete the picture.

Amateurs who have been active for many years over several sunspot cycles may develop an instinct for judging band conditions. Routine checking of DX broadcasting stations on adjacent bands is often helpful, as are the 28MHz worldwide and 14MHz sequential beacons. However, it is possible to carry out basic forecasting oneself to supplement and update the propagation information given during the GB2RS Sunday news bulletins. Ignoring the multiplicity of solar events which cause variations in the ionosphere,

Fig 1.5. Sunspot cycles since 1959. The day-to-day numbers of sunspot activity vary widely. In order to view the trends the data is averaged over a month (shown in the grey lines) or smoothed over a wider period (shown by the black line). The smoothed data enables us to make predictions (shown with a dashed line), which are useful when planning HF and 50MHz antenna installations

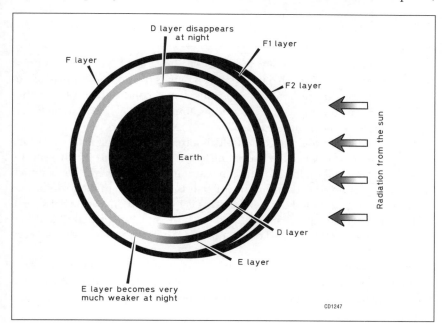

Fig 1.6. Simplified view of the layers of the ionosphere over the period of a day. Although the F layer remains intact at night its density decreases and the MUF may only allow propagation on the 1.8 or 3.5MHz bands

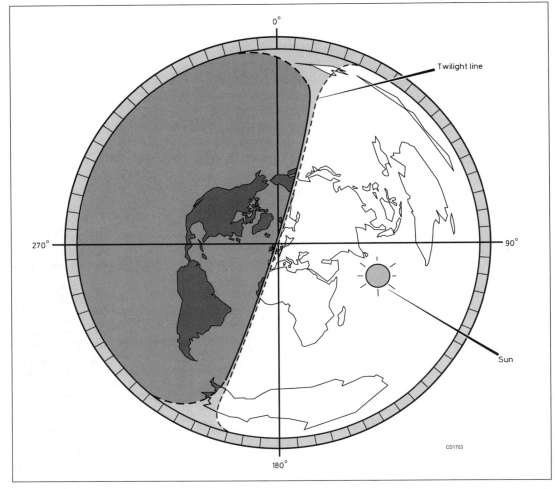

0°

Twilight line

270°

90°

Sun

CD1703

180°

Fig 1.7. Great-circle map (showing direction and range from the UK) of the world with the grey-line path to New Zealand and Australia for 0800UTC, mid February 1999

we need to consider two main items. First, the 'solar flux' which is noise measured on 2800MHz each day and which ranges from a minimum of about 66 units to a maximum of about 300 units. Good conditions on the higher HF bands require a high flux. Second, 'geomagnetic activity', which acts against the benefits of high flux.

At times the Earth's magnetic field is affected by solar activity. These geomagnetic disturbances often result from bombardment of low-energy particles from the Sun. In turn this can result in an ionospheric storm which can disrupt communications on the HF bands. It is given in the form of two indices. The first is called the *K index*. This is measured on a scale between 0 and 9 where 0 is the quietest and 9 indicates the most disturbed. It is based on values measured at several points around the Earth and is updated every three hours.

Another index called the *A index* is also available. This can vary between 0 and 400. However, the A index is in a 24-hour form and is therefore less immediate than the K index. A conversion between the two indices is given in Fig 1.8.

This diagram shows, in approximate terms, the relationship between solar flux and geomagnetic activity to determine expected propagation conditions. On the chart, solar flux is plotted vertically. The geomagnetic index is shown horizontally with the two scales: the K scale is based on readings taken eight times a day, each covering the previous three hours. The A scale is based on the eight K values for the previous day. The intersection of the flux and geomagnetic activity values determines the expected conditions, divided into eight zones as given in the caption.

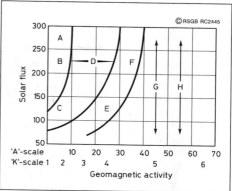

Fig 1.8. Chart relating to solar flux and geomagnetic activity to likely band conditions as published by G3ENI in the *TVARTS Newsletter*. Zone A: Above normal 50MHz open, 21 to 28MHz open up to 24 hours. Zone B: Above normal, 21 to 28MHz open up to 24 hours. Zone C: 21 to 28MHz alive. Zone D: Normal conditions. Zone E: Below normal, unsettled. Zone F: Below normal, disturbed. Zone G: Disturbed, sub-storm level, auroras may form. Zone H: Storm level, auroras

The Sunspot Index Data Centre in Brussels now prepares the numbers from information supplied by a number of observatories. They appear in DX propagation information available from a wide variety of sources, including the RSGB. The 12-month smoothed sunspot number correlates quite closely with the prevailing HF radio propagation conditions. The latest flux, geomagnetic level and other information can be obtained from the US National Bureau of Standards station WWV which provides these at 18 minutes past each hour simultaneously on 2.5, 5, 10, 15 and 20MHz. A more immediate source of sunspot data is on the Internet, and is given in the Appendix.

REFERENCES

[1] *Planning Application Booklet*, free to RSGB members.
[2] Bob Price, G4BSO, quoted in *HF Antennas for all Locations*, L A Moxon, G6XN.
[3] *The Radio Amateurs's Guide to EMC*, Robin Page-Jones, G3JWI, RSGB, 1992.
[4] 'Technical Topics', *Radio Communication* April 1992, quoting John Pegler, G3ENI, in the monthly newsletter of the Thames Valley Amateur Radio Transmitters Society.

2 Centre-fed antennas for HF

THE RESONANT DIPOLE

Of all antennas the half-wave dipole is the most sure-fire, uncomplicated one that you can make. In its basic form it is essentially a single-band, half-wave, balanced antenna, normally fed in the centre with coaxial cable. The current and voltage in one half of the dipole is matched by those values in the opposite half about the centre feed point – see Fig 2.1. The half-wave dipole will also present a low feed impedance on the third harmonic so a 7MHz dipole will operate on 21MHz, also shown in Fig 2.1. Dipole lengths for each band are given in Table A.1 in the Appendix.

In most cases the dipole is better than 95% efficient and because it has a low-impedance feed point it can be connected the transceiver via a length of 50Ω coaxial cable without the need of an ATU. The elements can be bent, within reason, to accommodate space restrictions.

A practical dipole installation with suggestions for optimising performance is shown in Fig 1.2, Chapter 1.

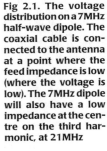

Fig 2.1. The voltage distribution on a 7MHz half-wave dipole. The coaxial cable is connected to the antenna at a point where the feed impedance is low (where the voltage is low). The 7MHz dipole will also have a low impedance at the centre on the third harmonic, at 21MHz

There are various methods of connecting the coaxial cable to the antenna – two of these are shown in Fig 2.2. Both these arrangements take the strain of the cable away from the connections. Also, having the ends of the cable facing downwards assists in preventing water entering the cable. The coaxial braiding and centre can be connected to the elements using terminal blocks. Cover these connections with grease to prevent corrosion.

The weight of the cable can be significant. Unless there is a good reason for using heavy cable, ie because you are running high power, it is best to use a lightweight cable such as RG-58 – see Chapter 9.

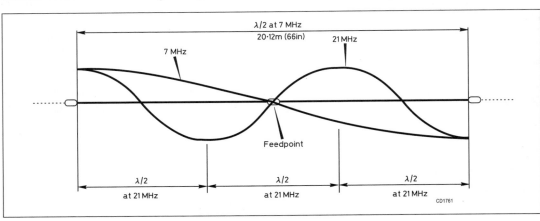

λ/2 at 7 MHz
20·12m (66in)

7 MHz

21 MHz

Feedpoint

λ/2 at 21 MHz   λ/2 at 21 MHz   λ/2 at 21 MHz

CD1761

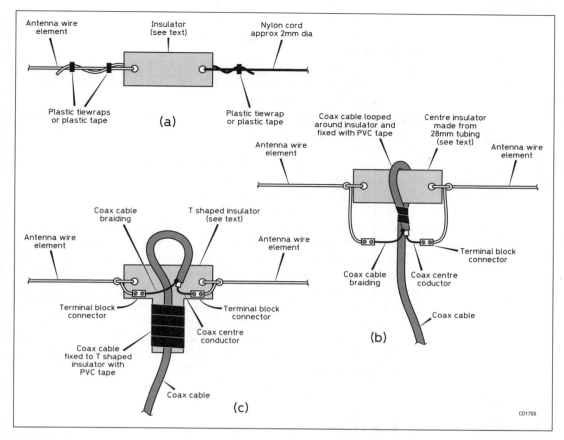

The dipole can be supported by 2mm or 3mm nylon rope with 'dogbone' or home-made insulators at the ends of the elements. The method of connecting the antenna element to the insulator, shown in Fig 2.2, allows the dipole element length to be adjusted for minimum SWR.

DO NOT use egg insulators and wire as element end supports – the end capacitance of such an arrangement will cause some very unpredictable results; something I found out the hard way.

The dipole is described as a half-wavelength antenna. In practice the dipole length is slightly shorter than half a wavelength because of 'end effect'. A true wavelength on 7.02MHz is 42.7m and a half-wave 21.35m. A half-wave dipole for the same frequency will be 20.78m (68ft 2in).

Dipole dimensions for each amateur band are shown in Table A.1 in the Appendix, where the wire lengths have been calculated using EZNEC and assume the use of 2mm diameter wire and an antenna height of 10m (33ft).

Most antenna books use the formula $143/f$ (MHz) = L (metres) or $468/f$ (MHz) = L (feet). This gives a close enough approximation on the higher frequency bands but may be a bit short for the lower bands. For example, the formula gives a dipole length of 40.6m for 3.52MHz while EZNEC calculates a length of 41.42m for the same frequency. Remember these lengths are total lengths and the wire has to be cut in half at the centre to connect the coaxial cable.

Fig 2.2. (a) A convenient arrangement for constructing a dipole so that the element lengths can be adjusted. Make the element longer than shown in Table A.1 and the excess can be taped back along the element. (b) Method of connecting coaxial cable to the centre of the dipole using a short length of tubing or a dog-bone insulator. (c) Method of connecting coaxial cable to the centre of a dipole using a specially constructed T-insulator

15

You also need to be aware that around 160mm (6in) at each end of each half of the dipole elements is required to connect them to the centre insulator and the end insulator.

The 80 and 160m dipoles are quite long and should be made of hard-drawn copper wire to reduce stretching and sagging due to the weight of the antenna and the coaxial cable.

The feed-point impedance of a dipole at resonance can vary either side of the nominal 75Ω, depending on height above ground, the proximity of buildings and any electromagnetic obstacles, together with any bends or 'dog-legs' in the wire. As a result an SWR of 1:1 is not always possible when the antenna is fed with 50Ω coaxial cable.

Because the dipole is a balanced symmetrical antenna, it should ideally be fed with balanced two-wire feeder. However, because almost all transmitters use a 50Ω coaxial-line antenna socket, coaxial cable is almost universally used to feed the dipole antenna. Connecting unbalanced coaxial cable to a balanced antenna does not normally affect the performance of the antenna provided the unbalanced current (antenna current) on the coaxial line is kept to a minimum. This can be done by making sure the coaxial line is not a multiple of an electrical quarter wavelength (see Chapter 9) and that it comes away from the antenna element at as close to 90° as possible.

Antenna currents on the line, which can cause the line to radiate (and cause TVI or BCI), should not be confused with SWR. A high SWR on transmission line does not cause it to radiate. A balun can also be used to reduce these antenna currents – see Chapter 9.

THE VERTICAL DIPOLE

The dipole antenna requires two supports and this may be a problem at some locations. The solution may be to mount the antenna vertically as shown in Fig 2.3. If the antenna is for the lower HF bands then it may finish up as a sloping dipole because of its length.

THE GROUND-PLANE ANTENNA

When a dipole is mounted vertically it has become common practice to call the top element of the antenna a *vertical* and the lower one a *counterpoise*. The terminology is derived from an antenna that was once quite popular called the *ground plane*. This antenna comprises a vertical element with a counterpoise made from four wires called *radials* as shown in Fig 2.4. The radials are made to slope down from the feed point although the angle is not critical. If the radials are at 90° to the vertical element the feed impedance is around 30Ω; with the radials sloping down at around 45° the feed impedance is around 45 to 55Ω (depending on height), which is a good match for coaxial cable.

The vertically orientated antenna is often cited as having a good low angle of radiation. From the graphic data obtained from EZNEC, see Fig 2.5, this appears to be true. The elevation plot shows a ground-plane antenna which has a feed point at only 0.2 wavelengths above the ground, which

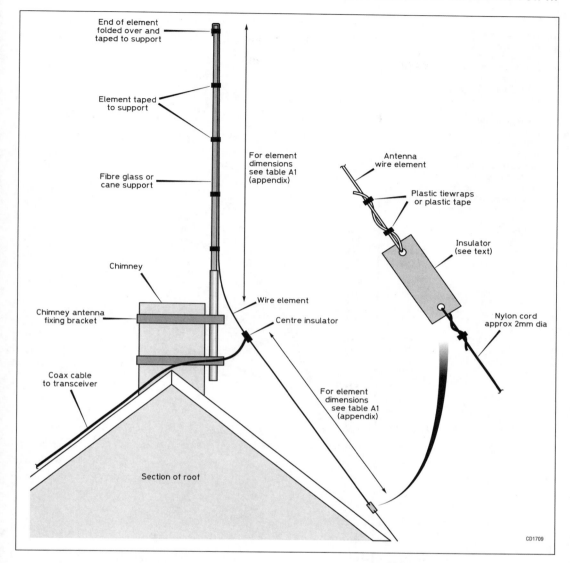

End of element
folded over and
taped to support

Element taped
to support

Fibre glass or
cane support

For element
dimensions
see table A1
(appendix)

Antenna
wire element

Plastic tiewraps
or plastic tape

Insulator
(see text)

Chimney

Chimney antenna
fixing bracket

Wire element

Centre insulator

Nylon cord
approx 2mm dia

Coax cable
to transceiver

For element
dimensions
see table A1
(appendix)

Section of roof

CD1709

equates to 3m (9ft) on 21MHz. It has a very deep vertical null but the maximum gain is only 0.45dBi.

If the 21MHz ground-plane antenna is raised so that the feed point is 10m above the ground the antenna has two elevation lobes, one at 12° (1.4dBi) and the other at 38° (2.6dBi), with a deep vertical null, similar to the vertical dipole shown in Fig 2.5.

The ground-plane antenna can also be used as a multi-band antenna and this is described later.

I have tried to give some idea of the performance of various antennas in Fig 2.5 but trying to make comparisons between such antennas is far from simple. While the performance of the dipole looks attractive for DX it is difficult to get the sort of height that would give this performance on the lower-frequency bands when you are restricted to a backyard type of site.

Fig 2.3. If horizontal space is restricted, the dipole can be orientated as a sloping or vertical antenna as shown. The dimensions are the same as for a horizontal dipole and they are given in Table A.1 in the Appendix. The element support can be weather-proofed cane or glassfibre. The elements can be made from plastic-covered wire

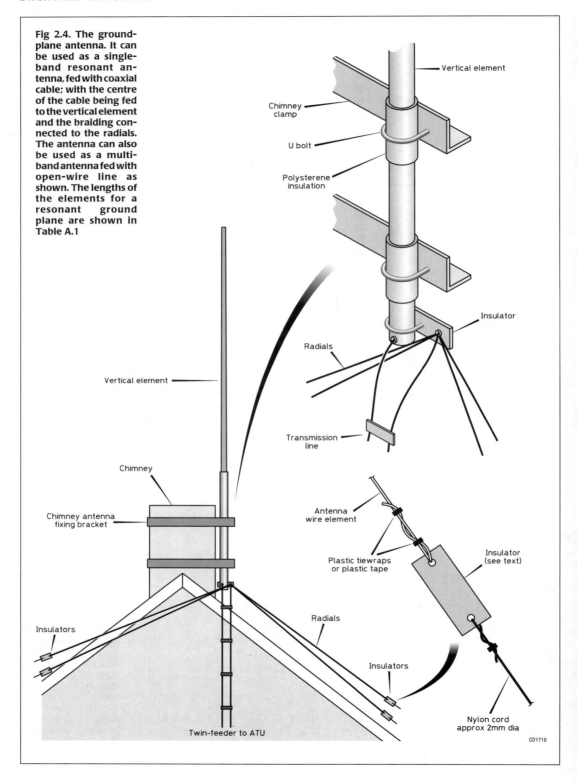

Fig 2.4. The ground-plane antenna. It can be used as a single-band resonant antenna, fed with coaxial cable; with the centre of the cable being fed to the vertical element and the braiding connected to the radials. The antenna can also be used as a multi-band antenna fed with open-wire line as shown. The lengths of the elements for a resonant ground plane are shown in Table A.1

Vertical element

Chimney clamp

U bolt

Polysterene insulation

Insulator

Radials

Transmission line

Antenna wire element

Plastic tiewraps or plastic tape

Insulator (see text)

Insulators

Nylon cord approx 2mm dia

Vertical element

Chimney

Chimney antenna fixing bracket

Insulators

Radials

Twin-feeder to ATU

CD1710

MULTI-BAND ANTENNAS

While the resonant dipole is a very efficient antenna, which can be connected to the antenna socket of the transceiver without an ATU, using separate dipoles for each of the bands can result in a mass of wires in the backyard. Solutions to the multi-band problem include using dipoles in their fundamental and harmonic modes, parallel dipoles, trap dipoles, the multi-band doublet using tuned lines and the multi-band doublet with the ATU.

Most multi-band systems can be improved using an ATU so it is probably a good idea to invest in one or build one. It is basic RF technology and does not date like computers or even modern transceivers. See Chapter 4.

Using a 7MHz dipole on 7 and 21MHz

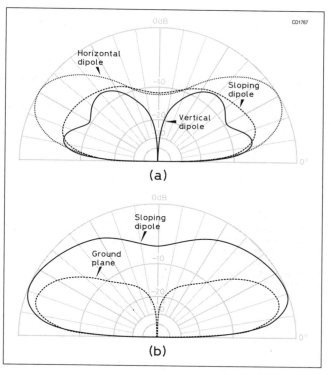

Fig 2.5. Elevation polar diagrams of verical antennas compared with a horizontal dipole. (a) Vertical dipole and sloping dipole. (b) Sloping dipole and ground plane 0.2λ high at feed point

Using dipoles on harmonically related frequencies without an ATU is possible but generally only on two bands. For example a 7MHz dipole will work on 21MHz bands as shown in Fig 2.1 (a dipole being used on its third harmonic). Because of the end effect the dipole isn't exactly resonant at the third harmonic but at some frequency slightly above it as shown in Fig 2.6.

The trick is to load the antenna to a lower frequency in the 21MHz region without affecting resonance on the 7MHz band. Fixing loading loops at the 21MHz high-voltage points of the antenna brings it to the correct resonant point without affecting the 7MHz resonance.

The size of the loops are determined experimentally and they should be equal in size. The shape of the loops is not important and you could use straight lengths of wire but you would need a method of tethering them. Try loops of around 300mm (1ft) to start with and fix them in place on the dipole element as shown in Fig 2.7.

The loops can be fixed to the element temporarily using battery terminal clips and the diameter adjusted for resonance using an SWR meter. The

Fig 2.6. The resonant length of a 7MHz dipole and its harmonic resonance at 21MHz

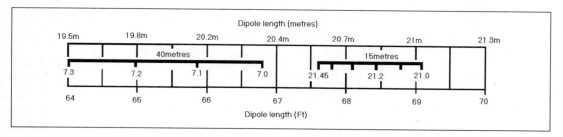

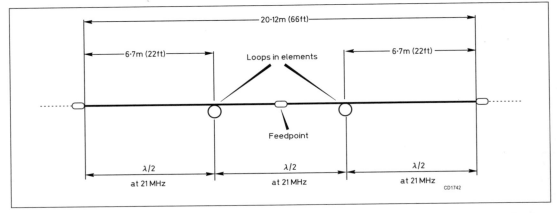

Fig 2.7. By using loops fixed to the 21MHz high-voltage point the antenna can be made to resonate on the 7 and 21MHz bands

loops can be soldered into position when the correct resonance point has been established.

A dual-band antenna could also be constructed for the 10.1MHz and 28.5MHz bands or for 3.6 and 10.1MHz.

Parallel dipoles

One of the best-known methods of constructing a multi-band antenna, where an ATU is unavailable, is to use several dipoles fed in parallel from the same feed line. The length of each separate dipole is a half-wavelength for each band so that each one presents a good impedance match to the feed line on the band for which it is intended and a poor match on all the others. It is an effective system because none of the dipoles takes power from the feed line except the one which is a half-wave at the operating frequency, and thus it is the only one matched to the feed line at that frequency.

However, there can be considerable interaction if the ends of the dipoles are spaced too close together. The ends of the dipoles must be arranged so they are far apart as practical and the best arrangement I have found is the one shown in Fig 2.8.

The multi-element structure is supported by the lowest-frequency dipole. The resonance of these dipoles can be interactive – when you adjust one it effects the resonance of the other. The ends of each of the dipoles can be connected to their respective insulators as shown in Fig 2.3 for ease of element length adjustment.

Each dipole in the parallel-fed combination may be supported from different directions if different directions of radiation are desired and the space is available. This also has the advantage of placing the ends of the dipoles some distance apart.

The ends of the lowest-frequency dipole can be bent to fit into an available area in necessary but the length will have to be lengthened slightly from that shown in Table A.1 to get the lowest SWR.

The G3BDQ [1] method of adjusting parallel dipoles (taking a 14/21/28MHz dipole cluster as an example) is to adjust the 28MHz dipole first. This will undoubtedly shift the resonances of the 14 and 21MHz sections, but when moving on next to adjust the 21MHz section, this should only affect the 14MHz dipole. Presumably this is because the ends of the 21MHz

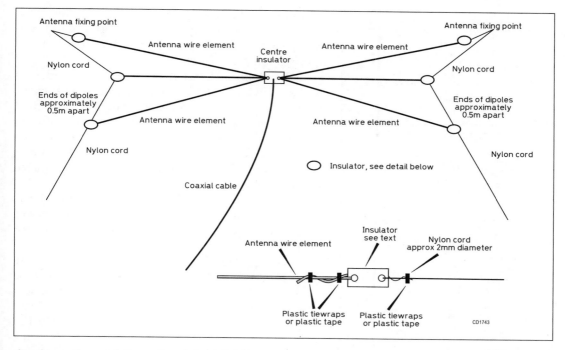

dipole are beyond the ends of the 28MHz one. Finally, adjust the 14MHz dipole and the set-up is ready for use.

The G5RV antenna

Newcomers (and some old-timers) often regard the G5RV antenna as a panacea to the multi-band antenna problem. Louis Varney, G5RV, designed his antenna over 40 years ago, primarily to give a clover-leaf pattern and a low feed impedance on the 14MHz band. The G5RV has a top of 102ft (31.27m), a total of three half-wavelengths on 14MHz, and is fed in the centre.

The feed impedance on 14MHz is low because the feed point is at the centre of the central half-wave section. The mid-band resonant feed impedance at that point is around 90Ω and a 34ft (10.36m) matching section of open-wire feeder is used as a 1:1 transformer, repeating the feed impedance at the other end, as shown in Fig 2.9.

Because of this the lower end of the matching section can be connected to a length of 75Ω impedance coaxial cable as a convenient way of routing the feed to the transmitter in the shack (see Fig 2.10).

In addition the antenna is presents low impedances on other bands, which were within the impedance range of earlier amateur radio transmitters with pi-output variable tuning and loading; thus the antenna could be connected directly to the transmitter without an ATU. This represented quite an advantage over routing open-line feeder into the shack.

However, for the G5RV to work the top dimension must be around 31.27m (102ft) and the dimensions of the matching section shown in Fig 2.10 are only true for open-wire feeder. If 300Ω ribbon or slotted line is used then the length must be adjusted to take account of the velocity factor. (Multiply 10.36m (34ft) by the velocity factor.)

Fig 2.8. Dipoles can be connected in parallel using a common co-axial feeder. Interaction can be minimised by keeping 500mm spacing or more between the ends of the wires. Each dipole end support should be adjusted to keep all the dipoles reasonably tight and tidy and to prevent them from getting tangled when they blow around in the wind

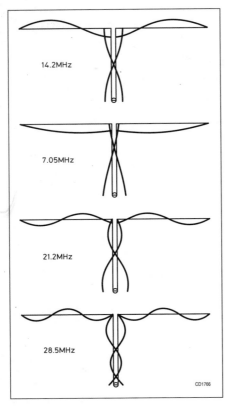

14.2MHz

7.05MHz

21.2MHz

28.5MHz

CD1766

Fig 2.9. Showing the current distribution on a G5RV antenna at 14MHz and also on 7, 21 and 28MHz

In addition the G5RV geometry cannot be altered by, for example, converting it into an inverted-V or bending the ends to fit into a small available space without modification to the length.

On the 10, 18 and 28MHz bands the feed impedances can be fairly awkward. Modern all-solid state amateur band transceivers have transmitter output stages that are easily damaged when operated with high SWR on the feed cable to the antenna, or they have an ALC circuit that reduces power in some proportion to SWR. It is obvious that an ATU between the low-impedance feeder and the transceiver is required.

ZS6BKW developed a computer program to determine the most advantageous length and impedance of the matching section and the top length of a G5RV-type antenna.

He arranged that his antenna should match as closely as possible into standard 50Ω coaxial cable and so be more useful to the user of modern equipment. The G5RV antenna total top length of 31m was reduced to 27.9m, and the matching section was increased from 10.37m (ignoring the velocity factor). This matching section must have a characteristic impedance of 400Ω which can be made up from 18SWG wires spaced at 250mm (1in) apart. The ZS6BKW gives improved impedance matching over the original G5RV but still cannot be used without an ATU with modern solid-state PA transmitters.

Some amateurs have reported that they get very low SWR readings on all bands. If you have consistently a low SWR using this antenna, I would suggest that a test of the coaxial cable from the transmitter to the bottom of the open-wire matching section might be in order – see Chapter 9.

G3BDQ notes [1] that many amateurs use the G5RV antenna with success, and that he prefers the use of either open-wire or 300Ω ribbon to feed the horizontal top. With an ATU such a feed will result in high-performance, all-band working.

G5RV mentions [2] that the most efficient feeder to use is the open-wire variety, all the way down from the centre of the antenna to the equipment, in conjunction with a suitable ATU for matching. He added that by using 25.6m (84ft) of open-wire feeder the system will permit parallel tuning of the ATU on all bands; which brings us to the open-wire tuned dipole.

The open-wire tuned dipole

This antenna, also known as the *tuned doublet* or *random-length dipole*, is very simple, yet is a most effective and efficient antenna for multi-band use. It is fed with open-wire tuned feeders, as shown in Fig 2.11, and an ATU is used to take care of the wide variations of feed impedance on the different bands.

This antenna should be at least a quarter-wavelength long at the lowest frequency of operation, where it radiates with an effectiveness of approximately 95% relative to a half-wave dipole. However, the feed impedance of

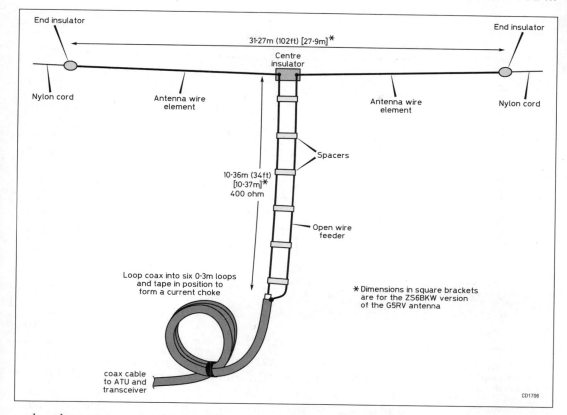

End insulator

End insulator

31·27m (102ft) [27·9m]*

Centre insulator

Nylon cord

Antenna wire element

Antenna wire element

Nylon cord

Spacers

10·36m (34ft) [10·37m]* 400 ohm

Open wire feeder

Loop coax into six 0·3m loops and tape in position to form a current choke

* Dimensions in square brackets are for the ZS6BKW version of the G5RV antenna

coax cable to ATU and transceiver

CD1706

such a short antenna results in SWR values of around 300:1 on 450Ω line. While the antenna is quite efficient the impedances at the end of the tuned feeder will be outside the matching range of the average commercial ATU using a toroid balun to provide a balanced feed to the tuned feeders.

If you have the space then use a doublet with a length of about 3λ/8 on the lowest frequency. This is halfway between quarter-wave and half-wave and will work very well if you can't erect a full half-wave on 3.5MHz. A 3λ/8 dipole has an effectiveness greater than 98% relative to a half-wave dipole, and the SWR values are far easier to match, being in the region of 25:1 on 600Ω line, 24:1 on 450Ω line, and 25:1 on 300Ω line.

A 3λ/8 dipole at 3.5MHz is approximately 30m (100ft) long, which means that any length from 27m (90ft) to 30m will make an excellent radiator on all HF amateur bands from 3.5 to 28MHz including the WARC bands.

If you don't have room for a 27m length of straight wire for operation on 3.5MHz, a 3 to 5m (10 to 16ft) portion of each end may be dropped vertically from each end support. There will be no significant change in radiation pattern on 3.5MHz and 7MHz. However, there will be a minor change in polarisation in the radiation at higher frequencies, but the effect on propagation will be negligible.

The W6RCA multi-band doublet

Many antenna designs feature combinations of doublet length and feed-line length, resulting in a convenient impedance (one easily matched by a

Fig 2.10. Construction of the G5RV antenna. The dimensions shown in square brackets are for the ZS6BKW version – see text

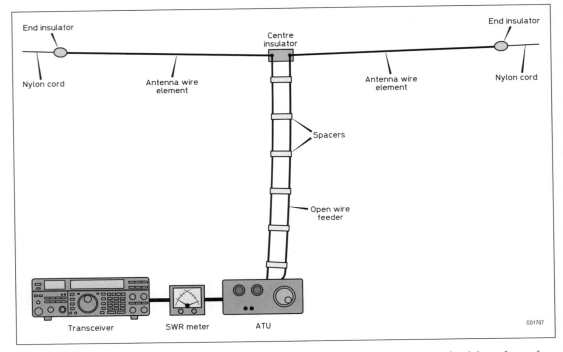

End insulator

Fig 2.11. The tuned open-wire dipole using a tuned transmission line. If you are short of space the antenna could be cut for 3/8 wavelength on 7MHz and it will tune all bands from 7 to 28MHz. The real advantage of this antenna is that dipole length is not critical because the tuner provides the impedance match throughout the entire antenna system, whatever the dipole length may be

transceiver's internal auto-ATU) at the bottom of the feed line for a few bands but never all of them. Hence the need for an ATU with the open-wire tuned multi-band dipole described above.

The following describes a more radical approach by Cecil Moore, W6RCA, and described by G3SEK [3]. His solution to the problem covers all the HF bands from 3.6 to 29.7MHz with no ATU at all. This is achieved by changing the length of the 450Ω tuned ladder-line – and this is much more practical than it looks at first sight. The line length is adjusted for each band, so that the current maximum always coincides with the bottom of the feed line. The feed impedance at this point is then by definition low and non-reactive, and in practice the SWR is usually low enough that you can use a 1:1 choke balun straight into coaxial cable and the transceiver. With reasonable lengths for the doublet and the permanent part of the feed line, you can always achieve an acceptable impedance match.

The requirement is that the physical half-length of the doublet (L1 in Fig 2.12), plus the total electrical length of the feed line (L2, allowing for the velocity factor v) must be an odd multiple of a quarter-wavelength on each band:

$$L_1 + L_2 \times v = n \, \lambda/4$$

where n is 3, 5, 7 etc. When you get out the calculator and start playing with figures, you can arrive at several possible solutions. The W6RCA arrangement is shown in Fig 2.13, with a 39.62m (130ft) centre-fed doublet and 27.5m (90ft) of 450Ω ladder-line. The doublet is approximately a half-wave at 3.5MHz and a full-wave at 7MHz, and the 27.5m (90ft) feed line brings the current maximum to the bottom at 7.2MHz. The big practical advantage of this combination is that all the other bands can be matched within a relatively small range of additional feed-line length. The longest additional length required is 9.5m (31ft) for 3.6MHz, which extends the feed line to an electrical half-wavelength.

All other bands require a line extension somewhere between zero and 9.5m, so W6RCA built a variable-length switcher shown in Figs 2.14 and 2.15. This consists of 300mm (1ft), 600mm (2ft), 1.22m (4ft), 2.44m (8ft) and 4.88m (16ft) loops of line, which can be individually switched in or out using DPDT relays, giving any length from zero to 9.5m in 300mm steps.

W6RCA found he could cover all amateur bands from 3.6 to 29.7MHz with a SWR of better than 2:1. The optimum dimensions will depend on a number of local factors. These include antenna height, earth properties, the use of other doublet configurations such as an inverted-V or inverted-U, and the exact type of feed line. So-called '450Ω' ladder-line varies considerably in characteristic impedance, velocity factor and quality (conductor diameter and insulation) between different brands; hence the need to experiment.

A battery-powered tuneable SWR analyser is the perfect tool for the job of experimenting with line lengths and it should used via a 1:1 balun. You can easily make temporary splices in ladder-line using screw connectors – or just twisting the wires together. The first step would be to increase the permanent length of line by say a metre from the recommended length, then trim the feeder so that the SWR minimum occurs around 7.05MHz. You may find that the same length works well enough for 21MHz and 24.9MHz too. Next, determine the maximum extra length you will need to tune all the way down to 3.5MHz with an acceptable VSWR. This extra length should not be much more than 9.5m, and the optimum lengths for all the other bands will all be shorter than that.

Unfortunately the popular 32m (102ft) G5RV-style doublet is not very well suited to this arrangement, because it requires a much wider variation in the feed-line length. If you're stuck with a 102ft 'flat-top', W6RCA recommends adding a 4.6m (15ft) vertical 'drop wire' at each end, and then you're back to the much more convenient situation of Fig 2.14. For a shorter doublet covering 7 to 29.7MHz, a 20.12m (66ft) doublet and a 18.3m (60ft) feed line as a good starting-point, again with a 0 to 9.5m variable section. Note also that the system can still be used as a shortened dipole on the next band below, but you will require an ATU and there may be significant losses in the ATU and feed line due to the very low impedance.

After the initial experiments, you can think about a more permanent arrangement. You don't have to build the complete line switcher. Practical solutions range from a fully manual system to a fully automatic

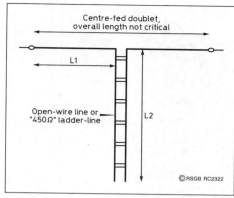

Fig 2.12. The HF multi-band doublet fed with ladder line can have a wide range of feed impedances. To estimate the impedance, measure half the length of the doublet (L1) plus the electrical length of the feed line (L2, allow for velocity factor)

Fig 2.13. W6RCA's novel line-length switcher makes his 39.62m (130ft) doublet cover all eight HF bands with no ATU. Optimum dimensions will depend on local factors, but you can always change the line length to compensate

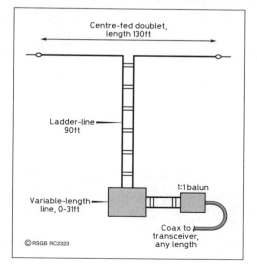

25

system linked to the transceiver's 'band data' output (ideal for HF contesting in the single-antenna section). For occasional visits to certain bands, you could insert the necessary lengths of feed line using 4mm banana plugs and sockets (the silver-plated variety can be used permanently outdoors).

It wouldn't be difficult to string something along a wooden garden fence, so long as the loops of line are suspended clear from other lines, metallic objects or the ground.

The 1:1 balun is worth a brief mention. It's important to use a balun, because any low-impedance path to ground from either side of the feed line is likely to result in very strong unbalanced radiation from the feed line itself. This is a consequence of the 'odd quarter-wavelength' principle used in selecting the feed-line length. A suitable choke balun is described in Chapter 9.

Fig 2.14. The practical line switcher. The horizontal rail holds the five pairs of DPDT relays. W6RCA points out that, with hindsight, it makes more sense to start with the 2.44m (8ft) and 4.88m (16ft) loops at opposite ends of the wooden rail that holds the relays. You could also change bands manually by using plug-in lengths of line for each band

The Comudipole (coaxial cable fed multi-band dipole)

While the open-wire tuned dipole is a very good antenna there are problems in many locations of bringing open-wire feeder into the shack. This may be particularly relevant for apartment dwellers. One solution for a multi-band antenna was first described by Ton Verberne, PA2ABV, and is an arrangement known as the *Comudipole* [4, 5].

PA9ABV lives on the second floor of a five-storey apartment building. The antenna on the roof is an inverted-V dipole of about 2 × 19m and a 4:1 coaxial balun – see Chapter 9. From there some 30m of RG213 coaxial cable

Fig 2.15. More details of W6RCA's line switcher, which uses five pairs of surplus DPDT relays. A suitable 1:1 choke balun is described in Chapter 9

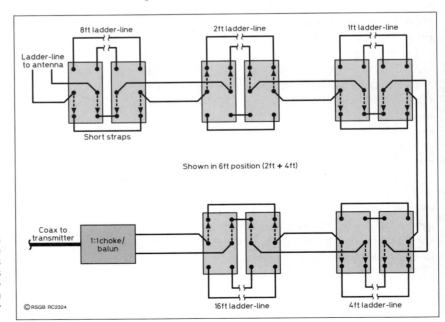

8ft ladder-line | 2ft ladder-line | 1ft ladder-line

Ladder-line to antenna

Short straps

Shown in 6ft position (2ft + 4ft)

Coax to transmitter

1:1 choke/ balun

© RSGB RC2324

16ft ladder-line | 4ft ladder-line

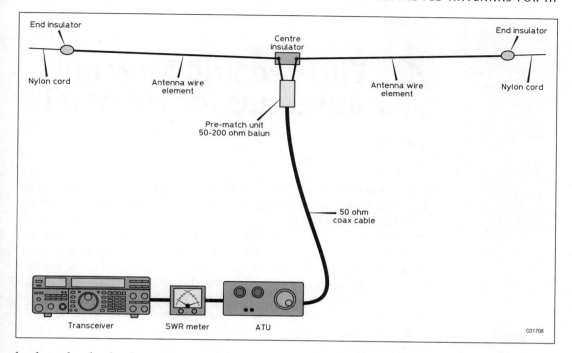

leads to the shack where an L-network takes care of matching to the transceiver. In practice the arrangement at PA2ABV gives a good match on all nine amateur bands from 3.5MHz to 28MHz. Even on 1.8MHz a match is possible but efficiency is low.

Fig 2.16. PA2ABV's Comudipole antenna

The trap dipole

I have not included the popular trap dipole in this chapter. The reason is that the modern solid-state transmitter is unable to provide an acceptable match to the input impedance of the feed line of this antenna except perhaps for a few kilohertz on either side of the resonant frequency of the trap. Hence, an ATU is necessary if any wider-frequency excursion is to be enjoyed. In addition traps can be quite lossy. In any case, if an ATU is employed them you might as well use the tuned doublet described earlier in this chapter.

REFERENCES

[1] *Practical Wire Antennas*, John D Heys, G3BDQ, RSGB, 1989.
[2] 'The G5RV multi-band antenna', *Radio Communication* July 1984.
[3] 'In Practice', *RadCom* August 1999.
[4] *Electron* (December 1992) and reported in 'Technical Topics' in *Radio Communication* May 1994.
[5] 'Eurotek', *Radio Communication* August 1992.

3 End-fed and Marconi antennas for HF and LF

THIS chapter is about the end-fed antenna, ie one which has its end connected directly to the transmitter or ATU. An example of an end-fed antenna is shown in Fig 3.1.

The antenna directly connected to the transmitter is often discouraged because of the close proximity of the radiating element to house wiring and domestic equipment. This undesirable feature is aggravated by the fact that considerable excursions of feed impedance occur when changing operation from band to band, and good matching can sometimes be difficult to achieve.

However, the end-fed antenna is simple, cheap and easy to erect; it suits many house and garden layouts; and it is equally amenable to base or portable operation.

There are two aspects of the end-fed antenna which need to be considered. The first is matching the transmitter to the range of impedances encountered at the end of a wire antenna on the different bands and the other is an effective and efficient RF earth or ground.

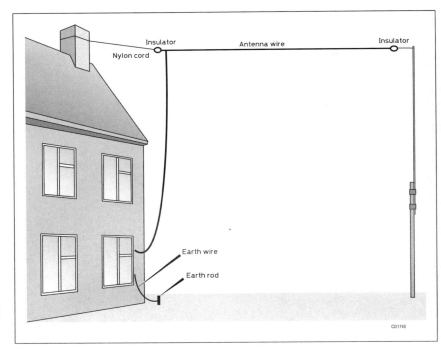

Fig 3.1. The end-fed antenna, the simplest of all multi-band antennas

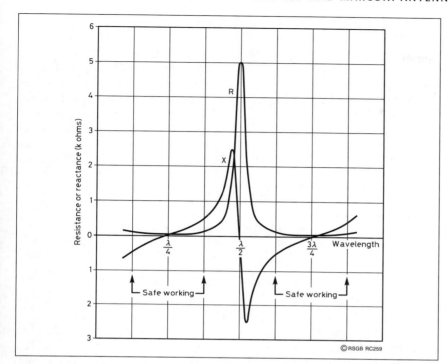

Fig 3.2. End-fed impedance characteristics of a wire from λ/4 to 3λ/4. Values of impedance that are more easily matched using a commercial ATU are designated 'safe working'

MATCHING THE MULTI-BAND END-FED ANTENNA

The end-fed antenna has traditionally been designed to resonate on one lower band in the HF spectrum, say a quarter-wavelength on 3.5MHz where the feedpoint will be around 50Ω. At a half-wavelength on 7MHz, the input impedance will rise to a high value, presenting a voltage feed to the source. The next band, 10MHz, will fall in the vicinity of current feed again at three-quarters-wavelength and present a fairly low impedance. The next move to 14MHz will encounter a high impedance again and then through an off-tune 18MHz to another high at 21MHz. The sequence continues with extra complications in that odd multiples of one wavelength will show generally increasing impedance with frequency whereas even multiples of wavelength (the half-wave points) will show decreasing impedance as the band is ascended.

Fig 3.2 illustrates resistance and reactance plotted against electrical length from below λ/4 to 3λ/4 and beyond. It can be seen that dramatic changes begin to occur as the λ/2 (half-wave) resonant point is approached. These changes are repeated at multiples of λ/2.

In spite of these wide variations of antenna feed impedance on different bands the transceiver can be matched to the antenna using a suitable ATU. Although ATUs are generally described in Chapter 4 the diagram in Fig 3.3 is included here because it is designed specifically for the end-fed antenna and will match the very high or very low impedances encountered in an end-fed half-wave antenna, as described above.

In its basic form this ATU is very simple when used for single-band operation. I use such a circuit and its layout is shown in Fig 3.4. This ATU is

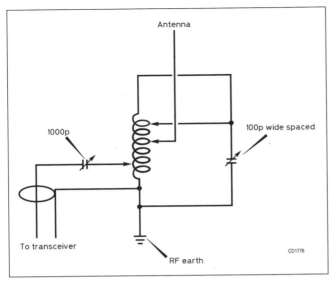

Antenna

1000p

100p wide spaced

To transceiver

RF earth

CD1776

Fig 3.3. A circuit diagram of an ATU for a multi-band end-fed antenna

Fig 3.4. A single-band ATU for 3.5MHz. The coil comprises 22 turns wound on a 80mm diameter former. The parallel capacitor and taps are preset and the ATU is used remotely in the garden shed

used for remote operation of a long wire for 3.5MHz. The ceramic coil is 80mm diameter with 22 turns wound over 70mm of its length and tuned with a wide-spaced 100pF capacitor.

In practice the ATU design shown in Fig 3.3 gets rather complicated when multi-band operation is required. Ideally, to match a whole range of impedances with all the various lengths of wire that may be encountered, the coil should be tapped every turn. There are three sets of taps and capacitor settings to be adjusted for each band. In practice, coil taps can be adjusted on test then fixed so that they can be selected using a switch or relay.

If the feed impedance swings which occur when changing bands can be moderated then a simpler ATU can be used. This is achieved by using antenna wire lengths which steer clear of the half-wave points. This would allow the end-fed antenna to be matched on all bands by any of the ATUs described in Chapter 4. The selection of an optimum antenna length was described in detail by Alan Chester, G3CCB, although this was done to meet the limitations of a wide-band matching transformer system [1].

In Fig 3.5, wire length is shown against each of the nine HF bands, including 1.8MHz. The heavy lines indicate areas where impedance excursions might fall outside the matching capabilities of many ATUs. These lengths were calculated by G3CCB from the lower band edge frequency in each case and no corrections were made for the 'end effect' on a real antenna.

To use the chart shown in Fig 3.5, a perpendicular straight edge is dropped from the horizontal axis and moved along until a clearest way through the gaps between the extreme impedance sectors is found. There is a minimum antenna length shown which depends on the band in use. This restriction, which may be of interest to those operating from a restricted size site, can be overcome by using a loading coil – this is described later.

OBTAINING A GOOD RF EARTH

A good RF earth is required for an end-fed antenna to operate efficiently. You can think of an

RF earth having electrical 'mass', which enables the energy source (the transmitter) to push current into the antenna. The analogous 'mass' can be real mass in a practical antenna system, such as a vehicle in a mobile installation; or it can be the central heating system or an outside earth connection (a copper pipe or bar driven into the ground) in a fixed installation. The 'mass' can also be achieved using a resonant conductor, often known as a *radial* or *counterpoise*.

A problem with not having a good RF earth is that the outside of the radio equipment can be at a high RF potential. Furthermore, the microphone, key or headset leads are also 'hot' with RF so you get RF feedback and BCI problems. Additionally, the IC circuits of modern communications equipment (keying or microphone circuits) are easily damaged in these circumstances.

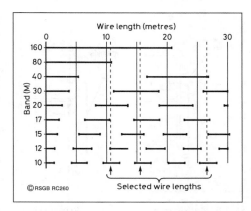

Fig 3.5. Antenna wire lengths, showing high-impedance lengths for various bands

Using real earth

In practice a good RF earth connection is hard to find and is only practicable from a ground-floor room. The problem with the 'earth stake' is that ground has resistance and the lead connecting the earth stake to the radio has reactance. This ground resistance is in series with the radiation resistance of the antenna so it is important to get the ground resistance as low as possible if you want an efficient end-fed antenna.

Many ways have been tried to reduce the ground resistance. In general, the more copper you can bury in the ground the better. I found that an old copper water tank, connected to the radio with thick short copper wire, made a very good earth. At my present location an RF earth is made from about 60 square metres of galvanised chicken wire. This was laid on the lawn early in the year and pegged down with large staples made from hard-drawn copper wire. The grass grew up through the chicken wire and as if by magic the wire netting seemed to disappear into the ground over a period of about two months. In the early stages, the lawn had to be cut with care with the mower set so that it did not cut to close and chew up the carefully laid wire netting.

Low-band DXers tend to use buried multiple radials; lots of wires radiating out from the earth connection. The rule seems to be is the more wires, the better. The length of the wires will be restricted in our backyard scenario but nevertheless they will contribute to lowering the RF ground resistance. These types of direct connection to earth can also provide an electrical safety earth to the radio equipment in the shack.

Artificial earths

If you operate from an upstairs shack, engineering a low-impedance earth connection at ground level using the method described above will probably be a waste of time. The reason for this is that the distance up to the shack is a significant fraction of a wavelength on the higher HF bands. G3SEK makes the point [2] that at frequencies where this length is near λ/4 or 3λ/4, the earth connector will act as a RF insulator, which is just the opposite of what

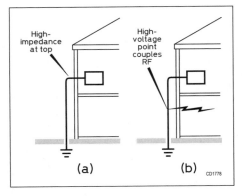

(a)   (b)

Fig 3.6. Why RF ground leads from upstairs seldom work. (a) Ground lead with quarter-wave resonance (or odd multiple) is ineffective; very little current will flow into it. (b) Ground lead with half-wave resonance (or multiples) will have high-voltage points which couple RF into house wiring

is wanted – see Fig 3.6(a). This is bound to happen in one or more of our nine HF bands.

On the other hand, if the lead resonates as a half-wave (a situation that is likely to arise on any band above 10MHz), it will may act as a good RF earth. However, it also has a high-voltage point halfway down which may couple RF into the house wiring – see Fig 3.6(b) – because electrical wiring within the wall of a house is generally perpendicular. In other words, although an earth wire from the radio in an upstairs shack to an earth stake will provide a safety earth its usefulness as an RF earth is unpredictable.

The favoured method of obtaining a good RF earth is to connect a quarter-wave radial for each band to the transceiver and ATU earth connector, and then run the free ends outside, away from the transceiver. Because the current at the end of the wire is zero and the impedance is high it follows that at a quarter-wave inward where it connects to the transceiver the RF potential is zero (the impedance is low). The problem is where to locate all these radials – such an arrangement will require some experimenting to find the best position for them. Radials can be bent or even folded but the length may have to be altered to maintain resonance. They are best located outside the house in the horizontal plane to reduce coupling into the electrical wiring. If the radial(s) are used indoors (say round the skirting board), use wire with thick insulation with additional several layers of insulating tape at the ends where the RF voltage can be fairly high when the transmitter is on.

The best way to check resonance of a radial is to connect it to the radio earth, make a loop in the radial and use a GDO to check resonance. If such an instrument is unavailable then use an RF current meter (see Chapter 10) and adjust the radial length for maximum current.

Alternatively, one single-length radial can be tuned to place a zero RF potential at the transceiver on any band by inserting an LC series tuning circuit between the transmitter and the radial. Such units are commercially available which have, in addition to the LC circuit, a through-current RF indicator which helps tuning the radial or earth lead to resonance (maximum current).

Another possibility is that you can make one yourself. The unit designed by SM6AQR and shown in Fig 3.7 uses a 200 to 300pF air-spaced tuning capacitor with at least 1mm plate spacing; the capacitor and its shaft must be insulated from the tuner cabinet [3]. The inductor is a 28µH roller coaster. Alternatively, a multi-tapped fixed coil plus with as many taps as possible could be used. See Chapter 4 regarding the use of multi-tapped coil in place of a roller coaster.

The tuning indicator consists of a current transformer, rectifier, smoothing filter, sensitivity potentiometer and DC microammeter. The 'primary'

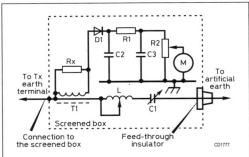

Fig 3.7. SM6AQR's earth lead tuner. T1: Amidon T-50-43 ferrite toroid; the primary is simply the earth lead through the toroid centre; secondary is 20t small-gauge enamelled wire. L1: 28µH roller coaster or multi-tapped coil with 10-position switch; see text. C1: see text. C2, 3: 10nF ceramic. D1: AA119. R1: 1kΩ. R2: 10kΩ pot. Rx: see text. M: 100µA or less

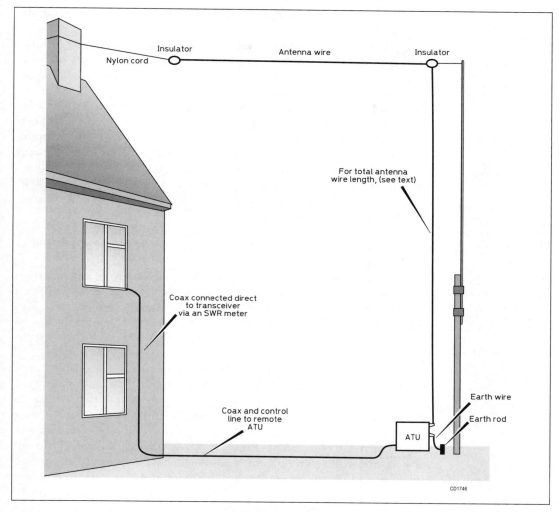

Fig 3.8. A remotely fed long-wire antenna arrangement. The ATU will require a control cable in addition to the coaxial cable feeder. The earth rod could be replaced with radials as described earlier in the text

of the current transformer is the artificial earth lead itself; it simply passes through the centre of the T1 ferrite toroid, onto which a secondary of 20 turns of thin enamelled wire has been wound. Rx, the resistor across the T1 secondary, should be non-inductive and between 22 and 1100Ω; it is selected such that a convenient meter deflection can be set with the sensitivity control R2 on each required frequency and for the RF power used.

A separate electrical safety earth should always be used in addition to the RF earth described above.

A REMOTE-CONTROLLED ATU

Having the antenna feed point remote from the shack as shown in Fig 3.8 can circumvent the disadvantages of bringing the end of an antenna into the shack, described at the beginning of this chapter and discussed in Chapter 1. Locating the long-wire antenna feed point away from the house minimises electrical noise on receive and EMC problems on transmit. Furthermore, it reduces the unpredictable effect on the antenna caused by possible conduit, wiring and pipe resonances.

The disadvantage of this arrangement is that the ATU is some distance from the transceiver, which can be rather inconvenient when it comes to making adjustments. There are automatic ATUs commercially available now although I have never tried one.

L B Uphill, G3UCE, devised a remote-controlled ATU with an end-fed antenna that has proved satisfactory on all the HF bands [4]. It sits in a rear porch and is connected to the shack by 10m of coaxial cable, plus an eight-way multi-core cable for remote control of the relays. Other suitable places to house an ATU may be used, such as the garage, outside shed, conservatory or greenhouse. Even mounting it on a post in the garden is feasible, provided the assembly is weatherproofed. A good RF earth or a counterpoise close to the ATU is necessary.

Once set up, this ATU provides instant selection of preselected settings. It will, however, need several hours to set up and so should be sited in an accessible position.

The ATU has been tested with several different lengths of antenna from 18m (60ft) to 61m (200ft). Some antenna wire lengths were more difficult than others to get all six bands working, and the best turned out to be 30m (100ft) and 40m (132ft). Around 40 turns are required if 160m is the lowest band to be used; if 80m is the lowest frequency then 20 to 25 turns are sufficient.

A junk box coil may be used provided the turns are of a reasonably heavy copper wire. The wire spacing should allow the use of an instrument-type crocodile clip with narrow jaws to be clipped to any turn during setting-up without shorting an adjacent turn. If a suitable coil is not available then a 40-turn coil can be wound on a 190mm (7.5in) length of 45mm diameter plastic pipe using 14 to 16SWG tinned copper wire. Fasten one end to a nut and bolt, and wind tightly using a similar thickness of string as spacing until 40 turns are wound on. Anchor the other end to a nut and bolt and carefully remove the string spacer. Apply three or four strings of cement across the turns to hold them in place.

The capacitors used are 100pF air-spaced types for higher-frequency bands and 500pF 500V working mica presets for the lower bands. A capacitor may not be required for 160m, where a direct connection is made from the co-axial cable to the coil.

The relays are 12V types and are not critical, provided the contacts can carry about 5A AC. A small control box with a two-pole, six-way Yaxley switch controls the relay switching in the shack. One pole switches the relays and the other pole switches small LED indicator lamps to show which band is selected. An eight-core miniature, screened cable is used to connect the ATU to the shack. With six bands to select this will leave two wires spare and these are used to switch the transmitter on and off via the CW socket during adjustments from the ATU end.

Setting up

Starting with the lowest frequency, tune up the transmitter on a dummy load to the centre of the band, connect the feeder, energise the appropriate relay, and pass a small amount of RF to the ATU. An SWR meter must be inserted at each end of the feeder. Find a tapping on the coil, working from the antenna tap where the SWR reduces, and adjust the appropriate capacitor until a combination is found which gives the lowest SWR. The shack SWR meter is now checked and if both give similar readings the top can be soldered permanently in place on the coil. Now carry on to the next lowest frequency, remembering to switch in the appropriate relay. On the highest frequencies (15, 12 and 10m) the tap should not need to be more than four or five turns from the antenna.

When all the bands have been satisfactorily set up, no further alterations must be made to the antenna length or the earth system or all adjustments will need to be repeated.

This method of remotely controlling an end-fed antenna is used in commercial and military installations. An example of such an ATU is shown in Fig 3.9.

Fig 3.9. A remote-control ATU made by Racal. The pre-selected connections to the coil are made using specially designed clips and connected via any one of the relays

ALTERNATIVE END-FED ANTENNAS
Using an existing HF wire beam on the lower HF bands

Any wire beam such as the quad, or any of the wire beams shown in Chapter 6, can be used as an end-fed antenna as shown in Fig 3.10.

In this case the coaxial cable is used as the antenna conductor rather than as a feeder. The inner conductor and the braid of the coaxial cable is shorted together using a PL259 socket with a shorting link and connected to the ATU. The beam itself forms a top capacitance which, provided the coaxial cable is reasonably in the clear, makes a very effective lower-frequency HF antenna. I employed such an arrangement using a 21MHz Double-D wire beam – see Chapter 6. This arrangement, together with the copper water tank earth mentioned earlier, was used to make regular DX contacts on 3.5MHz.

Other antennas can be used in this way. A dipole for 14MHz can be used on the lower-frequency bands by connecting the coaxial cable to the ATU, as already described, so that the dipole forms a capacitance top. A good RF earth is required for this antenna.

Electrically short antennas with a loading coil

If you are very short of space then an electrically short antenna, with a loading coil to bring it in to resonance, may be the solution. Short antennas with a loading coil can be reasonably effective – mobilers use them all the time.

Fig 3.10. Using a wire beam as an end-fed antenna on the lower LF bands

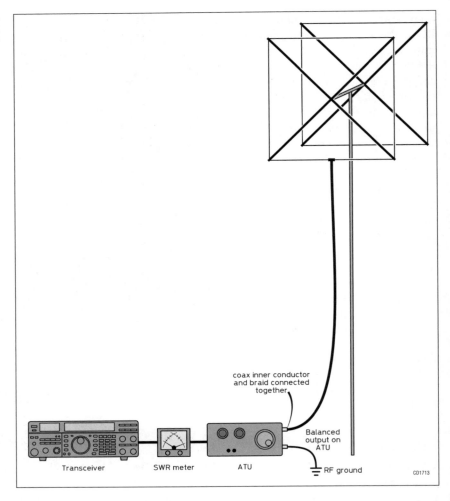

coax inner conductor and braid connected together

Balanced output on ATU

RF ground

Transceiver   SWR meter   ATU

The simplest solution is just to use a mobile antenna. The Texas Bugcatcher, which has become very popular in the USA, is described here as a solution for multi-band operation on HF from a very restricted site (see the Appendix).

This commercial mobile antenna uses the older traditional centre loading with a low-loss coil or resonator. The lower section of the antenna below the coil is 600mm (24in) long, with an optional 400mm (16in) extension rod. The antenna screws into a standard $\frac{3}{8} \times 24$in threaded antenna mount.

The coil (resonator) is 300mm (12in) long and 63mm (2½in) outside diameter. The coil has 90 turns wound over 254mm of the former and the bands are selected using a shorting lead with a crocodile clip to connect to preselected coil clips.

The top whip section is 2.2m (48in) long with a capacitance hat in the centre to reduce the length of the antenna. If the capacitance hat is not desired for any reason, it may be removed and a 1.37m (54in) long whip substituted.

Coil clips are provided which are fastened to the appropriate tapping

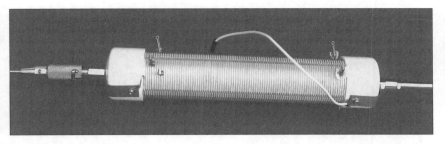

Fig 3.11. The Texas Bugcatcher loading coil with most of the coil clips fitted. Small insulating tabs have been fixed to some of the coil clips to prevent shorting to adjacent windings

point on the coil for each band. Some care is required when setting the clips so they do not short on adjacent turns. If a short occurs the effect is to cause an unexplained HF frequency shift on all bands. I fitted small insulating tabs – see Fig 3.11.

I had a recent request for advice on an antenna for 1.8 and 3.5MHz to go in a loft space, because planning restrictions ruled out the use of an outside antenna.

My first suggestion was to try a large tuned loop but the person concerned was in his eighties and wanted a commercial solution. I decided to try the Bugcatcher in this situation. However, I was unable to put the antenna into my loft so I fixed it to the frame of the upstairs window with a counterpoise wire to the copper pipe of the central heating system.

An earth plate, available from the manufacturers (see Fig 3.12), will convert the Bugcatcher into a short outdoor vertical. The antenna loaded up quite well with the built-in ATU of the shack TS-850S and I had many QSOs around the UK and Europe on 3.5 and 7MHz. If the top whip were replaced with a T-shaped wire structure fitted into the apex of the loft, the antenna should work on 1.8MHz.

The longer the element below the coil is made, the more efficient the antenna will be on the lower frequencies.

If you are restricted to a loft antenna then there is nothing to stop you making a similar coil to that described above. Because the coil does not have to be weatherproof you could make the G3UCE coil, described earlier in this chapter, and use it as a loading coil. The size and inductance is not critical provided that taps can be made anywhere on the coil. Shorting out the unused turns with the link from the bottom of the coil to a tapping point varies the inductance value.

Fix the coil about halfway up an upright roof support in the loft. Take one wire from the base of the coil to the floor of the loft near to any copper plumbing pipe. Connect the centre of the coaxial feed to the wire element and the braiding to the plumbing. If there is no plumbing pipes in the loft then use radials as described in 'Artificial earths'. Connect a T or inverted-L section of wire to the top of the coil and fix to the inside of the roof using insulators; there will be high RF voltages here if you are using a lot of power.

Fig 3.12. An earth plate, available from the manufacturers of the Bugcatcher, which can be fixed in the lawn to make a fixed grounded vertical. *The top of the coil is not very high in such an installation and there will be a high RF voltage at the top of the coil if you are using a lot of power. It is important that the arrangements are made so that no one can come into contact with the coil or the top of the antenna when you are operating*

Fig 3.13. A pressurised plastic bottle used as a coil former. The coil is fixed to the top element of the antenna using plastic tape around the neck of the bottle. An additional 'neck' is cut from another bottle of the same size and glued to the bottom of the coil former. This forms a fixing point for the bottom wire element of the antenna

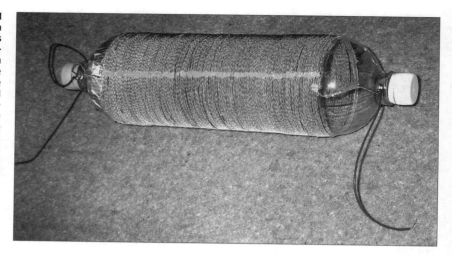

The antenna is set up by adjusting the shorting tap for the lowest SWR for each band using the lowest power possible (or use an SWR analyser). Wires can then be soldered to the tapping points and marked with the band they are used for.

It is possible to arrange for the tapping points to be switched remotely if you can get high-voltage, low-capacitance contact relays.

Another possibility is to feed the loft antenna with the G3UCE remote ATU. Setting up would require setting the loading coil to some optimum point.

A lightweight loading coil

Any electrically small antenna can be improved with a loading coil. Most of the radiation takes place from the element below the loading inductance so the coil should be in some elevated position. The problem with a wire antenna is how to elevate coils. They can be supported by the wire element itself but a good high-Q coil can be fairly heavy.

A lot of work has been done by the LF experimenters since the introduction of the 136kHz band and the following description of the coil is the result of experimental work by Mike Dennison, G3XDV.

The coil former is made from a large one-litre size plastic soft drinks bottle. The plastic used with these bottles is rather thin and is normally held on shape by the pressure from the gas in the soft drink. When the bottle is empty it is rather floppy and no good as a coil former. The trick is to pressurise it. This is done by simply putting the bottle in to the freezer compartment of a refrigerator for a couple of hours. When the bottle is taken out of the freezer the top is screwed on firmly. As the air in the bottle warms up it expands and pressurises the bottle, which then makes a good lightweight coil former.

The wire can now be wound around the bottle using the G3UCE technique. The wire can be held in place using hot-melt glue and finally fixed using plastic cement. A complete loading coil is shown in Fig 3.13.

The loading coil can then be weatherproofed by coating it in clear silicone rubber.

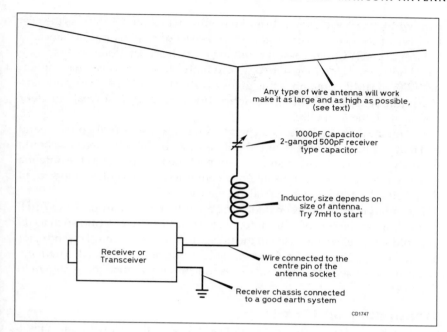

Fig 3.14. An experimental arrangement to use an existing HF wire antenna for receiving 136kHz signals

Any type of wire antenna will work make it as large and as high as possible, (see text)

1000pF Capacitor
2-ganged 500pF receiver type capacitor

Inductor, size depends on size of antenna. Try 7mH to start

Receiver or Transceiver

Wire connected to the centre pin of the antenna socket

Receiver chassis connected to a good earth system

CD1747

MARCONI ANTENNAS FOR LF

On 30 January 1998 a new frequency band of 135.7 to 137.8kHz was made available in the UK on the basis of non-interference to other services (inside or outside the United Kingdom).

A half-wave dipole on this band is over 1000m long and an end-fed quarter-wave over 500m long so these antennas are not a practical proposition for the backyard location. However, as already mentioned, electrically short antennas can be made to work using a loading coil and you will need a fairly large inductance to resonate the antenna at this low frequency.

There is nothing particularly special about making an antenna for the 136kHz band. In fact you might already have one – an antenna of 1.8 or 3.5MHz will probably work quite well. The most traditional of the LF antennas is the T or inverted-L. An 1.8 or 3.5MHz dipole, with both conductors of the feeder shorted, makes a good T-antenna. An end-fed antenna will make an inverted-L antenna for LF.

Receiving on 136kHz

Because very few of us have experience on this new band I have included this 'how to get started' by receiving on 136kHz.

Many commercial receivers/transceivers do not cover the LF bands (or if they do the performance is often not very good). Consequently most of the early LF work was done using a converter ahead of a commercial receiver or transceiver.

John More, G4GVC, who has been very successful receiving low-frequency signals, found that his Kenwood TS-850S performed very well on this band. His receiver has useful options which include three CW filters: 500Hz bandwidth at 8.83MHz, 270Hz bandwidth at 8.83MHz and 500Hz bandwidth (xtal) at 455kHz. He is of the opinion that the TS-850 was the best transceiver Kenwood ever produced in respect of receiver performance.

Most of G4GVC's successful receiving work has been done using a resonated horizontal 60m long wire only 24ft high. He also has used loop antennas with a MMIC preamp – this gives excellent-strength signals and very sharp tuning, but it STILL gives noticeably poorer copy of weak amateur signals than the 60m wire.

Assuming that you have a receiver that has good sensitivity on the band and that you have converted your dipole as described above, then you should be ready to receive 136kHz signals. Connect the transceiver to the antenna as shown in Fig 3.14, with the antenna connected to the centre connector of the receiver or transceiver coaxial antenna socket.

The antenna must be resonated using an inductance of around 5 to 7mH, depending on the size of your antenna. Sometimes you can find such a coil in an old scrap television, used in the line-scan linearity circuit. This inductor may have the advantage having a variable ferrite or iron core. Alternatively you can use a fixed inductor and series tune it with a capacitor as shown in Fig 3.14.

Transmitting on 136kHz

Constructing antennas that can radiate a signal for these low frequencies is a challenge. The most effective antenna used so far is the old inductively loaded Marconi.

The problem with antennas for this band is that they are only a fraction of a wavelength long and the radiation resistance is very low, often in the region of 0.01Ω. The loading coil resistance and the earth resistance is in series with the radiation resistance so only a small part of the transmitter power is dissipated in the radiation resistance and radiated.

However, with some ingenuity and lateral thinking, practical antennas have been constructed. Tuned loops, loaded Marconis and short dipoles have all been used with some success.

The secret of getting an antenna to work on LF is the loading coil and a good earth.

You will probably need an inductor of around 3 to 5mH. I found the best solution to be plastic lattice fencing. This can be rolled into coil formers of any size. There is very little plastic material used in the support so the coils wound on them are almost air-spaced. Using this construction a multi-tapped inductor coil wound on a 300mm diameter, 500mm long was found to be suitable.

When you feed power into such an antenna system the voltage across the coil is very large. The coil is wound in small multi-layer bunches distributed over the full length of the former, thereby distributing the RF potential gradient over the length of the coil.

To be able to tune the antenna exactly to resonance you need to make the value of the loading coil variable. The traditional method of making a loading coil variable is to use a variometer.

The other method is to use a ferrite core whose position inside the coil can be adjusted, thereby varying the inductance of the coil, as described by G3KAU [5]. By using a ferrite core the coil can be made much smaller but

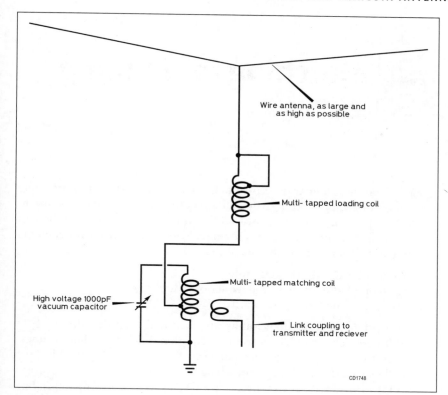

Wire antenna, as large and as high as possible

Multi- tapped loading coil

Multi- tapped matching coil

High voltage 1000pF vacuum capacitor

Link coupling to transmitter and reciever

CD1748

Fig 3.15. An experimental arrangement to use any existing wire antenna for transmitting and receiving 136kHz signals. A better method is to build a variometer into the loading coil and feed the bottom of it via a multi-tapped ferrite cored transformer

care is required in the construction to ensure that it can stand the high RF voltages on transmit.

An experimental transmitting arrangement is shown in Fig 3.15 but the construction of a 136kHz station is beyond the scope of this book and you should consult reference [5] to proceed further with this band.

REFERENCES

[1] 'Taming the end-fed antenna', Alan Chester, G3CCB, *Radio Communication* September 1994.

[2] 'In Practice', *Radio Communication* May 1994.

[3] 'Eurotek', *Radio Communication* September 1993.

[4] 'A remote controlled ATU', L B Uphill, G3UCE, *Radio Communication* February 1989.

[5] *The LF Experimenter's Source Book*, Peter Dodd, G3LDO, RSGB.

4 | Matching and tuning

MOST of the antennas described in Chapters 2 and 3 may require some degree of impedance transformation before they can be connected to the station transmitter. A unit for providing this transformation is called an *ATU* (antenna tuning unit). There are three different antenna arrangements that may need coupling to the transmitter:

- The antenna fed with coaxial cable
- The antenna fed with twin-line feeder or ladder line
- The wire antenna fed against earth

The descriptions of ATUs that follow are classified roughly into pi- or T-network tuners for coaxial lines and link-coupled ATUs for balanced lines. T-network tuners may be used for balanced lines with suitable additions; these will be described where appropriate.

An ATU for use with the end-fed wire was described in Chapter 3, but some of the units for feeding coaxial or twin-line feeder may also be used for end-fed antennas. These will be described where appropriate.

THE T-NETWORK ANTENNA TUNER

The basics of the pi- and T-networks were described by G3VA in 'Technical Topics' [1] as follows.

The classic pi-network or LC/CL two-component matching networks can be used as the basis of an antenna tuning unit (ATU). These are theoretically capable of matching any transmitter to any antenna impedance (resistive or reactive). However, in practice the matching range is dependent on the component values. For the widest step-up and step-down transformations, the high-voltage variable capacitors need to have low minimum and very large maximum capacitance values – a significant disadvantage these days. The pi-network and the standard LC configurations, see Fig 4.1, do however possess the advantage that they not only transform impedance but also form a low-pass filter; and so provide additional harmonic and higher frequency spuriae attenuation.

But modern solid-state transceivers include built-in low-pass filtering tailored to the individual bands,

Fig 4.1. Some basic ATU configurations. (a) Pi-network in conventional 'low-pass' form. (b) Inverse pi-network with components interchanged but providing high-pass filter. (c) Switched LC network providing either step-up or step-down of the impedance with a degree of low-pass filtering. (d) T-network (high-pass)

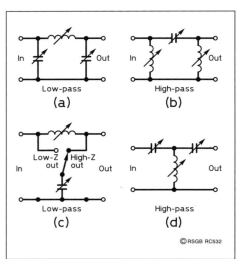

In — Low-pass **(a)**

In — High-pass **(b)**

In — Low-Z out / High-Z out — Out — Low-pass **(c)**

In — High-pass **(d)**

©RSGB RC532

with the result that there is far less requirement for the harmonic attenuation previously provided by the ATU. This has opened the way for much greater use of the T-network which can provide an acceptably wide range of impedance transformations without a requirement for large-value variable capacitors. The fact that they form a high-pass rather than a low-pass filter is no longer regarded as a real disadvantage.

The T-match ATU has enjoyed considerable popularity in the USA, being described as the *transmatch*. Anyone who has seen several editions of the *ARRL Handbook* will be aware that the transmatch has, over the years, undergone a number of circuit changes.

The following is a description of how to construct a T-match ATU by M J Grierson, G3TSO.

The G3TSO Transmatch

In his article [2] G3TSO gives us a short history of the development of the transmatch. The original design, Fig 4.2(a), used either a differential or a split-stator input capacitor. The differential capacitor is less common than the split-stator type and has one section at a maximum capacitance while the other section is at minimum capacitance. This has the effect of providing a synthetic sliding tap on the inductor L, whereas the split-stator capacitor tunes the inductor L but maintains the tap centrally.

The use of a dual-type input capacitor for harmonic suppression lost all credence some years ago and the circuit was amended to the simpler T-match of Fig 4.2(b). This circuit is that of a high-pass filter and provides no suppression of harmonics. More recently the SPC (series-parallel capacitance) transmatch, Fig 4.2(c), has emerged with a dual-output capacitor to providing a degree of harmonic suppression. In any event all three designs perform the task of matching a range of impedances quite successfully. As stated earlier, with the advent of SSB and linear amplifiers, and more recently solid-state transmitters with built-in low-pass filters, harmonic suppression is not the problem it was when using Class C AM power amplifiers.

G3TSO decided in the interest of simplicity to adopt the T-match variant of the transmatch, shown in Fig 4.2(b), in his general-purpose antenna tuning unit. This is the route taken by most ATU manufacturers at the time of writing – more of this later.

The circuit diagram of the G3TSO general-purpose antenna tuning unit is shown in Fig 4.3.

The tuning unit to be described provides operation on all bands from 1.8 to 28MHz. Other features have been added to permit the selection of different antennas as well as the facility to ground all inputs when the station is not in use. This unit also includes an SWR meter and a balun to allow the unit to feed balanced lines. You may not wish to include all these features.

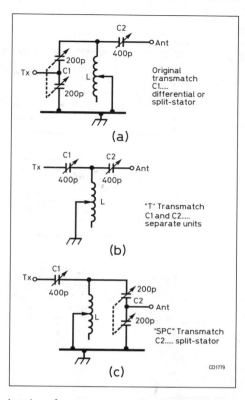

Fig 4.2. Variations of the 'Ultimate transmatch' (a) Original transmatch; C1: differential or split-stator type. (b) T-transmatch; C1, 2: separate units. (c) SPC transmatch; C2: split-stator type

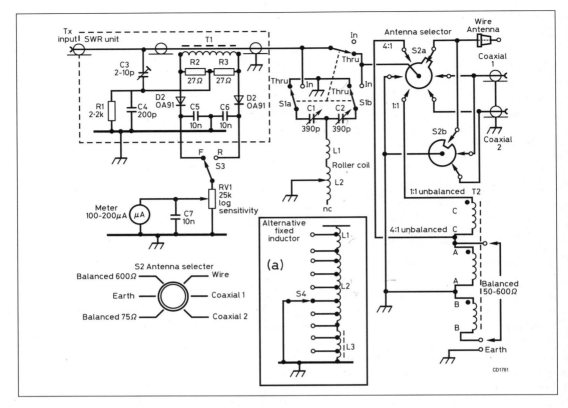

Fig 4.3. Circuit diagram of the G3TSO ATU

Component selection

New components suitable for use in antenna tuners are not readily available or very expensive, so the use of surplus components is the most economical answer. Fortunately the values of capacitors required are not too critical, and almost any high-quality wide-spaced variable capacitor can be put to use. Ideally a value of between 200pF and 400pF is suitable, and a number of surplus Johnson and Eddystone 390pF units have been seen over recent years. These units have ceramic end-plates and are tested to 2000V DC working. If in doubt, aim at a plate spacing of at least 1.5mm between the stator and rotor plates; this is necessary to cope with the high voltages which can be developed when matching high-impedance long-wire antennas.

Inductors can be either fixed, with a number of taps selected by a rotary switch, or variable such as the *roller coaster*, which allows maximum flexibility in matching. Roller coasters come in a variety of different shapes and sizes, but in general are not available in other than small numbers and one-offs.

All switches used are of the Yaxley type and use ceramic wafers; large numbers of this type of switch can often be found in junk boxes at rallies, and several switches can be broken down and reassembled to achieve the desired configuration. Paxolin wafers can be used, though they are not as good as the ceramic type.

The antenna selector switch uses a double-spaced switch unit giving six stops/revolution rather than the usual 12. The switch wafers are modified by removing alternate contacts, thus reducing the likelihood of arcing between them.

Balanced feeders

As the T-match is an unbalanced antenna tuner, some type of balun transformer must be incorporated if it is to be used successfully with balanced feeders. While a balun transformer provides a very simple solution for coupling a balanced feeder to an unbalanced tuning unit, it is not likely to be as efficient as a properly balanced ATU. Many published designs use a 4:1 balun to provide a balanced input for impedances in the range 150 to 600Ω. However, if a low impedance feeder from either a G5RV or W3DZZ type of antenna is connected to a 4:1 balun, significant losses may occur. For this reason it was decided to use a 1:1 balun which, if fitted inside the tuning circuit, can easily be switched to 4:1 by use of the antenna selector switch. This now provides a range of balanced inputs from about 45 to 600Ω without introducing too many losses into the system.

Balun construction

The balun transformer is wound on a single Amidon T200-2 powdered-iron core, colour coded red. For sustained high-power operation, 400W plus, two such cores can be taped together by using plumbers' PTFE tape, which can also be used to provide an added layer of insulation between the core and the windings.

Balun construction is simple but a little cumbersome; some 14 turns of 16SWG enamelled-copper wire have to be wound trifilar fashion onto the toroidal core. That is to say, three identical windings are wound on together. Care must be taken to ensure that the windings do not overlap or cross one another and that neither the core nor enamel covering is badly scratched during construction.

14 turns will require approximately 97cm (38in) of 16SWG (1.6mm) wire, so cut three equal lengths of 16SWG wire slightly longer than required and pass all three wires through the core until they have reached about halfway. This now becomes the centre of the winding and it is easier to wind from the centre to either end rather than from one end to the other which involves passing long lengths of wire through the toroid. The T200 size core will accommodate 14 turns trifilar without any overlapping of the start and finish of the winding. Close spacing will occur at the inside of the core, and a regular spacing interval should be set up on the outside. A small gap should be left where the two ends of the winding come close together.

Connection of the balun is requires care and it is necessary to identify opposite ends of the same windings, which can be done with a continuity meter, with some form of tagging or colour coding being worthwhile. On the circuit diagram a dot is used to signify the same end for separate windings. It is essential that the various windings are correctly connected if the balun is to work properly.

Details of how the balun transformer is wound and connected are shown in Fig 4.4. In this tuning unit, the balun is supported directly by soldering to the balanced input terminals, which are spring-loaded connectors. A sheet

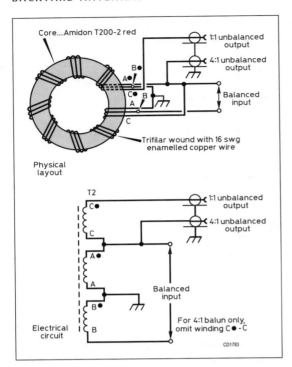

Fig 4.4. The balun transformer (G3TSO)

of 8mm (^{5}/16in) Perspex is then used to insulate the balun from the aluminium case. Construction of a 4:1 balun only is slightly simpler and only requires two (bifilar) windings.

SWR measurement

It is often convenient to be able to connect the antenna tuner directly to the transmitter without the need for extra cables and external SWR bridges, so a built-in SWR bridge has been included in the design.

The circuit, shown in Fig 4.3, is fairly conventional and is of the current-sampling type of bridge which, unlike the voltage-sampling stripline type of bridge, is not frequency conscious.

The current transformer T1 uses a small ferrite ring of about 12mm (0.5in) diameter and, while the size is not critical, the grade of ferrite is. Ferrite having an AL value of at least 125 should be used, and the Amidon FTSO-43 ferrite core is ideally suited to this application.

A short length of coaxial cable is passed through the ferrite core to form the primary after the 18-turn secondary has been wound on. The braid of the cable can be earthed at one end to form an electrostatic screen, but on no account should both ends of the braid be earthed or it will form a shorted turn.

The diodes D1 and D2 should be a matched pair of germanium diodes, which can be selected from a number of similar-type diodes by comparing their forward and reverse resistances. While this is best done with a high-frequency signal, adequate matching can be achieved by using a simple multimeter.

Fig 4.5 gives a suggested layout and PCB track. The size is not at all critical but a symmetrical layout should always be attempted.

The completed SWR bridge should be tested away from the antenna tuner by placing it in line between a suitable transmitter and a 50Ω dummy load. The trimmer capacitor is adjusted to produce a zero-reflected reading with the forward reading at full scale. By connecting the bridge the reverse way around, some check of the diode balance can be judged by comparing the meter deflections in both directions. The forward and reverse switch selection will be reversed if the signal direction through the bridge is reversed. It is advisable to check that the bridge balances on a number of different bands, as C3 may be more sensitive at the higher-frequency end of the operating range.

The sensitivity of the bridge is very dependent upon the resistance of the meter used. Comparison with a calibrated SWR bridge will enable a simple calibration of 1.5:1, 2:1 and 3:1 to be made, and in most cases a mental note of where these occur is the only calibration required, unless you wish to dismantle the meter in order to recalibrate the scale.

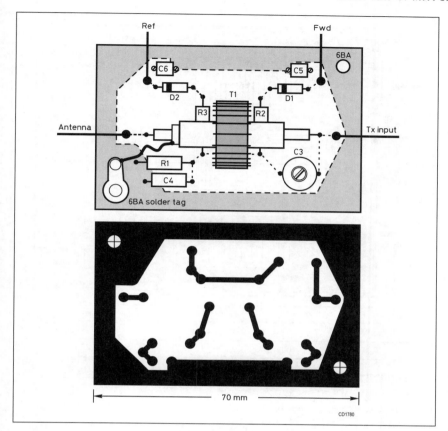

Fig 4.5. PCB and lay-out for the SWR bridge

Construction of the antenna tuner

The complete tuner layout is illustrated in Figs 4.6 and 4.7, with a components list in Table 4.1. It is advisable to collect all the components and lay them out on a sheet of paper before committing oneself to a particular size. Layout is not over-critical, but a sensible approach is needed to minimise lead lengths and unnecessary stray capacitance which could render 28MHz operation impossible.

Cases can be purchased, or prefabricated using 16 or 18SWG aluminium sheet bent into two interlocking 'U' shapes. Half-inch aluminium angle provides stiffening as well as a means of joining the sections together. Roller coaster connections should be arranged so that minimum inductance is located at the end closest to the connections, ideally the rear of the unit. A small heavy-duty coil, L1, is included for ease of 28MHz operation and is more efficient than half a turn on the roller coil. An alternative arrangement to the roller coaster is shown in Fig 4.3(a). Here a switched inductor is used. The switch should be of the ceramic type with substantial contacts. A third toroidal inductor is included to permit operation on 1.8MHz, and it is recommended that the bottom end of this could be shorted to ground to prevent the build-up of high voltages which could arc over.

G3OHK has described a further switched inductor [1], and this is shown in Fig 4.8.

Fig 4.6. Component layout of the G3TSO ATU

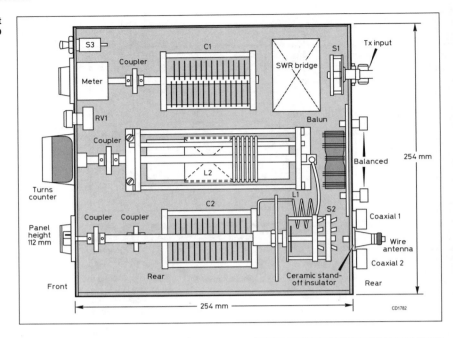

Fig 4.7. Front and rear panels of the G3TSO ATU

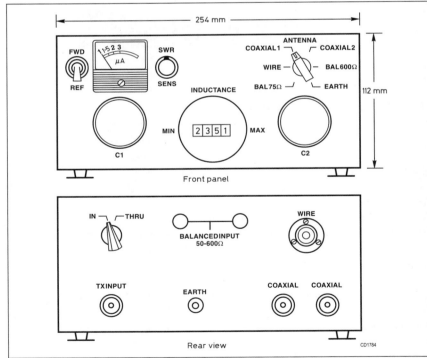

The capacitors C1 and C2 are electrically above ground and must be mounted on insulators, a problem greatly reduced if the capacitors are constructed using ceramic end-plates. Ceramic pillars or even Perspex may be considered for mounting capacitors with metal end-plates. Additionally the

Table 4.1. Components list

ATU

C1, 2	390p 2000VDC wkg, ceramic end-plates, eg Eddystone or Jackson
L1	3t 10SWG, 25mm (1in) ID, 25mm (1in) long
L2	Roller coaster 36t, 38mm (1.5in) dia, 16SWG
T2	Amidon T200-2 (red); 14t trifilar 16SWG enamel
S1	Three-pole two-way ceramic Yaxley
S2	One-pole six-way double-spaced ceramic Yaxley
	One-pole six-way shorting water (one pole open)

ALTERNATIVE ATU CIRCUIT

L1	2.5t 14SWG 25mm (1in) ID tapped at 1.5t
L2	14t 16SWG 1.25in ID tapped at 1, 2, 6, 9 and 14t
L3	Amidon T1 57-2; 31t 18SWG enam tapped at 6 and 27t
L4	One-pole 11-way ceramic (three wafers to include S1 function)

SWR BRIDGE

R1	2k2
C3	2–10p trimmer
C4	200p mica
C5, 6, 7	10n disc ceramic
R2, 3	27R
RV1	25k log
D1, 2	Matched OA91 etc (germanium diodes)
T1	18t 22SWG 13mm (0.5in) OD ferrite ring (Amidon FT50-43, Fairite 26-43006301). Primary: 38mm (1.5in) coaxial cable, braid earthed one end only to form electrostatic shield.
Meter	100–200µA
S3	SPCO miniature toggle

Note: For equipment and parts suppliers see Appendix.

shafts of the capacitors must be insulated, and the use of Eddystone spindle couplers is recommended. To ease the rather sharp tuning characteristics that can be encountered on 21 and 28MHz, slow-motion drives were tried but they made tuning on the lower frequencies rather laborious and their use is not advisable. A turns counter on the roller coaster makes for much simpler operation, and may be as simple as a slot in the cabinet with a Perspex window for monitoring the position of the jockey wheel or a more sophisticated geared or direct-drive counter.

Antenna switching can introduce excessive lead lengths as well as stray capacitance, and for this reason the antenna selector switch is located on an extension shaft at the rear of the unit adjacent to the antenna inputs and the balun transformer. The wiring of the antenna switch is done strictly to achieve minimum lead lengths rather than to provide front-panel selections in any logical order. A separate IN/THROUGH switch enables the tuner to be by-passed and the antennas routed directly to the trans-mitter. It is located on the rear panel adjacent to the input socket to minimise lead length, and is only intended for occasional use. It is necessary to ground the tuning components in the THROUGH position to minimise capacitance effects.

Wiring of the tuner should commence after the mounting of all components, and fairly heavy wire such as 16SWG tinned wire, coaxial cable braid or copper strip should be used. It has not been found

Fig 4.8. A variable-inductance ATU coil described by Hector Cole, G3OHK. This arrangement uses two switches and just 14 taps to permit selection of from one to 50 turns of a 50-turn coil. It can be quickly reset to any number of turns previously found suitable without the turns counters required for roller coaster coils

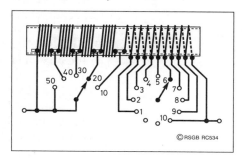

necessary to screen the SWR bridge, but it should be located directly adjacent to the transmitter input socket and all meter leads kept away from tuning components.

The antenna selector switch has two ceramic wafers and is arranged so that every other contact is removed to give double spacing. The second wafer is used for shorting and provides a ground for all unbalanced antennas not in use, and is largely to prevent capacitative coupling to other antennas. The balanced input is grounded to DC through the balun. Balun switching is simply achieved by either taking the input from one side of the balanced input, giving a 4:1 ratio, or by selecting the third winding, giving a 1:1 ratio. An earth position enables the transceiver input to be grounded to prevent static discharge into the receiver.

Operation of the antenna tuning unit

If the SWR bridge is included in the design it should be checked and balanced independently of the ATU, using a dummy load, and ideally be compared and calibrated against an SWR measuring device of known accuracy.

To use the antenna tuner, select the required antenna and ensure that the IN/THROUGH switch is in the IN position. Set both C1 and C2 to halfway positions, adjust the inductance for maximum signal on receive, and one at a time adjust C1 and C2 for maximum received signal. Using low CW transmitter power, further adjust C1, C2 and the inductance to eliminate any reflected reading on the SWR meter. All tuning controls are interdependent, and settings may need to be adjusted several times before minimum SWR is achieved. In addition, more than one setting may give a matched condition, in which case the settings requiring the highest value of C1 should be used. Once the transmitter is matched on low power, increase to the operating power for any final adjustments. Never attempt to tune the ATU initially on full power or with a valve power amplifier that has not been tuned up.

Generally, the higher the frequency, the lower the value of inductance required but exceptionally high impedances may require more inductance than expected. Capacitance values may vary considerably, and it is not uncommon on the higher frequencies for one capacitor to be very sharp and require a minimum value while the other is flat and unresponsive. Using the components recommended it is possible to match a wide range of impedances from 1.8 to 28MHz, but operation on 1.8MHz may become impossible if lower values of capacitance are used. However, fixed silver mica capacitors may be switched across C1 and C2 to compensate. Higher values of capacitor will almost certainly prevent operation on 28 and maybe 14MHz.

Conclusion

The antenna tuner described is not new or revolutionary in design but probably represents the ultimate in flexibility. Performance is good and it is not inhibited by a lack of balanced input or restricted to a very narrow range of low impedances. The power handling capability of the tuner will to a large extent depend upon the impedances encountered and the spacings of the capacitors. As a rule, very high impedances should be avoided, as arcing can occur in the switches and the efficiency of the unit may well suffer.

Adjustment of antenna or feeder length can remove any exceptionally high impedances that may be encountered.

G3TSO used this tuner with a 60m (180ft) doublet fed with an unknown length of 300Ω slotted ribbon feeder, where it could be tuned to give a 1:1 SWR on all amateur bands from 1.8 to 28MHz. Using Eddystone capacitors of the type recommended, the tuning unit should be capable of handling 100W into a fairly wide range of impedances up to several thousand ohms, and the full 400W into impedances up to 600Ω.

Two versions of the tuner have been built using the same basic circuit, one for base station operation using a roller coaster coil, and a smaller portable version using a range of switched inductors. The portable version has a slightly different layout, largely as a result of trying several other designs, and combining the IN/THROUGH facility on the inductor switch has necessitated several wafers. The balun used in this version is also the simpler 4:1 type and is connected with a flying lead.

For those who wish to adopt the SPC circuit, the value of C2 should be made approximately 200pF, and an additional similar-value capacitor should be ganged to C2 and connected between the antenna side of C2 and ground. Both capacitor rotors should be connected together and the stator of the new capacitor should be grounded.

The construction of the described antenna tuning unit should be well within the capabilities of most newly licensed amateurs, and it can represent a considerable financial saving when compared to the commercial alternative.

The MFJ VersaTuner V

This is a commercial ATU from MFJ (see Appendix). It uses a T-match tuning arrangement very similar to the G3TSO tuner described above. It also uses similar antenna switching and has a cross-needle power and SWR meter that is particularly convenient to use. The ability to switch in a dummy load is also a useful feature. In fact this is more than an ATU – it is an antenna management system.

The circuit is shown in Fig 4.9 and the layout in Fig 4.10. The toroid balun is fixed at 4:1, with its limitations as described below.

BALANCED ATUS

Many of the antennas described in Chapter 2 require a balanced feed. The following is material by W4RNL, who describes methods [3] to adapt unbalanced antenna tuners (ATUs or transmatches) to service with balanced lines. Among the schemes used the following are the most common ones:

1. Float the tuner from ground and install a balun at the input end.
2. Install a balun, usually 4:1, at the antenna side of the tuner, to convert the balanced line to an unbalanced line.

Either system is subject to limitations. Floating the tuner does not guarantee freedom from common-mode currents that defeat balance. A 4:1 balun often reduces the already low impedance at the antenna terminals to a still lower one, and high reactances are often unfriendly to the cores used in such baluns.

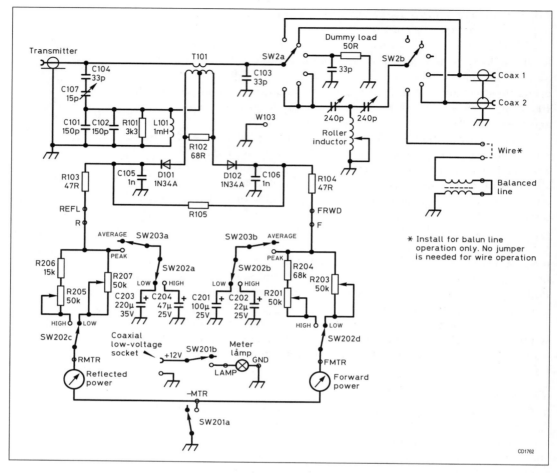

Fig 4.9. Circuit diagram of the MFJ VersaTuner V

The more classic alternative is the link-coupled or inductively coupled ATU; the basic circuitry is shown in Fig 4.11. The unbalanced input is inductively coupled to the main inductor. Since the mutual inductance between the coils is critical for maximum efficiency, the coupling is varied either by a movable link or by a series input capacitor.

Likewise, a single coil and link for all HF bands does not provide the best coupling ratios for all possible conditions. Without provision for coil tapping and series connections, the most efficient operating mode may be inaccessible, despite a 1:1 match.

For an operator who likes to change bands frequently, these inconveniences may be worse than the losses inherent in current systems pressed into balanced-line duty. However, for operators seeking the most efficient transfer of power to balanced lines, nothing beats a properly designed and constructed link-coupled ATU.

Commercial balanced-line tuners

You won't find many of these around. Two such tuners, described by W4RNL [3], are the Johnson Matchbox and the Annecke (made in Germany). A simplified diagram of these units is shown in Fig 4.12.

The Johnson Matchbox circuit is a straightforward link-coupled circuit. The input with the relay and associated circuitry includes taps for a 50Ω transmitter connection and a 300Ω receiver connection, since receivers continued to used balanced input strips long after transmitters had gone to shielding, pi-networks, and 50Ω outputs. The Johnson Matchbox uses a single link for all bands with no variability.

The Annecke design does away with the relay, receiver tap, and other pre-50Ω transceiver features. Instead, it uses a larger (overcoupled) link with taps for the various bands (3.5, 7, 10–14, 18–21, and 24–28MHz) mechanically linked to the secondary coil tap switches. In addition, it employs a series variable capacitor to adjust coupling (or input impedance, which amounts to the same thing). The Annecke design is superior in this regard.

The secondary systems of both the Matchbox and the Annecke are almost identical, differing only in output connection options. The secondary coil is

Fig 4.10. Layout of the MFJ VersaTuner V

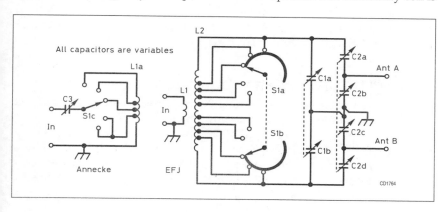

Fig 4.11. Typical link-coupled antenna tuner circuit

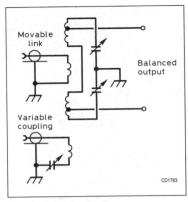

Fig 4.12. Simplified diagram of the Johnson and Annecke link-coupled tuning units

tapped at reasonable positions for 3.5/7/14/21/28MHz, shorting out the unused turns toward the outer ends. Although the Annecke is marked with the preferred settings for the WARC bands, Matchbox users will have to experiment on these bands. Across the outer limits of the coil is a split-stator capacitor, with the moving vanes earthed, which is used to set the tank at resonance. The required value of capacitance will vary somewhat as the reactance and resistance at the antenna terminals is varied.

The terminals are not connected directly to the out limits of the tank. Each side of ground passes to a differential capacitor. The centre of each differential goes to the antenna terminal. As mentioned earlier, a differential capacitor is a split-stator variable arranged so that as capacitance on one side goes up it decreases on the other. The antenna terminal on each side of ground is thus set at a certain reactance from ground and certain series reactance from the tank. This arrangement forms a voltage divider. It also forms a means of compensating for reactance at the antenna terminal of the tuner, allowing it to match a wide range of $R \pm jX$ combinations that might be present at the antenna terminals and still present the requisite high impedance to the tank circuit ends.

The Johnson design goes back to AM days, so the 275W rating is conservative to the power of the carrier plus sidebands of a 100% modulated AM signal. Capacitors appear to be spaced for at least 3kV or better. The Annecke unit is rated at 200W and appears (from the photo of the case and the control arrangement) to use slightly lighter components than the Johnson, even though the 200W rating is also conservative.

One bad tendency of all antenna tuner makers is to list a simple impedance range for the antenna matching capabilities, for example, 50–3000Ω for the Annecke. Actually, the ability of any tuner to effect a match is determined by the combination of R and jX at the antenna terminals. Whatever the reactance-compensating scheme, it will have some limitations, usually being more effective with large values of either jX or $-jX$, but not both. Moreover, the range of impedances for which any given tuner design can achieve maximum efficiency is ordinarily quite a bit narrower than for achieving a mere 1:1 SWR on the transmitter side. However, bringing the impedance presented to the antenna terminals within the range of the tuner's maximum efficiency potential is usually only a transmission line length change away – see the W6RCA antenna in Chapter 2.

BALANCED TUNER WITH PLUG-IN COILS

As stated earlier by W4RNL, nothing beats a properly designed and constructed link-coupled ATU for the most efficient transfer of power to balanced lines, but they are hard to find. You could make one and the description of the ATU that follows [4] is by Ted Garrott, G0LMJ. It uses plug-in coils rather than switching, each HF band having its own plug-in coil. A total of nine coils are therefore needed to cover all bands 1.8–28.0MHz.

The ATU uses a conventional circuit, see Fig 4.13, except that L1 and L3

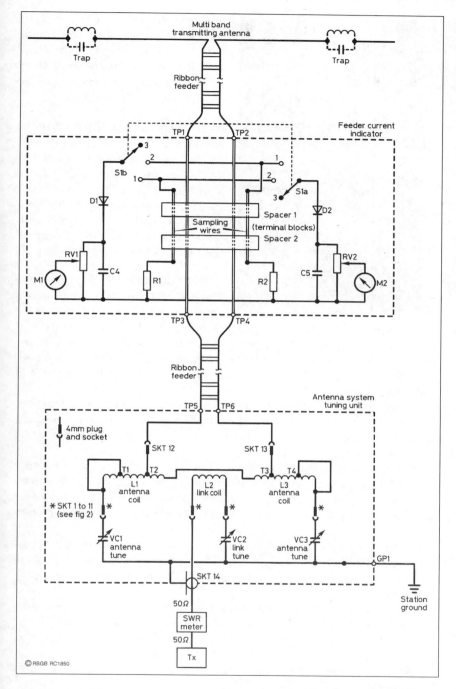

Fig 4.13. The G0LMJ balanced-line ATU circuit diagram. The ATU is shown in the lower dotted box, and the feeder current indicator in the upper dotted box

are not tuned by a split-stator capacitor. Instead, two separate capacitors VC1 and VC3 are used. This arrangement provides the facility of adjusting the ATU to give equal current into the two halves of the antenna. The relative values of RF current in the two feeder wires is monitored using with two meters M1 and M2.

Fig 4.14. General view of G0LMJ's balanced line ATU

A general view of the ATU is shown in Fig 4.14. As can be seen, the unit is built in two parts: the tuner and feeder current balance indicators.

An SWR meter is used between the transmitter and the ATU.

Materials and components

Medium-density fibreboard (MDF) is used for the chassis and plastic drainage piping for the coil construction. These materials were used because they were easy to obtain and inexpensive. In fact all the materials and components have been chosen because they are relatively easy to obtain.

Construction

The general layout and dimensions is shown in Fig 4.15. A components list is given in Table 4.2. The chassis is made from 6mm MDF and the joins fixed with wood adhesive. The outside of the chassis is smoothed with sandpaper and wiped with a damp cloth to remove the dust, and then treated with four coats of varnish. VC1 and VC3 are mounted below the chassis and bolted to the side walls.

VC2 is also mounted below the chassis on its own fabricated brackets. The output terminal posts TP5 and 6, together with two 4mm coil sockets, SKT12 and 13, are mounted on a bracket glued to the rear of the chassis, as shown in Fig 4.16.

The coil and VC1, 2 and 3 are mounted to the rear of the chassis, in order to avoid hand-capacitance effects when tuning. VC1, 2 and 3 are driven by calibrated slow-motion drives via lengths of insulated rod. To reduce backlash this rod is both screwed and glued to the coupler and slow-motion drive.

The 4mm coil sockets, SKT1 to 11, are arranged along the rear of the chassis to accommodate the plug-in coils. The seemingly odd spacing of these sockets is to accommodate the various lengths of coil formers and plug spacings.

Note that some of the 4mm sockets are connected together under the chassis (see Fig 4.15). Some of the sockets are too close together to use the fixing nuts, so these are glued into their holes. The sockets *must be* accurately set out on the chassis.

Self-adhesive rubber feet are attached via pieces of 25 × 25mm MDF, glued to the corners of the chassis.

The general layout of the feeder current indicator section is shown in Fig 4.17. This is fixed into a convenient place so that it can be seen when adjusting the ATU. In Figs 4.14 and 4.16 the unit is shown fixed to a shelf.

Note the use of five-way mains terminal blocks for spacing the sampling wires; 1.25mm wire is used for all wires through the terminal blocks.

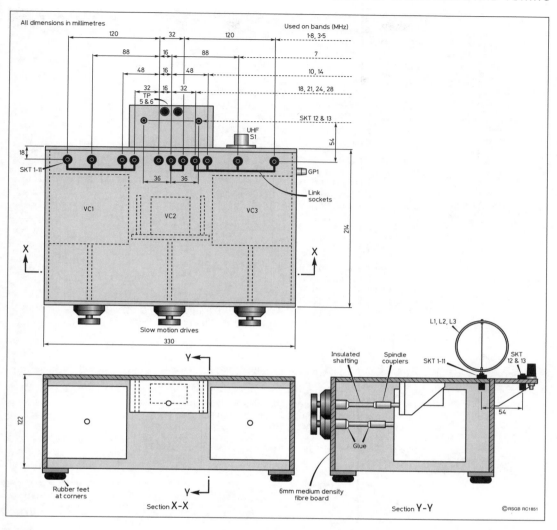

Fig 4.15. Dimensions and physical layout of the ATU section

Coils

The nine plug-in coils are shown in Fig 4.18. The formers are plastic pipes, as used for drainage. Winding details for coils to cover all nine HF amateur bands are given in Table 4.3. The turns are held in place with beads of epoxy resin; four beads for 68mm and three beads for 36mm formers. The link coils L2 all resonate within the band they are wound for, using the 400pF capacitor VC2.

The method of fixing the 4mm plugs to the formers is shown in Fig 4.19. 5mm (³/₁₆in) diameter holes are fine for the Maplin 4mm plugs, and they will self-tap into the plastic. If any other type of plug is used, the hole size should be determined by testing on scrap material first. The plugs *must be* accurately set out on the former. A 45W large-tipped soldering iron can be used to solder the 1.6mm wire into the plugs.

The method of terminating the ends of L1 and L3 and joining them over the top of L2 is shown in Fig 4.20.

Table 4.2. Components list

RESISTORS
R1, 2   150R 2W metal film
RV1, 2   47k linear potentiometers with plastic shafts, Maplin FWO4E

CAPACITORS
VC1, 3   13–250p, 7.8kV, type TC250, ex Nevada
VC2   14–400p, 1.25kV, Jackson type LAT, ex Cirkit
C4, 5   10n 50V ceramic disc

SEMICONDUCTORS
D1, 2   1N914

MISCELLANEOUS
M1, M2   100µA, Maplin RX 33L
S1   4-pole 3-way rotary switch, Maplin FF76H. Two poles are spare. Use spare
          tags as junctions for D1, C4, VR1, and D2, C5, VR2
GP1   Grounding post, Maplin JL99H
TP5, 6   Terminal posts, Maplin HFO2C
SKT1–13   4mm sockets, Maplin KC49D
SKT14   UHF chassis socket
TP1–4   Terminal posts, Maplin HF02C

Small vernier dials (3 off), Maplin 141 RX39N
Pointer knob, Maplin RW75S
Spindle couplers (3 off)
Knobs (2 off), Maplin FK40T
4mm banana plugs (54 off), Maplin JB24B (sufficient for 9 coils)
3mm panel head steel bolts, 16mm long, with nuts and washers (8 off)
Self adhesive rubber feet (4 off)
Spacer 1,2, terminal block (one 12-way strip, cut to suit), Maplin FE78K
MDF, 6mm thick, 35cm × 1.2m approx
Perspex, 4mm thick, 100 × 300mm approx
Plastic tube, 68mm OD, 1.25m
Plastic tube, 36mm OD, 0.5m
Enamelled copper wire (159g), 1.25mm (18SWG)
Tinned copper wire (450g), 1.25mm (18SWG)
Tinned copper wire (150g), 1.6mm (16SWG)

Note: For equipment and parts suppliers see Appendix.

Fig 4.16. Rear view of the ATU. Note the bracket which carries coil sockets SKT12 and 13, and the output terminals TP 5 and 6

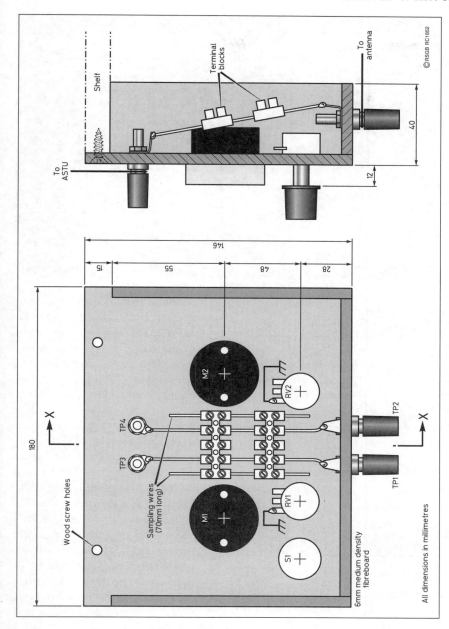

Fig 4.17. Dimensions and physical layout of feeder current indicator

This method only works well for 68mm formers. For 36mm formers the ends of L1 and L3 can be terminated using solder tags, held down to the former with self-tapping screws. The coil ends are then joined with a jumper wire over the top of L2.

The construction for fixing the 4mm plugs to the coil former at SKT12 and 13 is shown in Fig 4.21. The two plugs are glued to a bracket, constructed from 4mm Perspex, which is glued to the coil former.

Wire was soldered to the plugs before assembling the plugs to the Perspex. Before applying glue, all components including the coil were put into place

Fig 4.18. The nine coils required to cover all the HF bands

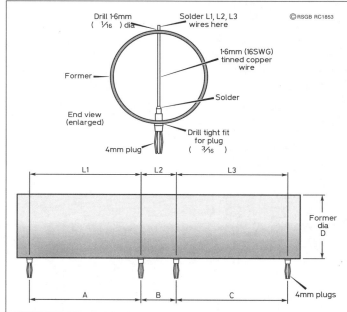

© RSGB RC1853

Drill 1·6mm (1⁄16) dia

Solder L1, L2, L3 wires here

1·6mm (16SWG) tinned copper wire

Former

Solder

End view (enlarged)

4mm plug

Drill tight fit for plug (3⁄16)

L1   L2   L3

Former dia D

A   B   C   4mm plugs

Fig 4.19. Basic construction and dimensions of the plug-in coils

on the chassis. The glue was then applied and allowed to set thoroughly. The result is a perfect fit of the coil plugs to the chassis sockets. In order to facilitate good bonding, the Perspex is thoroughly roughened to provide a key for the epoxy resin. The bracket arms are glued to L2 on top of the 1.8, 3.5 and 7MHz coils, and direct to the former for all other coils. Coil taps T1 to T4 are determined by testing, using flexible wire and crocodile clips for attaching to the coil and sockets SKT12 and 13. All taps are made symmetrically about the coil centre. When the correct tap positions are found, the final, permanent wiring can be made. An SWR of 1.0 is aimed for, and when achieved VC1, 2 and 3 should be comfortably within their working range (ie not at maximum or minimum). VC1 and 3 should be set at about the same dial readings.

Set-up procedure

To determine the correct positions for taps T1 to T4, the following procedure is recommended:

1. Set T1 and T4 one turn from each end of the coil.
2. Transmit low power at the low-frequency end of the band.

Band (MHz)	L1 (turns)	L2 (turns)	L3 (turns)	D (mm)	A (mm)	B (mm)	C (mm)
1.8	28	18	28	68	120	32	120
3.5	28	11	28	68	120	32	120
7.0	19	5	19	68	88	16	88
10.1	10	3	10	68	48	16	48
14.0	9	3	9	68	48	16	48
18.068	3	2	3	68	32	16	32
21.0	4	4	4	36	32	16	32
24.89	4	4	4	36	32	16	32
28.0	4	4	4	36	32	16	32

Table 4.3. Coil turns and dimensions

L1 and L3: 1.25mm tinned copper wire to fill available space and wound in same direction. L2: 1.25mm enamelled copper wire close wound

3. Try various positions for T2 and T3, tuning VC1, 2 and 3 for minimum SWR.
4. If an SWR of 1.0 is not achieved, carry out step (3) again, but with T1 and T4 set nearer the centre of the coil.
5. When an SWR of 1.0 is achieved, connect the permanent taps T1, 2, 3 and 4.

Having established the correct tap positions, the settings for VC1, 2 and 3 must be determined for various frequencies in the band. This is done by trying various settings until one is found that gives an SWR of 1.0. VC1 and VC3 should be kept at about the same settings.

Current sharing

The next stage is to ensure that the two halves of the dipole are taking the same current. Meters M1 and M2 must be adjusted to the same sensitivity before this can be done. The adjustment is carried out as follows:

1. Set RV1 and RV2 fully anti-clockwise.
2. Transmit at low power.
3. Set S1 to position No.1.
4. Adjust M1 to mid-scale, using RV1.
5. Set S1 to position 2.
6. Adjust M2 to mid-scale, using RV2.
7. Reset S1 to position 1.

Both meters now have the same sensitivity and will show the relative currents in each half of the dipole. If these currents are not the same, they may be equalised by further adjustments to VC1, 2 and 3. It will be found that there are a number of VC1, 2 and 3 settings that will give an SWR of 1.0, but only one that will also give equal currents in each half of the dipole.

When the correct settings are found they should be logged. Use Table 4.4 (the results were obtained at G3OLM's QTH with his multi-band dipole) as a guide.

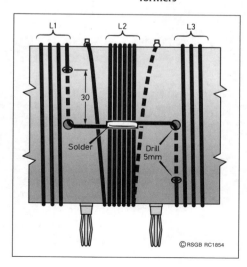

Fig 4.20. L1 to L3 junction on the 68mm formers

© RSGB RC1854

Fig 4.21. Coil connections to the 4mm plugs which connect with SKT13 and 14

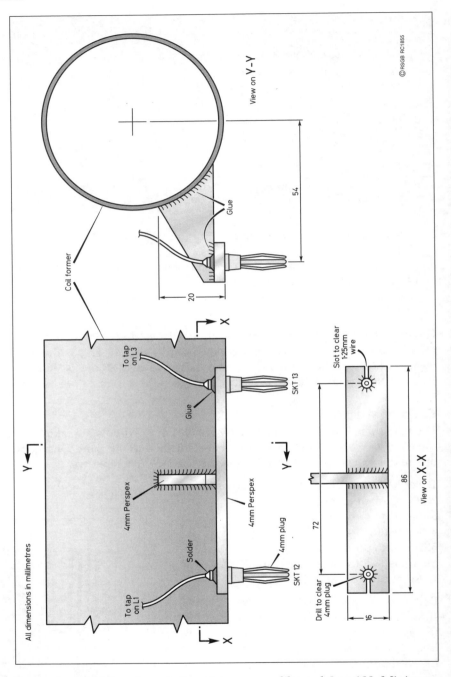

Remember that the slow-motion drives are calibrated 0 to 100. Minimum capacitance is 0, maximum is 100.

If you are using an ATU that feeds into a 450Ω line using a voltage balun it may be an interesting exercise to construct the feeder current indicator and check the feeder currents and see what the balance is like on your antenna.

Safety

There are two safety points which must be stressed:

1. Use a dust mask when working on MDF.
2. In thundery weather, earth both sides of the ribbon feeder to avoid a build-up of high voltage on the antenna.

THE Z-MATCH

Another link-coupled ATU that has been around a long time is the Z-match. Originally it was designed as a tank circuit of a valve PA [5], the anode of which was connected to the top or 'hot' end of the multi-band tuned circuit. It was fed directly from the PA valve, with its internal (source) impedance of several thousand ohms.

When the circuit was adopted as an ATU [6] the tank circuit is fed directly from a source which requires a 50Ω load via a 350pF variable coupling capacitor connected to the top (or 'hot') end of a multi-band parallel-tuned LC circuit.

In spite of the great disparity between the required 50Ω load for the transmitter and the relatively high impedance of the tank circuit the Z-match enjoyed considerable popularity, probably due to its simplicity. Z-match ATUs were produced commercially and they are described here because they are easily available and cheap. An example of such a unit is shown in Fig 4.22.

The design of the Z-match was improved and described by Louis Varney, G5RV. All of what follows is from his article [7].

As you can see in Fig 4.23, on the 3.5, 7 and 10MHz bands the main inductance L1 is connected in parallel with the two sections of C1 which are also paralleled.

The effect of the much smaller inductance L2 can be considered as a rather long connecting lead between the top of C1a and the top of C1b. Since the

Table 4.4. Example of dial settings at G3OLB			
MHz	VC1	VC2	VC3
1.81	70	50	72
2.0	32	47	38
3.5	56	55	56
3.8	39	40	37
7.0	86	50	87
7.1	79	47	79
10.1	17	34	19
10.15	16	34	20
14.0	24	27	30
14.35	22	24	28
18.068	52	60	68
18.168	51	53	66
21.0	38	27	55
21.45	37	30	48
24.89	37	15	18
24.93	37	15	18
28.0	25	26	11.0
29.7	15	43	16.5

Fig 4.22. The original KW E-Zee Match shows the general construction of a Z-match ATU. The construction allows plenty of space for switches if you wish to modify it as described later

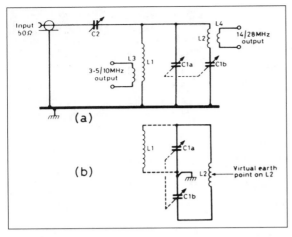

Fig 4.23. (a) The basic Z-match circuit. (b) The 14–28MHz tuned circuit shown in a more conventional form

inductance of L2 is very much less than that of L1, this assumption is valid for the relatively low frequencies of 3.5 and 7MHz. For these bands, therefore, L1, C1a plus C1b may be considered as a simple tuned circuit with one end earthed.

Provided that the capacitance range of C1a plus C1b is sufficient, the circuit will also tune to 10MHz. It may be necessary to reduce the inductance of L1 by one or two turns to achieve resonance on that band. However, it should be noted that care must be taken to avoid the occurrence of harmonic resonance between the two circuits comprising the multi-band tuned circuit and the values of the inductances. L1 and L2 must be selected with this in mind. On the 14, 18, 21, 24 and 28MHz bands the active tuned circuit consists of the two variable capacitor sections C1a, C1b as a split-stator capacitor, with the moving vanes earthed, and L2 connected between the two sets of stator vanes. Because its inductance is much greater than that of L2, L1 may be considered as an HF choke coil connected in parallel with C1a; it has no noticeable effect on the performance of the split-stator tuned circuit L2, C1a, C1b. This can be proved by first tuning this circuit to any band from 14 to 28MHz, noting the dial-reading of C1a, C1b and then disconnecting the top of L1 and retuning for resonance. It will be found that the effect of L1 is negligible.

Fig 4.23(b) shows the effective 14 to 28MHz tuned circuit in a more conventional manner.

The relatively high impedance LC circuits L1, C1a and C1b (paralleled for the 3.5, 7 and 10.1MHz bands) and L2, C1a, C1b (as a split-stator capacitor for the 14 to 28MHz bands) must be detuned slightly off resonance at the frequency in use, so as to present an inductive reactance component. This, in conjunction with the coupling capacitor C2, functions as a series-resonant input circuit which, when correctly tuned, presents a 50Ω non-reactive load to the transmitter output.

Modifying the Z-match

Because feeding the RF energy from the output of a transmitter requiring a 50Ω resistive load to the top of a parallel-tuned LC circuit cannot be the most efficient method, G5RV felt that the circuit would benefit from modification. He performed a number of tests which involved tapping the coils L1 and L2 to obtain a better match. The circuit of the modified Z-match is shown in Fig 4.24.

The final modified Z-match

The final design is shown in Fig 4.25. The circuit incorporates switching for the appropriate coil coupling taps and selects the appropriate output-coupling coil (L3 or L4) to the feeder.

For maximum output coupling efficiency on 7MHz and 10MHz a tap on

L3 is selected by S1b. Provision is made for coaxial cable antennas to be fed either direct or via the Z-match.

The transmitter output can be direct to a suitable 50Ω dummy load. The layout is not critical but it is advisable to mount the coils L1 and L2 with their axes at right-angles to prevent undesirable inter-coupling. Also, all earth leads should be as short as possible and the metal front panel should of course be earthed. The coupling capacitor C2 should be mounted on an insulating sub-panel and its shaft fitted with an insulated shaft coupler to isolate it from the front panel to prevent hand-capacitance effects. The receiving-type variable capacitors used in the experimental model Z-match have adequate plate spacing for CW and SSB (peak) output powers of up to 100W.

For higher powers it would be necessary to use a transmitter-type split-stator capacitor (or two ganged single-section capacitors) for C1a, C1b. However, C2 requires only receiver-type vane spacing even for high-power operation. Tests with additional feed-point taps on both L1 and L2 in the modified Z-match circuit showed no practical advantage. However, the tap on the output coupling coil L3 was found to be essential on 7MHz and 10MHz. The very tight coupling between L1/L3 and L2/L4 tends to reduce the operating Q value of the LC circuits. This renders them more 'tolerant' of the complex reactive loads presented at the input end of the feeder(s) to the antenna(s) used.

G5RV noted that the efficiency of a conventional link coupled ATU was

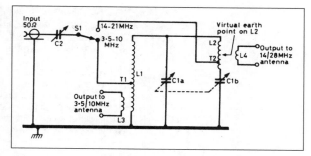

Fig 4.24. The basic Z-match circuit showing the tapped-down feed arrangement

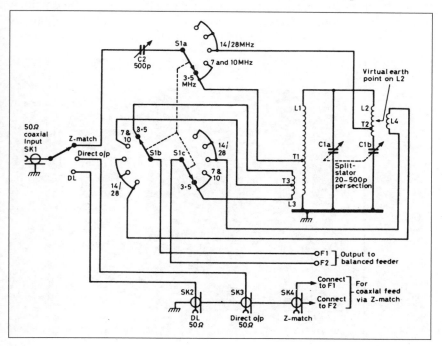

Fig 4.25. The final modified Z-match circuit

Table 4.5. Components list for Z-match

C1a–1b	Split-stator variable capacitor, 20–500p per section.
C2	500p single-section variable capacitor (shaft insulated)
L1	10t 4cm ID CIW 14SWG enam copper wire. Tap T1 4t from earth end
L2	5t 4cm ID, turns spaced wire dia 14SWG enam copper wire. T2 1.5t from centre of coil (virtual earth point)
L3	8t 5cm ID C/W enam copper wire over L1. T3 at 5t from earth end
L4	3t 5cm ID C/W over L2. 14SWG enam copper wire
S1	Ceramic wafer switch. All sections single-pole five positions
S2	Ceramic wafer switch, single-pole three positions

Notes:
1. A suitable 250 + 250p (split-stator or twin-ganged) variable capacitor can be used since the capacitance required to tune L1 to 3500kHz is approximately 420pF, and for 7100kHz approximately 90pF. If C1a, C1b (paralleled) have a combined minimum capacitance of not more than 20pF, it should be possible also to tune L1 to 10MHz. Otherwise it may be necessary to reduce L1 to nine turns, leaving T1 at four turns from the 'earthy' end of L1. A lower minimum capacitance of C1a, Clb as a split-stator capacitor would also be an advantage for the 28–29.7MHz band.
2. Taps on L1 and L2 soldered to *inside* of coil turn. Tap on L3 soldered to *outside* of coil turn.

better than that of either form of Z-match; and that by virtue of its design, the Z-match cannot satisfy all the required circuit conditions for *all* bands. However, in its original form it does provide the convenience of 3.5 to 28MHz coverage without the necessity for plug-in or switched coils. Nevertheless, the inclusion of the simple switching shown in Fig 4.25 is an undoubted advantage.

COMPONENTS FOR ATUS

While components for handling QRP levels of RF power can be obtained from some electronic catalogues the same cannot be said for components for higher power. This tends to discourage building of ATUs, which is a

Fig 4.26. An example of an ex-government remote-controlled ATU. The switch unit is driven by a stepper motor. The variable capacitor and roller coaster (just visible) is driven by a servomotor

Fig 4.27. Remote-controlled ATU by Collins. In addition to the special variable inductor described in the text it also has a vacuum tuning capacitor and a high-voltage vacuum antenna change over switch. This unit was bought for the components but so far I haven't had the heart to take it apart

pity because this sort of equipment is relatively simple, especially when compared with the transceivers now in use.

However, these components are available at rallies and usually come in the form of an ex-military or commercial unit. An example of such a unit is shown in Fig 4.26. This unit has excellent-quality components suitable for building an ATU.

The unit shown in Fig 4.27 deserves special mention. It uses a variable inductor, which comprises the coil former and a silver-plated metal drum of the same diameter. When these two mechanically coupled drums are rotated the silver-plated phosphor-bronze tape is wound on or off the coil former to the metal drum, thereby shorting out the unused turns. This arrangement ensures that no unwanted resonances exist on the unused section of the coil.

REFERENCES

[1] 'The T-network antenna tuner', Pat Hawker, 'Technical Topics', *Radio Communication* April 1995.

[2] 'A general-purpose antenna tuning unit', M J Grierson, G3TSO, *Radio Communication* January 1987.

[3] 'Link coupled antenna tuners: a tutorial', L B Cebik, W4RNL, on the Internet at http://funnelweb.utcc.utc.edu/.

[4] 'A balanced line ASTU', Ted Garrott, G0OUJ, *RadCom* July/August 1998.

[5] 'To turrets – just tune', King, W1CJL, *QST* March 1948.

[6] 'The Z-match antenna coupler', King, W1CJL, *QST* May 1955.

[7] 'An improved Z-match ATU', Louis Varney, G5RV, *RadCom* October 1998.

5 Loops and slot antennas for HF

IF YOU are restricted to a very small backyard, with no place to put up a wire antenna, then the compact HF transmitting loop antenna may be a suitable option. A surprising amount of information is available on these types of antennas. This chapter concentrates on the construction of small loop antennas, starting with one by Roberto Craighero, I1ARZ, who began experimenting with small transmitting loops in 1985. What follows are details of his experiments, including detailed constructional details of a 1m diameter loop antenna, tuneable over the range 14 to 29MHz [1].

This book concentrates on the practical side of antennas. If you wish to read more about the theory of the small loop antenna then I recommend an article by A J Henk, G4XVF, entitled 'Loop antennas, fact not fiction' [2].

GENERAL COMMENTS ON SHORT LOOP ANTENNAS

It must be recognised that good efficiency can be achieved only by ensuring the loop has a very low RF resistance. Additionally its high-Q characteristic results in a narrow effective bandwidth, requiring accurate retuning for even a small change in frequency.

This can be overcome by the use of complex and expensive automatic tuning systems or, more realistically for amateurs, by remote control of the tuning capacitor forming part of the loop. Another disadvantage is that even on low power, there will be very high RF voltage across the tuning capacitor, resulting in the need for either a high-cost vacuum capacitor or a good-quality, wide-spaced transmitting capacitor.

Against these disadvantages should be set the fact that a well-constructed loop just 15m high can have a radiation efficiency close to that of a ground-plane antenna – see Fig 2.5. Furthermore, the short loop utilises the near-field magnetic component of the electromagnetic wave, resulting in much less absorption in nearby objects: this means that a short loop can be used successfully indoors or on a balcony. For reception a 'magnetic' antenna is much less susceptible to the electric component of nearby interference sources. The reduction of man-made noise is particularly important on the lower-frequency bands, and is further enhanced by the directional properties of a rotatable loop. The loop can work effectively without an artificial ground plane.

The high-Q characteristics of a low-loss loop also means that it forms an excellent filter in front of a receiver, reducing overload and cross-modulation from adjacent strong signals. On transmit, these properties dramatically reduce harmonic radiation and hence some forms of TVI and BCI.

Basics

To achieve good radiation efficiency in a small transmitting loop it is essential to minimise the ratio of RF ohmic losses to radiation resistance. In a small resonant loop the RF ohmic losses are made up of the resistance of the loop and that of the tuning capacitor (which will have much lower resistive loss than a loading coil). The tendency of HF current to flow only along the surface of a conductor (skin effect) means that large-diameter continuous copper tubing (or even silver-plated copper) should be used to achieve a maximum high-conductivity surface area.

Provided that the circumference of a loop is between 0.125λ and 0.25λ, it can be tuned to resonance by series capacitance. If the loop is longer than 0.25λ it will lose its predominant 'magnetic' characteristic and become an 'electric' antenna of the quad or delta type but, unless approaching one wavelength in circumference, will still have relatively low radiation resistance.

The radiation resistance of a small loop is governed by the total area enclosed and is a maximum for a circular loop. It is possible to build a transmitting loop antenna with a circumference less than 0.125λ but in these circumstances the bandwidth becomes so small that it becomes difficult to tune the loop accurately. It is thus advisable to restrict the operating range of a transmitting loop to a ratio of 1:2, that is to say 3.5 to 7, 7 to 14, or 14 to 28MHz. Extending the tuning range will tend to result in a rapid falling-off in efficiency. The most convenient solution for complete HF coverage is to use two loops; one for the higher-frequency bands (14, 18, 21, 24 and 28MHz), the other for 3.5 and 7MHz or 7 and 10.1MHz. For 1.8MHz it is advisable to use a loop designed for this band, or for 1.8 and 3.5MHz.

A 14 TO 29MHz LOOP

The main physical characteristics of this antenna are:

Circular loop: 1m diameter made from copper pipe of 22mm OD, circumference 3.14m.

Capacitor: Split-stator or 'butterfly' type, about 120pF per section. Minimum capacitance (for 28MHz) 16pF.

Feed: Inductive coupling with a small loop made from coaxial cable.

Maximum power: This is governed primarily by the spacing of the capacitor vanes. Suggested rating 100W maximum.

Tuning method: Remote control of capacitor by means of electric DC motor and reduction gear. Rotation speed not faster than one turn per minute.

The electrical characteristics, calculated from the formulae given by W5QJR [3], are set out in Table 5.1. The overall design of the loop is shown in Fig 5.1.

Table 5.1. Calculated electrical characteristics of a 1m diameter transmitting loop antenna using 22mm copper tubing			
	14MHz	21MHz	28MHz
Radiation resistance (Ω)	0.09	0.46	1.68
Conductor losses (Ω)	0.04	0.05	0.05
Efficiency (%)	67.3	89.5	93.3
Loop inductance (μH)	2.4	2.4	2.4
Inductive reactance (Ω)	214	321	443
Q factor	789	311	127
Theoretical bandwidth (kHz)	17.7	67.5	228
Voltage across tuning capacitor (100W) (kV)	4.1	3.1	2.3
Tuning capacitance (pF)	53	23	12

The loop

Copper pipe of 22mm OD is generally sold in straight lengths 5m long. In some cases it may be possible to obtain such pipe already coiled into circular shape; in such cases it is relatively easy to change this to the required diameter of 1m. I1ARZ modified the diameter of circular pipe by making a chalk mark on the floor of the correct 1m diameter and then manually adjusting the pipe to this diameter; this requires two people, one keeping the pipe on the floor and the second slowly enlarging its diameter.

If you are unable to obtain a coiled pipe, it is possible to bend a straight pipe around a circular object of correct size; for example a round table or a large truck tyre. Before starting to bend the pipe, this should be filled with dry sand and the ends sealed. Sand must be pressed firmly inside while continuously shaking the pipe. This prevents pipe buckling or the formation of sharp bends during bending. A better alternative is to have the pipe bent at a workshop with a pipe-bending machine.

Both ends of the loop must be cut longitudinally along the vertical diameter of the pipe for about 5cm, then cutting one half away. The remaining half is flattened to form strip that can later be inserted through the insulated board used to support the tuning capacitor and connected to the stator plates. In this way only one joint will be necessary for each stator, reducing the soldering losses. At the bottom of the loop, opposite the tuning capacitor, a small copper bracket should be soldered to the loop – see Fig 5.2. On this bracket will be fixed the coaxial connector and the connector for the twin lead for powering the tuning motor. The bracket should be soldered to the loop using a flame-torch to ensure good electrical contact.

Fig 5.1. Electrical diagram of the I1ARZ loop antenna, plus the tuning motor connections

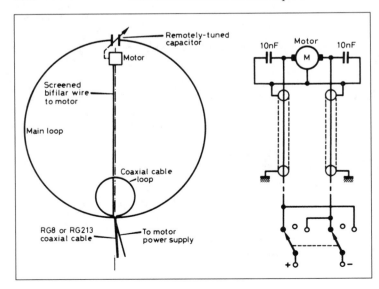

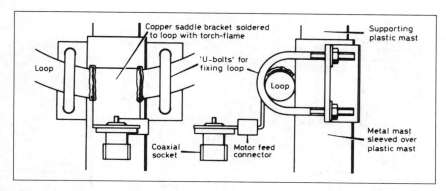

Fig 5.2. Details of the bottom of the loop – front view

The supporting mast

Where a loop is to be used outside the house, it is imperative to provide a supporting mast across the loop, otherwise there is the risk that high winds will deform or break the latter. This can happen for two main reasons: the combined weight of the motor, tuning capacitor, plastic board and watertight cover is considerable; additionally 22mm copper tubing is not sufficiently strong to remain rigid in the presence of high dynamic stress unless supported. A thick PVC pipe of about 40 to 50mm diameter can be used for this support. Alternatively a glassfibre tube (lighter but more expensive) or a wooden mast waterproofed with plastic compound may be used. The length of this mast should be about 1.5m with about 200mm used at the top for fixing the plastic board carrying the tuning capacitor; the remaining length is used at the base for fixing the loop to a rotor or another short mast. For obvious reasons, never use a metallic pipe across the loop.

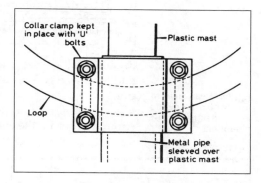

Fig 5.3. Method of fixing the bottom of the loop to the support mast

The loop is fixed to the mast using two U-bolts at the base – see Fig 5.3.

The ends at the top of the loop are held in place by means of two collar-clamps. (The source of these clamps is cross-joints in cast aluminium normally used to connect the boom of television antennas to the mast.) These clamps are connected with nuts and bolts (stainless steel) to the back of the plastic board supporting the capacitor – see Fig 5.4(b). The bolts should be of sufficient length to act as adjustable spacers in order to have the loop completely upright. The plastic supporting mast is fixed to the back of the board by means of two semicircular clamps with stainless steel nuts and bolts of sufficient length to reach the front side of the plastic board. The two copper strips of the loop must be bent at 90° and inserted in suitable cuts in the board to reach the stators of the capacitor on the front side of the board – see Fig 5.4(a) and Fig 5.5. The cuts should later be waterproofed with silicone compound.

Tuning board and cover

The size of the tuning board depends upon the dimensions of the variable capacitor and motor. The best material for high-power operation is 10mm thick Teflon; alternatively Plexiglas of the same thickness can be used. When

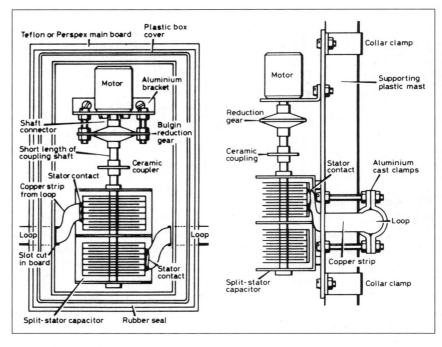

Fig 5.4. The loop tuning board. (a) Front view and (b) side view

calculating the size of the board, allow space for fixing the clamps of the loop and for a waterproof cover to protect the complete tuning unit. For protection, a plastic watertight box of the type used for storing food in a refrigerator was used. The original cover was cut in the centre with an opening just wide enough to permit the entry of the capacitor and motor. A layer of soft rubber is inserted between the surface of the supporting board and the cover to act as a seal. The cover is then fixed in place with several small stainless nuts and bolts, fastened tightly so that the seal is compressed between the board surface and cover to make it watertight. The plastic box can now be put against its cover, keeping it in place with a tight nylon lashing. Silicone compound should now be applied all round to keep out the moisture. To prevent gradual deterioration of the plastic box it is advisable to use white self-adhesive plastic sheet to protect it against ultra-violet radiation from the Sun.

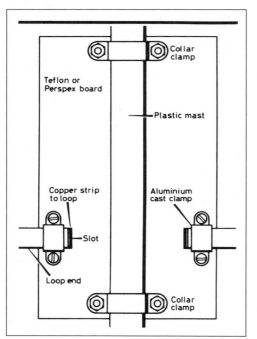

Fig 5.5. Rear view of tuning board showing loop and support mast mountings

The tuning capacitor

It is most important to use a very-good-quality transmitting-type variable capacitor; otherwise the efficiency of the antenna will be reduced. Owing to the high Q of this antenna, the RF voltage across the capacitor is very high (directly proportional to the power). With 100W power, this voltage will be between 4 and 5kV; with 500W it can be as high as 28kV!

It is most advisable to use a split-stator (or 'butterfly') capacitor of about 120pF per section. The advantage of this arrangement is that the two sections are connected in series, thereby eliminating the rotor contact losses which occur in conventional capacitors. Assuming that the loop is intended for use with a transmitter power of not more than 100W, the spacing between the vanes should be at least 1.5 to 2mm. The 'surplus' market remains a good source of excellent transmitting-type split-stator capacitors and it is worth taking time to locate a source rather than attempt to use a cheap capacitor which will almost certainly result in reduced efficiency of the loop antenna.

A vacuum capacitor would seem a good choice. However, the high loop currents tend to heat and thereby distort thin metal in vacuum capacitors, and consequently detune the loop [4]. Experiments with a vacuum-capacitor-tuned, low-frequency loop show that with SSB (about 60W PEP) with its low power factor there is no need to retune the antenna. However, when used with CW, with its greater power factor, there is a need to retune the loop from time to time.

The tuning motor

The motor forms an important part of the system; it requires a DC motor with a reduction gear capable of providing very fine control, with the capacitor shaft rotating at only about one turn per minute or even less. Ideally, a variable-speed motor is required to provide slow rotation for accurate tuning but a faster rate for changing bands.

I1ARZ used a motor that could operate between 3 to 12V, which ran slowly at the lowest voltage and fast at 12V. Again, it is the surplus market that may provide such a motor. Should you be unable to find a motor incorporating a suitable reduction gear it is possible to use a receiver-type slow-motion tuning drive; a Bulgin gear with a reduction drive ratio of 25:1 was used on the prototype.

An alternative motor control method by GW3JPT is described later.

Construction of the tuning system

Construction of the tuning system calls for care and attention to detail, otherwise there is the risk of damaging the various components unless they are accurately aligned.

When estimating the dimensions of the insulated supporting board, bear in mind the following:

- The space required for the watertight cover.
- The aluminium bracket for mounting the motor.
- The external reduction gearing, together with the various couplings between the capacitor spindle and the motor.

The first step is to mark with a pen the centre line of the board (ie major axis). Bolt the capacitor to the board, taking great care to ensure that the shaft is aligned with the centre line marked on the board. A split-stator capacitor must be placed with the respective stator contacts symmetrically in the vertical plane so that the copper strips coming from the back of the board on either side of the capacitor have the same length (one being bent upwards, the other downwards). With a butterfly or conventional capacitor, the copper strips must be bent horizontally as both contacts are the same height.

Once the capacitor has been bolted to the board, measure with callipers or dividers the exact distance of the board from the centre of the capacitor shaft. Transfer this dimension to the centre line of the vertical side of the L-shaped aluminium bracket to be used for supporting the motor and any external reduction gear.

Drill a small pilot hole just large enough to take the motor shaft. It is important that this operation is carried out carefully since it is vital to the accurate alignment of the system.

Once it has been determined that motor and capacitor shafts are in accurate alignment, the motor may be fixed permanently to the bracket, enlarging the pilot hole and drilling holes for the motor-fixing bolts, but do not yet fix the bracket to the board.

The next step is to adapt the motor shaft to a shaft extension (as normally used for lengthening potentiometer shafts), taking care not to introduce any eccentricity. If your motor does not require external reduction gear, you can insert the motor shaft into a ceramic coupler (circular shape with ceramic ring and flexible central bush), again making sure there is no eccentricity. The lower flange of the aluminium bracket can now be fixed to the board by means of two nuts and bolts.

If you use the Bulgin drive external reduction gear, drill two 4mm holes in the bracket; one in each side of the motor at the same distance as the mechanical connections of the gear and at the same level as the centre of the motor shaft. If the size of the motor is wider, it is necessary to join to the Bulgin gear two short strips of brass or aluminium so as to obtain an extension of the fixing points of the drive. Two long brass bolts (4mm diameter) should be inserted in the holes to hold the gear in place with the nuts. The Bulgin gear can now be fixed to the motor shaft, with the other side of the gear connected to the ceramic coupler by means of a very short piece of potentiometer-type shaft. Make a provisional check of the tuning system by temporarily connecting the power supply to ensure that everything is working smoothly. The copper strips of the loop can now be soldered to the stator capacitor vanes. This requires the use of a large-wattage soldering iron, taking care that the best possible electrical contact is achieved.

Motor feed line

The feed line can be made from twin screened cable, as normally used with high-fidelity audio amplifiers etc. The braid should be connected through a soldering lug to the aluminium bracket or to the motor casing. The motor must be bypassed for RF, using two 10nF ceramic capacitors connected to the braid. The cable is kept in place by means of nylon clamps along the supporting plastic mast. At the base of the loop solder a connector on the small copper bracket, with the braid soldered to the bracket. From this point to the operating position, normal electrical twin cable can be used. Some constructors have suggested inserting the feed line inside the loop pipe but this reduces the efficiency of the antenna. A small box containing the DC power supply and switch for reversing polarity of the supply is operated from the shack.

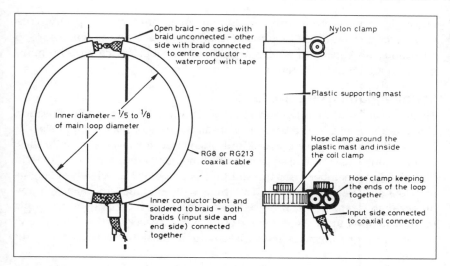

Fig 5.6. Detail of (a) the construction of the coaxial loop feed and (b) the plastic support mast

Coupling loop and matching procedure

A variety of methods for feeding the loop are shown later. I1ARZ found the most satisfactory method of coupling was a small single-turn (Faraday) coupling loop formed from a length of coaxial cable (RG213) with a diameter one-eighth of the main loop. In practice, the optimum diameter of the coupling loop will vary slightly from this figure and it may prove worthwhile to experiment with slightly different size loops. This is done by aiming for the lowest SWR over a wide frequency range and is best achieved by constructing several coupling coils.

With the I1ARZ antenna the optimum diameter proved to be 18cm rather than the theoretical 12.5cm. The coil should have the braid open at top-centre; at this point one side is connected to the inner conductor of the coaxial cable. At the base of the loop, inner conductor and braid are connected together and jointed to the braid on the input side of the coil as shown in Fig 5.6(a).

The ends and braid of the coupling loop are held together using a stainless hose clamp. This in turn is fixed to the mast at 90° to another hose clamp on the plastic mast – see Fig 5.6 (b). This provides a very simple method of adjustment by sliding the small loop up or down the mast to find the best SWR position.

The upper opening should be protected with tape and, to avoid any subsequent movement of the coil, then fixed to the mast by means of nylon clamps mounted in the same way as for the hose clamps at the base. Final matching of the antenna has to be carried out after determining the final position of the installation. An SWR bridge is connected at the base of the loop close to the input coaxial connector. If your transmitter covers 18MHz make your adjustments on this band; otherwise use 21MHz. Apply minimum power, just sufficient to deflect the SWR meter. After finding loop resonance, move the coupling coil up and down or deform it slightly to check how the SWR varies. The coupling coil must be maintained in the same plane as the loop. After finding the lowest SWR, tighten the hose clamps and nylon clamps to keep the coil in position. Coaxial line and tuning motor power line must be kept vertical for about 1m or more from respective connectors at the base of the loop to avoid undesirable coupling with the loop itself and subsequent difficulty to achieve a proper matching. The minimum SWR should be better than 1:1.5 on all bands.

Installing and using the loop

The loop can conveniently be installed on a terrace or concrete floor or roof. One method is to use as a base or pedestal the type of plastic supports that can be filled with water or sand and often used for large sun umbrellas. Light nylon guys can be used to minimise the risk of the loop falling over in high winds. Remember that a transmitting loop operates effectively at heights of 1 to 1.5m above ground, and nothing will be gained by raising it any higher than, say, 2 or 3m at most. I1ARZ tested his loop using a telescopic mast at heights up to 9m above ground but with very little difference in performance; and normally it was used with the mast fully retracted to about 3m high.

With a garden, the loop could be fixed directly to a short metallic mast driven into the ground. A small TV rotator could be used but this is not essential; maximum radiation is in the plane of the loop, minimum off the sides of the loop. Large metallic masses like fences; steel plates, pipes etc reduce the efficiency of the antenna if in proximity in the direction of the plane of the loop. The radiation is vertically polarised at all vertical angles, making the loop suitable for DX, medium-range and short-range contacts. The loop could be used in the horizontal plane from the balcony or window of a high-rise apartment. If the loop is used this it must be raised well above ground, as for a conventional horizontal element, to obtain good efficiency.

There is nothing particularly complicated about operating with a small loop antenna other than the need to tune it to resonate it at the operating frequency. Using the SWR meter, tune carefully with the aid of the polarity-reversing switch to the precise point where minimum reflected power is achieved. To avoid keeping the transmitter too long in the 'tune' position and to minimise the radiated interference to other band users, it is most advisable to tune initially for maximum signal in the 'receiving' mode; this will bring the loop close to the tuning point for transmission. The 'receiving-mode' procedure should always be used when changing bands.

Use of an indoor loop

A transmitting loop performs well indoors and there is a temptation to have the loop alongside the operating desk since it can then be tested with manual, rather than remote, tuning. This is not advisable unless you use only very low power. With full power, the RF voltages developed on the bare copper tubing are very high, with the risk of RF burns. There is also the potential hazard of prolonged exposure to strong magnetic RF fields, although the degree of risk remains unknown.

Conclusion and final comments

I1ARZ began experimenting with transmitting loops of small diameter in 1985 and he is now convinced that the loop is a thoroughly practical antenna that should not be written off as either a compromise or emergency

Fig 5.7. Some experimental loops used by GW3JPT

antenna. Its performance, provided the RF ohmic losses are kept very low, is very good. With a home-made QRP (2W) transceiver he was able to contact a number of US stations, receiving reports better than S7. With his normal transceiver (maximum power 50W), results have been excellent, commonly resulting in S7 reports; similarly with stations in the Far East. From European stations, a report of S9 + 10dB is customary.

WIRE LOOP ANTENNA FOR THE LOWER HF BANDS

As already mentioned, it is necessary to ensure that the resistance of the loop is as low as possible.

However, larger loops for the HF bands may be impractical due to the weight. C R Reynolds, GW3JPT, constructed many magnetic loop antennas, all of which were made from 22mm copper tubing or strip aluminium. Some of the experimental loop antennas used are shown in Fig 5.7.

He wanted to operate on the lower HF frequency bands and, although he found that it was possible to tune a small loop to Top Band using a very large 1000pF capacitor, there were two problems. On 1.8MHz the efficiency is rather low and on 7MHz tuning is rather critical because it only takes a few picofarads of tuning capacitor variation to tune the whole of this band. This represents a very small percentage of 1000pF, requiring only a fraction of capacitor rotation to cover the band.

In an article [5] GW3JPT described a different design of a practical loop antenna for the 1.8, 3.5 and 7MHz bands. This uses a much larger square loop of a size shown in Fig 5.8. If this were to be made from copper tube it would be very heavy so he used a 19.5m (64ft) length of plastic-covered wire. This antenna requires a 250–300pF tuning capacitor.

The Faraday coupling loop is shown in Fig 5.9. It is close coupled for about 0.77m (30in) each side of the centre of the triangle section of the element.

This wire loop will also work on 40m. This is done by using a relay or a

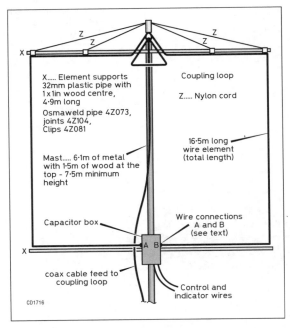

X..... Element supports
32mm plastic pipe with
1x1in wood centre,
4·9m long
Osmaweld pipe 4Z073,
joints 4Z104,
Clips 4Z081

Coupling loop

Z..... Nylon cord

16·5m long
wire element
(total length)

Mast..... 6·1m of metal
with 1·5m of wood at the
top – 7·5m minimum
height

Capacitor box

Wire connections
A and B
(see text)

X

A B

coax cable feed to
coupling loop

Control and
indicator wires

CD1716

Fig 5.8. Overall view of the LF band magnetic loop

Fig 5.9. The Faraday coupling loop

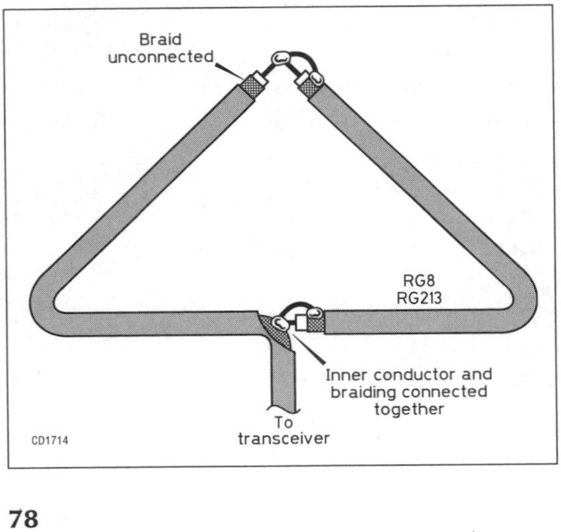

Braid
unconnected

RG8
RG213

Inner conductor and
braiding connected
together

To
transceiver

CD1714

switch to disconnect the capacitor at points A and B as shown in Fig 5.8. The loop is then tuned by the stray capacitance of the switch or the relay. Because this stray capacitance cannot be varied, the antenna element length is adjusted for correct matching using an SWR meter.

The antenna and mast can be fitted to a good ground post. It does not need any guy wire support and can be raised or lowered easily. For portable use it can be erected in a few minutes using three or four guy wires.

Capacitor drive motor

There is a reasonable range of motors available suitable for rotating the loop capacitor. The cheapest and one of the best available was a barbecue spit motor. Although this is already geared down it does require extra reduction using a 6:1 or 10:1 epicyclic drive for more precise tuning.

The motor will rotate slowly if energised by a 1.5V battery. With 3V applied the motor will run much faster. By switching from 1.5 to 3V a fast or slow tuning speed can be selected. This switching is shown in Fig 5.10. The positive lead of the 3V battery is connected to H and the positive lead of the 1.5V battery is connected to L. The negative leads of both batteries are connected to D.

The direction of rotation is achieved using a two-pole, three-way switch. When the switch is set to the centre position the motor is disconnected from the battery (OFF position). The battery polarity to the motor is selected by the two other positions of the switch and should be labelled 'DOWN' or 'UP'.

The drive mechanism must be electrically isolated from the high RF voltages present at the capacitor. An insulated coupler can be made from plastic petrol pipe. This pipe size should be chosen so that it is a push fit on to the drive mechanism and capacitor shafts. The pipe can then be fixed to the shafts by wrapping single-strand copper wire around the ends of the pipe and tightening with a pair of pliers.

All the capacitors made by GW3JPT have the spindle extending both sides of them. One spindle is used to couple the capacitor to the drive mechanism. The other is used to connect the capacitor to a position indicator. This indicator circuitry must be electrically isolated from the capacitor as described above.

The control unit is housed in a plastic box. The fast/slow and rotation direction switches are fixed to the front, together with the capacitor position meter.

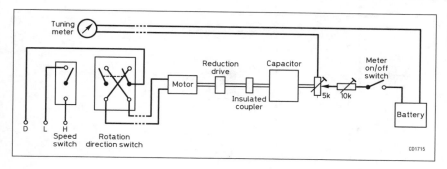

Fig 5.10. Control and indicator system for the magnetic loop antenna

Capacitor unit housing

One of the main problems of constructing any electrical circuits associated with antennas is protecting them from wind and rain. One option is to try and find some sort of suitable plastic housing and then organise the components to fit, but GW3JPT prefers to make the tuning housing from exterior plywood. The bottom and sides of the box are fixed together using 1in square strips of timber. Glue and screws are used to make the joints waterproof. The top must, of course, be made so that it can be removed fairly easily. Paint or varnish the box as required.

Construction of capacitors

The capacitors for tuning loop antennas can be very difficult to come by so GW3JPT makes his own – an example of one of his home-made capacitors is shown in Fig 5.11.

GW3JPT uses aluminium and double-sided circuit board for the vanes. Nuts and washers are used for the spacers and various types of insulation material can be used for the end plates.

The centre spindle and spacing rods are constructed from 6mm-threaded plated steel rod.

Make the 76mm × 76mm (3 × 3in) end plates first – see Fig 5.12. These can be taped together back-to-back for marking and drilling. The same can be done with the vanes. Masking tape is used so the surface is not scratched around drill holes, which are drilled to clear 6mm with the centre hole acting as a bearing.

The number of vanes required dictates the length of the 6mm spindle. For double-sided board use washer/nut/washer spacers so that there is no need to bond the copper sides. The resulting spacing is about 6mm (0.25in).

The first capacitors made by GW3JPT used the conventional shape for the moving vanes, but

Fig 5.11. An example of one of the GW3JPT home-made capacitors

Fig 5.12. Details of home-made capacitor. (a) Moving vanes; (b) fixed vanes; (c) fixed and moving vanes geometry showing minimum capacitance; (d) capacitor assembly

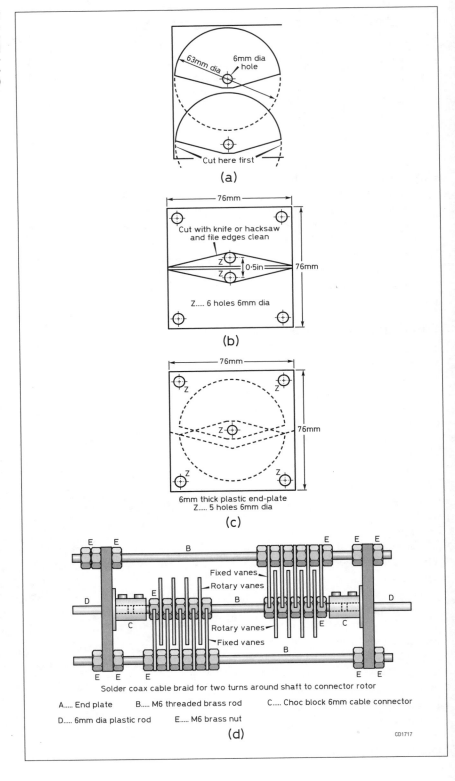

63mm dia

6mm dia hole

Cut here first

(a)

76mm

Cut with knife or hacksaw and file edges clean

Z
Z
0·5in

76mm

Z..... 6 holes 6mm dia

(b)

76mm

Z   Z

Z

76mm

Z   Z

6mm thick plastic end-plate
Z..... 5 holes 6mm dia

(c)

E E   B   E E E

Fixed vanes
Rotary vanes

D   E   B   D
C   E C

Rotary vanes
Fixed vanes

E E E   B   E E

Solder coax cable braid for two turns around shaft to connector rotor

A..... End plate   B..... M6 threaded brass rod   C..... Choc block 6mm cable connector

D..... 6mm dia plastic rod   E..... M6 brass nut

(d)

CD1717

this is very difficult to cut out and fragile to use. The shape illustrated in Fig 5.12(a) is much easier.

The fixed vane is a simple rectangle, which can be modified to reduce the minimum capacitance. See the dotted line in Fig 5.12(c). For the size shown, six pairs of vanes with 6mm (0.25in) spacing work out to about 150pF. Units using both printed circuit board and aluminium vanes have been in use for over two years and they are both still in good working condition.

Operation

Tuning of the loop needs to be adjusted precisely for minimum SWR, which should coincide with maximum power out. This tuning is critical: a few kilohertz off tune and the SWR will rise dramatically. The best way of finding the correct position of the tuning capacitor is to listen for maximum noise or signals whilst tuning the loop. Then fine-tune using an SWR meter.

The performance of this antenna on 3.5MHz was at least as good as my G5RV. It tuned all of Top Band and gave quite good results when compared with local signals on the club nets.

A 2m DIAMETER LOOP FOR 3.5MHz

This loop antenna [6] is very compact and, although designed for mobile use, it would be suitable for 3.5MHz operation from a very restricted location. The loop was designed by PA2JBC to have a diameter of 2m and, for transportation purposes, be capable of being dismantled into two pieces. This feature would make it easy to get through a small loft access hatch. It also has a most interesting tuning arrangement. However, bearing in mind what has already been said about loops, an antenna this small does not have the efficiency of the larger models. The specification of the PA2JBC loop is given in Table 5.2.

The electrical characteristics in Table 5.2 were calculated for 22mm copper tubing. For practical reasons this antenna was built as an octagon. Measurements on the final antenna correlated closely with the calculations in Table 5.2 and PA2JBC has concluded that soft-soldered (rather than brazed or silver soldered) 45° elbows and the compression couplers do not spoil the Q. This is slightly at odds with the above description of I1ARZ's loop. The structure of the antenna is shown in Fig 5.13.

The eight 820mm lengths of copper tubing are prepared by thoroughly cleaning the ends with fine emery paper and coating with flux. The pipe must be cut with a pipe cutter so that the ends fit snugly into the connector.

Two of the pipes to be joined are fitted into the 45° connecting elbows. Heat the

Table 5.2. Calculated data for the PA2JBC 3.5MHz, 2m diameter loop antenna made of 22mm tubing, using a 100W transmitter at 3.74MHz	
L	5.8µH
Loaded Q	1273
Resistance	7.4mΩ
Loss resistance	46mΩ
Efficiency	14%
Bandwidth −3dB	2.94kHz
C at resonance	314pF
Capacitor voltage	8.3kV
Loop current	43.3A RMS

Fig 5.13. The PA2JBC 80m compact loop antenna

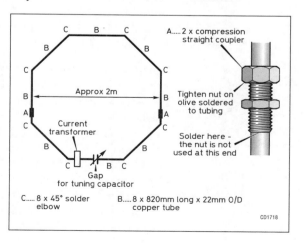

A.....2 x compression straight coupler

Approx 2m

Current transformer

Gap for tuning capacitor

Tighten nut on olive soldered to tubing

Solder here – the nut is not used at this end

C.....8 x 45° solder elbow   B.....8 x 820mm long x 22mm O/D copper tube

CD1718

joint with a blowtorch while at the same time applying multi-cored solder at the point where the pipe joins the connector. When the solder flows freely the joint is complete. Repeat for all the other joints, making sure the alignment of the loop is flat. Also make sure you fit the current transformer on to one of the sections of tubing (see later) before completing the loop. The completed loop is then cut in two sections as shown in Fig 5.13 and compression joints fitted at point A. If the antenna has to be frequently dismantled and reassembled then the 'olive' should be soldered to the tubing to reduce wear.

The tuning capacitor

The required capacitance variation to cover 3.5 to 3.8MHz is 300pF to 360pF. This capacitance is made up using a fixed capacitor of 260pF and a 100pF maximum variable in parallel. Using a small variable capacitor reduces the cost and improves the bandspread tuning.

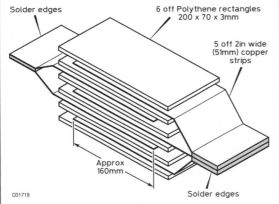

The 100pF variable must be able to handle up to 9kV peak and 13A RMS when used with a 100W transmitter. A wiper connection to the rotor is unsuitable at 13A so a 2 × 200pF split-stator capacitor is used. Even then, the current path between all rotor plates must be low resistance, preferably soldered or brazed; the same goes for the stator plates and their connections to the loop tubing. At 9kV, conservative design requires 9mm spacing between the plates, or 4.5mm in a split-stator (each half takes 50% of the voltage).

The fixed capacitor is made from 51 × 0.3mm copper strips interleaved with slabs of dielectric as shown in Fig 5.14. Polyethylene works well as a dielectric and is inexpensive; if it gets hot, it is not polyethylene! The capacitance is set by adjusting the meshing of the two sets of copper 'plates' but the dielectric must extend beyond the copper by at least 6mm. After adjustment, the capacitor can be wrapped with glassfibre-reinforced tape. Four parallel 3mm copper wires connect the fixed capacitor to the loop tubing. The 3mm-thick polyethylene is just adequate for 100W. On test the power was increased to 180W before it broke down.

Fig 5.14. This fixed 260pF home-made capacitor is good for 8kV at 40A

Loop-to-feeder coupling

With a loop of this design PA2JBC could not get a gamma match to work. A coupling loop also proved unsatisfactory as its shape had to be adjusted when changing frequency. The final solution was a current transformer. This transformer must match the 53mΩ loop to a 50Ω coaxial cable, an impedance ratio of 940:1. This means it has to have a turns ratio of the square root of 940 which is approximately 30:1. With this transformer the '1' is the loop tubing fixed in the centre of a toroid. With the loop at resonance the feeder 'sees' inductance. By increasing the transformer winding to 36 turns and adding a series capacitor a 1:1 SWR can be obtained anywhere in the band. This capacitor is a receiver-type air-dielectric 250pF variable. A 1:1 balun keeps the outside of the coaxial cable 'cold'. An electrical diagram of the transformer and balun is shown in Fig 5.15.

Construction of the current transformer is shown in Fig 5.16. 6 × 6 turns of 1mm PTFE-insulated copper wire gave the best results. Ferrite (Philips 4C6, violet) and iron powder (Amidon, red) both gave good results. The transformer can be placed anywhere on the tubing, eg next to the capacitors where both they and the coupler can housed be in a weatherproof box.

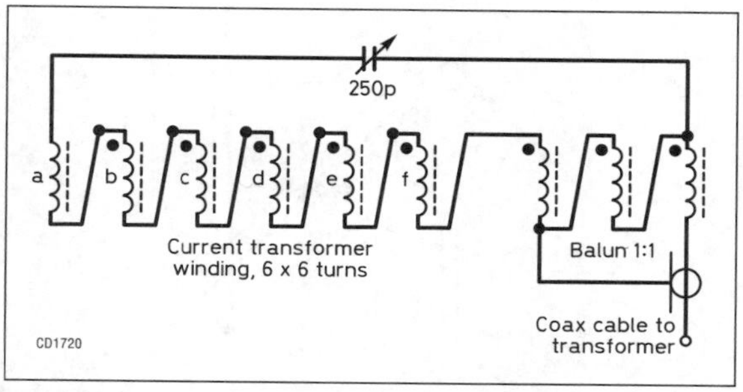

Fig 5.15. An electrical diagram of the matching transformer and balun

Installation and operation

PA2JBC installed the antenna in his loft 3m above ground level and above all the electrical wiring. It should be fixed using good insulating material such as plastic pipe, as used in the I1ARZ loop. The antenna's location close to wooden rafters and clay roofing tiles does not noticeably affect the Q of the loop, even when the roof is wet. If the loop is rotated with a TV rotator then it can be used to null out sources of QRM.

With 100W PEP, only 14W is radiated from this indoor antenna, which is probably as good as the best mobile antenna for the band. Certainly there is no problem with normal 80m countrywide QSOs in the daytime and occasional DX contacts at night. The high-Q characteristics of the antenna give a marked improvement in the signal-to-noise ratio in the presence of general electrical interference and QRN. This antenna could be used as a 'receive only' antenna in conjunction with a larger antenna for DX.

Tubing of 28mm would raise the Q and efficiency but it would also reduce the bandwidth; fine for CW but too narrow for 3.5MHz SSB! As it is, the loop must be re-tuned for every QSY.

For outdoor use, the loop should be degreased and painted.

Fig 5.16. Construction of the current transformer

ROOF-SPACE MULTI-BAND MAGNETIC LOOP

The following is yet another example of a loft antenna, which has the distinction of being able to operate from 3.5 to 28MHz [7]. It was described by Eric Sandys, GI2FHN. The main loop and the coupling loops are made from coaxial cable although the type, and hence the diameter, is not specified. It can be safely assumed that the larger-diameter cable, such as RG213, will give a more efficient antenna than the thinner varieties, although it will be more critical to tune. The antenna design borrows the dual-tuning technique from the Z-match tuner and the circuit of the loop is shown in Fig 5.17.

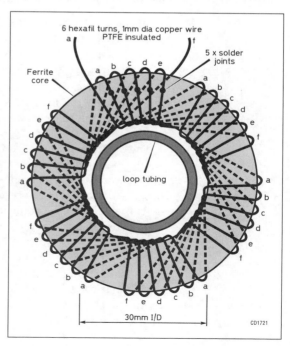

6 hexafil turns, 1mm dia copper wire PTFE insulated

5 x solder joints

Ferrite core

loop tubing

30mm I/D

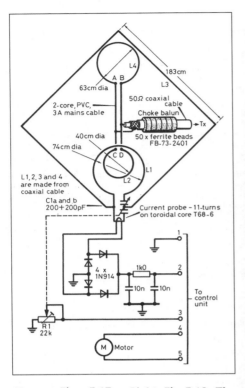

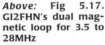

Above: Fig 5.17. GI2FHN's dual magnetic loop for 3.5 to 28MHz

Right: Fig 5.18. The multi-band loop antenna located in the roof space at GI2FHN

On 14, 18, 21, 24 and 28MHz, L1 is tuned by C1a and C1b in series. Because L3 presents high impedance at these frequencies it can be ignored. On 3.5 and 7MHz, L3 is tuned by C1a placed in parallel with C1b through L1.

The coupling links L2 and L4 are connected in parallel and RF is fed in through a 1:1 choke balun. The diameters of the coupling links were selected to give the lowest SWR, which is better than 1.5:1 on all bands. If coverage of the 10MHz band is required, L4 needs to be reduced slightly in size.

The diameter of the coaxial cable is used for the loops and coupling links should be the same. Note that the connections between the two coupling links should not be transposed. A should go to C and B to D. Failure to observe these points can result in degradation of the SWR.

At the GI2FHN QTH the loop is housed in the roof space using a timber framework to provide the necessary support – see Fig 5.18.

All frequency adjustments are carried out from a control box at the operating position (see Fig 5.19). Changing bands is made easy by using a Wheatstone bridge to give a visual indication on M1 of the travel of C1. The variable arm R1 is gear driven from the shaft connecting the motor and reduction gearing to C1. The direction of rotation is controlled by S1, a DPDT switch (centre-off). Fine-tuning is provided by a speed control R2. A current probe enables exact resonance to be established at the operating frequency.

GI2FHN finds that results have exceeded all expectations and the arrangement can be recommended for anyone who has a loft space but does not have space for a full-size wire antenna.

COMMENTS ON SMALL LOOP ANTENNAS

The compact loop antenna is a viable solution for these not able to erect a wire antenna. The compact loop by I1ARZ is, in the worst case, about 4 or 5dB down on a dipole half a wavelength high. This is less than one S-point. It is obvious that, under conditions of normal HF QSB, difficulties might be experienced when making meaningful comparisons.

The compact wire loop by GW3JPT is about 60% efficient on 1.8MHz. Making comparisons on this band is even more difficult – getting a 160m comparison dipole up half a wavelength high is a challenge.

There are numerous ways of coupling a low-impedance loop to coaxial cable and most of these are shown in Fig 5.20. The favoured method is the Faraday loop shown in Fig 5.20(e). There has been some comment that the Faraday loop connections found in most descriptions of loops (including the I1ARZ and GW3PJT designs above) are incorrect. The coaxial cable inner and braid at the top or apex of the loop in Fig 5.9, for example, is shown joined, which would make a Faraday half loop. The inner-to-braid connection should be removed but the gap in the braid halfway round the loop should remain.

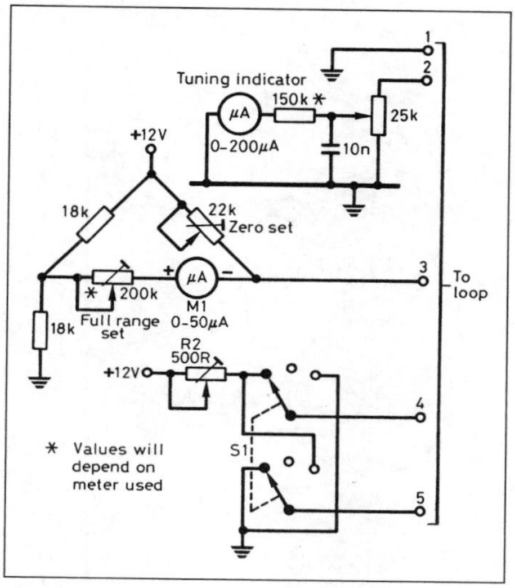

The matching methods in Fig 5.20(a) and (b) have been used with 10m or more diameter loops for 136kHz, for both transmit and receive. The PA2JBC compact loop for 80m, with its transformer and balun, is worthy of further development for more conventionally sized loops.

Fig 5.19. Control and indicator unit for tuning the GI2FHN dual loop

MULTI-BAND DELTA LOOP ANTENNA

If you have the space then a larger loop is well worthwhile. If the loop is larger than 0.25λ it will lose its predominant 'magnetic' characteristic and become an 'electric' antenna of the quad or delta type. From the previous descriptions of loop antennas it can be seen that the efficiency improves with an increase in size, and the resistive losses of a loop of full wavelength circumference are very small.

A full-wave loop on 7MHz can be fed with coaxial cable and will also operate on the 14 and 21MHz bands, and without an ATU, provided that a transformer and 4:1 balun are connected between the coaxial cable and the antenna. The shape of the loop is not too important.

If a loop antenna in the form of an equilateral triangle is used then only one support is required. If this support were a mast fixed to the chimney then it will probably circumvent UK planning restrictions.

The antenna is shown in Fig 5.21. As you can see, part of this antenna is close to the ground. This means there is a possible danger of someone

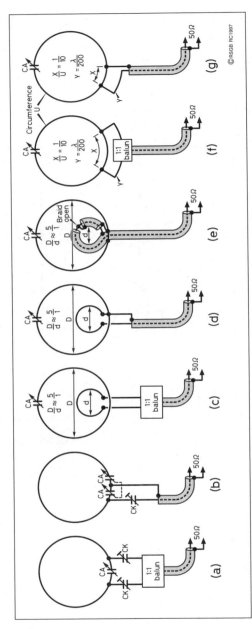

© RSGB RC1997

Fig 5.20. Matching a transmitting or receiving antenna to 50Ω coaxial cable as described in 1983 by DL2FA and reported in 'Technical Topics' in *Radio Communication* October 1996. The Faraday loop method (e) is favoured, but see text

receiving an RF burn if the antenna was touched when the transmitter is on. For this reason insulated wire for the lower half of the antenna is recommended. This loop antenna is not a high-Q device so very high voltages, such as those found at the tips of a dipole, do not occur.

The top half of the antenna can be constructed with bare copper wire. You could use insulated wire for all the loop but lightweight wire for the upper half of the loop (and a lightweight support) has a low visual impact. Using lightweight thin wire does not affect the antenna performance because the radiation resistance of a loop is fairly high.

The first experiments were carried out with the coaxial cable connected directly to the loop but the SWR was over 3:1. However, most literature puts the feed impedance of a loop greater than 100Ω. A 4:1 balun was fitted (see Chapter 9), enabling the antenna fed directly with 50Ω coaxial cable with minimum mismatch.

The best results occurred when the antenna was fed about one-third up from the bottom on the most vertical of the triangle sides. This antenna will give good results even when the lowest leg of the triangle is only 0.6m from the ground. Fig 5.21 shows the corner insulators fixed to the ground with tent peg type fixtures.

It can be run along a fence with shrubs and small trees being used for fixtures for the lower corner insulators.

The apex support in the experimental model was a 2.5m length of scaffolding pole fixed to the chimney with a double TV lashing kit.

The top of the chimney is about 9m above the ground. The pole gives the antenna enough height and a reasonable clearance above the roof. The apex of the loop is nearly 11m high.

This antenna proved to be a good DX transmitting antenna on 7MHz but it does tend to pick up electrical noise from the house on receive. It could be used with a smaller tuned loop on receive if electrical noise or QRM is a problem.

SKELETON-SLOT ANTENNA

This is a loop antenna with a difference and is known as the *skeleton slot*. With the dimensions given it will operate on the 14, 18, 21, 24 and 28MHz bands using a balanced ATU.

It is very easy to construct and is a simple design with no traps or critical adjustments. This antenna has a turning radius of only 1.5m (5ft) although it is 14m (47ft) tall. However, its construction means that it has a much lower visual impact than a conventional multi-band beam. The antenna is bi-directional and has a calculated gain, over average ground, of 8dBi on 14MHz and 11dBi on 28MHz.

The skeleton-slot antenna was first documented in an article by B Sykes, G2HCG, in *RSGB Bulletin* [8].

A non-resonant slot for HF

The main exponent of the HF skeleton slot, other than G2HCG, is Bill Capstick, G3JYP, whose version of this antenna was described in reference [9].

My version of the HF skeleton slot uses wire for the vertical elements, resulting in a more simplified and rugged construction. I was at first concerned that this method of construction would not work because references [8] and [9] gave minimum tube diameters for the elements. However, computer modelling with EZNEC2 reassured me that this method of construction would be suitable for this particular application so I went ahead.

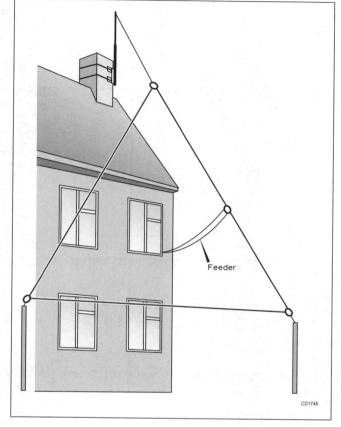

Fig 5.21. Loop antenna of one wavelength circumference on 7MHz

Construction

The antenna essentially comprises three aluminium tube elements fixed to the mast at 4.6m (15ft) intervals, with the lowest element only 4.6m from the ground. The mast is an integral part of the antenna, as a boom is to a Yagi. The general construction is shown in Fig 5.22.

The centre element is fed in the centre with balanced feeder and the upper and lower elements are fed at the ends by copper wire from the driven dipole.

The aluminium tubing and copper wire are fixed using hose clips. These dissimilar metal connections present no corrosion problems, even in a location like mine close to the sea, provided they are well coated with grease.

The centres of the upper and lower elements can be fixed directly to a metal earthed mast using an aluminium plate and U-bolts as shown in Fig 5.22. I insulated the elements from the mast by using oversized U-bolts and wrapping the element in an insulating material I happened to have at hand; this was because I wanted to try the option of using the antenna as the top loading for a lower-band antenna. If you want to insulate the elements from the mast then the method shown in Fig 5.22 is probably the best way.

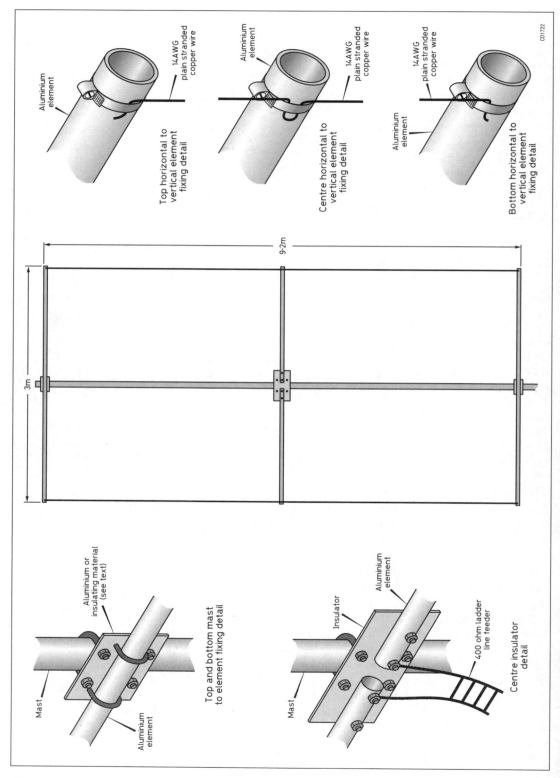

Aluminium element

14AWG plain stranded copper wire

Top horizontal to vertical element fixing detail

Aluminium element

14AWG plain stranded copper wire

Centre horizontal to vertical element fixing detail

14AWG plain stranded copper wire

Aluminium element

Bottom horizontal to vertical element fixing detail

0D1722

9·2m

3m

Aluminium or insulating material (see text)

Mast

Aluminium element

Top and bottom mast to element fixing detail

Insulator

Aluminium element

Mast

400 ohm ladder line feeder

Centre insulator detail

The performance of the antenna on the normal HF bands is unaffected by grounding or insulating the upper and lower elements.

The dimensions of this antenna regarding aluminium tube/wire diameters and length are not critical.

Feeding

The antenna requires a balanced feed and is fed with 450Ω slotted-line feeder, although the feeder impedance is not critical. The feeder should be fixed on stand-off insulators about 6in from the mast until clear of the lower element to prevent them blowing about in the wind and affecting the impedance, although this was not done in the antenna shown in Fig 5.23.

An ATU with a balanced output is required. I used a conventional Z-match with the two sets of balanced outputs, one ostensibly for the higher HF frequencies and the other for the lower ones.

In practice the lower-frequency output worked best for all frequencies. Experiments show that the antenna can be fed with any of the ATUs described in Chapter 4.

Performance

I built my skeleton slot to the size specified by Bill Capstick and these dimensions seem nearly optimum for the five higher HF bands. While the DX performance of this antenna is good up to 30MHz it deteriorates at frequencies higher than this.

On the 21, 24 and 28MHz bands the antenna performs very well, particularly when conditions are marginal. On 21MHz DX stations consistently gave me two S-points better than I received when I used the linear. Early-morning contacts with the Pacific on 21MHz had very noticeable echoes, probably due to the bi-directional nature of the antenna.

REFERENCES

[1] 'Electrically tuneable loop', Roberto Craighero, I1ARZ, *Radio Communication* February 1989.

[2] 'Loop antennas, fact not fiction', A J Henk, G4XVF, *Radio Communication* September and October 1991.

[3] *Small High-Efficiency Antennas – Alias the Loop*, 100-page booklet published by Ted Hart, W5QJR.

[4] DK5CZ's comments on the use of vacuum cap, 'Eurotek'column in *Radio Communication* October 1991, p39.

[5] 'Experimental magnetic loop antenna', C R Reynolds, GW3JPT, *Radio Communication* February 1994.

[6] 'A magnetic loop for 80m mobile', Loek d'Hunt, PA2JBC, 'Eurotek' column in *Radio Communication* May 1993.

[7] 'Roof-space dual-band magnetic loop', Eric Sandys,

Opposite: Fig 5.22. The G3LDO multi-band skeleton-slot antenna for 14 to 28MHz. The elements are fixed to the mast and the whole mast is rotated. The wire elements are fixed to the horizontal elements with hose clips. The centre insulator, as shown, is home-made but a commercial one would be suitable

Below: Fig 5.23. The G3LDO multi-band skeleton-slot antenna for 14 to 28MHz

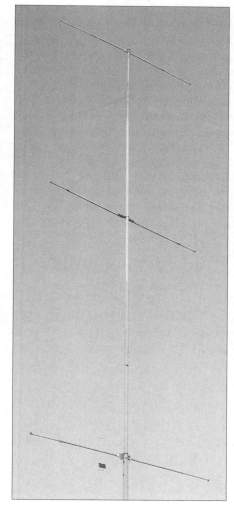

GI2FHN, 'Technical Topics' column in *Radio Communication* February 1993.

[8] 'Skeleton slot aerials', B Sykes, *RSGB Bulletin* (forerunner of the RSGB's *RadCom*) January 1953.

[9] 'The HF skeleton slot antenna', Bill Capstick, G3JYP, *Radio Communication* June 1996.

6 Small rotary beam antennas for HF

THE rotary beam antenna has become standard equipment for the upper HF amateur bands and the best-known icon of amateur radio is the three-element Yagi. It offers many advantages, such as power gain, reduction in interference from undesired directions, compactness and the ability to change the azimuth direction quickly and easily. All this is attractive for a restricted site. All the beam antennas described in this chapter are parasitic beam antennas. The basic design is the Yagi and, while a full-sized 14MHz three-element monobander Yagi is normally too large for a small garden, it may worth considering this antenna for the higher-frequency bands.

Optimum dimensioning of spacing and element lengths, moreover, can only be obtained over a very narrow frequency range, so the parasitic beam will work only over a relatively restricted band of frequencies. In most cases, the bandwidth of such an array is compatible with the width of the HF amateur bands.

The compactness of a parasitic beam antenna more than outweighs the disadvantage of the critical performance and no other antenna exists that can compare, size for size, with the power gain and directional characteristics of the parasitic array.

This chapter also contains more compact designs of beam antenna that may be suitable for your location.

TWO-ELEMENT YAGI

A two-element Yagi is shown in Fig 6.1. The parasitic element (Ep in Fig 6.1) is energised by radiation from the driven element, which then re-radiates. The phase relationship between the radiated signal from the driven element and the re-radiated signal from the parasitic element causes the signal from the antenna to be 'beamed' either in the direction of Ep or away from it, depending on the length of the parasitic element.

This phase relationship is effected by the length of the parasitic element. When the parasitic element is longer than the driven element it operates as a reflector and causes the power gain in a direction away from Ep. When the parasitic element is shorter it operates as a director, causing the power gain in a direction towards Ep.

When the parasitic element is to be used as a director, optimum spacing between it and the driven element is around 0.1λ. Optimum spacing when using the parasitic element as a reflector case is approximately 0.13λ.

The effect of these options can be seen in the computer simulation shown

Fig 6.1. Construction of a two-element Yagi beam with dimension references for the 14, 18, 21, 24 and 28MHz bands

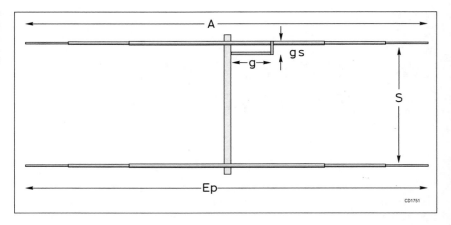

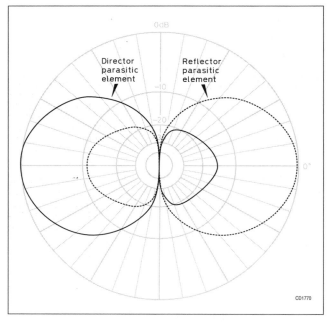

Fig 6.2. Computer analysis of a two-element beam with the parasitic element as (a) a reflector and (b) as a director

in Fig 6.2. There is very little difference in performance with a two-element beam when the parasitic element is used either as a director or reflector, with perhaps just a marginal improvement in the front-to-back ratio when the parasitic element is a director. Additionally, a two-element beam with a parasitic director will be slightly smaller and lighter of the two options.

Practical dimensions for this option are shown in Table 6.1. These dimensions have been calculated using EZNEC for a non-critical design to give a free-space gain better than 6dBi and a front-to-back ratio greater than 14dB as shown in the director parasitic element polar diagram of Fig 6.2. These calculations assume an average tube diameter of 20mm (0.75in) on 21MHz, which is scaled to an average of 30mm on 14MHz and 15mm on 28MHz. In practice the diameter of the tube is not critical and the diameter

Table 6.1. Dimensions for a two-element beam					
Frequency (MHz)	14.1	18.1	21.2	24.9	28.5
S – element spacing (m)	2.11	1.66	1.41	1.20	1.05
Ep – director length (m)	9.66	7.58	6.47	5.50	4.81
A – driven element (m)	10.30	8.08	6.90	5.88	5.13
S – element spacing (in)	83	65	56	47	41
Ep – director length (in)	380	298	255	217	189
A – driven element (in)	406	318	272	231	202

Refer to Fig 6.1 for dimensions S, Ep and A. These dimensions have been calculated using EZNEC for a non-critical design to give a free-space gain better than 6dBi and a front-to-back ratio greater than 14dB.

should be such that the antenna is mechanically stable. The elements should be made of, say, five sections that telescope into each other as shown in Fig 6.1. Aluminium scaffolding pole 50mm (2in) in diameter is useful material for the boom for any of the bands. The construction of the elements and methods of fixing the boom to the mast are described in Chapter 8.

As with all parasitic beams the dimensions of the parasitic elements determine their performance. The length of the driven element is less critical and its length only determines the feed impedance.

The feed-point impedance of this antenna is approximately 30Ω. To match it to 50Ω coaxial cable a matching arrangement is necessary. The gamma match is described later.

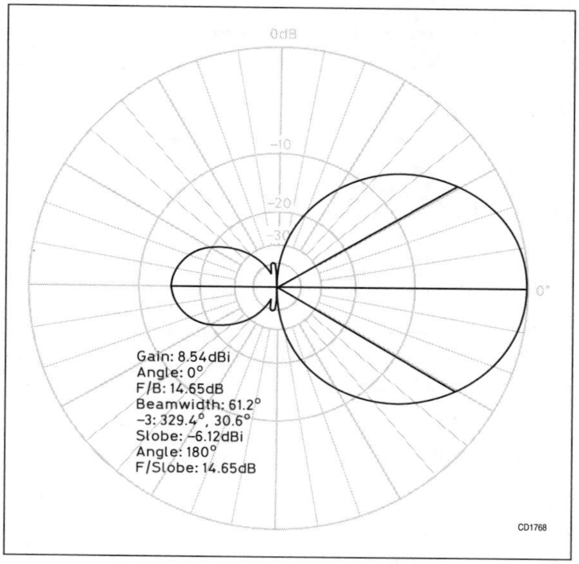

THE THREE-ELEMENT YAGI

By adding a reflector and a director to a driven element to form a three-element parasitic beam the free-space gain is increased to over 8dBi with a front-to-back (F/B) ratio greater than 20dB, although this depends on whether the antenna is tuned for maximum gain or maximum front-to-back ratio. I tend to tune beam antennas for maximum F/B ratio. The reason for this approach is that adjustments to the F/B ratio make a marked difference that is easy to measure. For example the polar diagram of the W3SAI antenna [1] shown in Fig 6.3 has a gain of 8.54dB and the F/B ratio is only 14.65dB.

On the other hand, the polar diagram of an antenna selected for a good F/B ratio (23.4dB), such as the one shown in Fig 6.4, is only 0.4dB down in forward gain on the W3SAI antenna. As 6dB is equivalent to one S-point, the improvement of 1.5 S-units on F/B is noticeable. The gain difference of 0.42dB is not going to be noticed on any S-meter.

The construction is similar to that described for the two-element beam. The dimensions for this antenna are given in Table 6.2 and are read in conjunction with Fig 6.5. A typical three-element beam, made from 'junk' aluminium tubing, see Chapter 8, is shown in Fig 6.6.

The feed-point impedance of this antenna is around 25Ω. To match it to 50Ω coaxial

Fig 6.3. The polar diagram of the three-element beam from the W3SAI *Beam Antenna Book* shows high gain and a F/B ratio of nearly 15dB

Fig 6.4. Polar diagram of a three-element beam designed using EZNEC for a high F/B ratio at the expense of gain

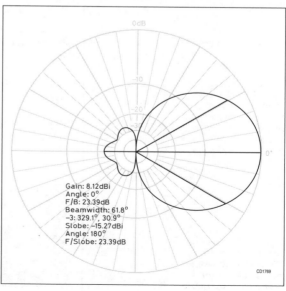

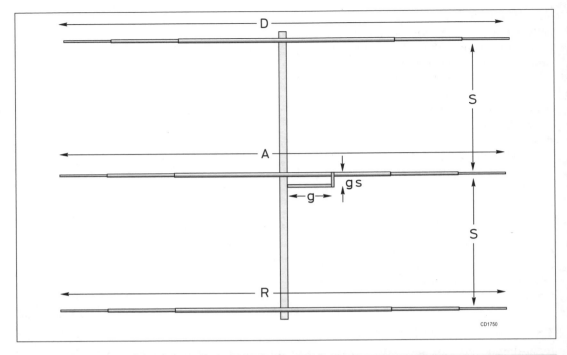

Fig 6.5. Construction of
a three-element beam
with dimension refer-
ences for the 14, 18,
21, 24 and 28MHz
bands

Table 6.2. Dimensions for a three-element beam

Frequency (MHz)	14.1	18.1	21.2	24.9	28.5
S – element spacing (m)	2.96	2.32	1.98	1.67	1.47
D – director length (m)	9.66	7.60	6.47	5.52	4.83
A – driven element (m)	10.30	7.92	6.76	5.76.	5.03
R – reflector length (m)	9.66	8.24	6.49	5.99	5.23
S – element spacing (in)	116	91	77	66	58
D – director length (in)	382	229	254	216	190
A – driven element (in)	402	314	268	229	200
R – reflector length (in)	414	324	276	236	206

Refer to Fig 6.5 for dimensions S, D, R and A. The dimensions are shown in metres and
inches and have been calculated using EZNEC for a non-critical design to give a free-
space gain better than 8dBi and a front-to-back ratio greater than 20dB.

Fig 6.6. A three-ele-
ment Yagi beam for
10m can be accommo-
dated on the roof of a
relatively small house

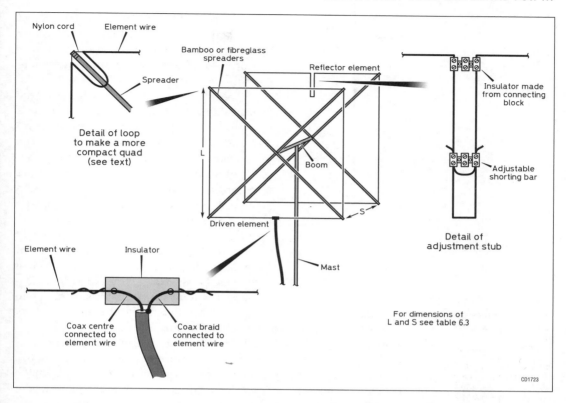

cable a matching arrangement is necessary. The gamma match is described later.

THE CUBICAL QUAD

The cubical quad beam is a parasitic array with elements consisting of closed loops having a circumference of one wavelength at the design frequency. The quad construction is shown in Fig 6.7 and the dimensions are given in Table 6.3.

Fig 6.7. Construction of a two-element wire quad, with dimension references in Table 6.3. The reflector can be constructed using the same dimensions as L, the driven element; a tuneable stub (see detail on right) is then used to lower the frequency of the reflector. This stub can be used to tune the reflector for the greatest front-to-back ratio of the beam. The stubs on the element corner supports (detail left) are discussed in the text

Table 6.3. Dimensions for a two-element quad beam					
Frequency (MHz)	14.1	18.1	21.2	24.9	28.5
S – element spacing (m)	2.98	2.34	1.99	1.70	1.49
ES – element support length (m)	3.93	3.1	2.64	2.24	1.96
L – driven element (m)*	5.33	4.18	3.57	3.04	2.65
S – element spacing (in)	117	92	79	67	59
ES – element support length (in)	155	122	104	89	77
L – driven element (in)*	210	164	140	120	105

Refer to Fig 6.7 for dimensions L and S. These dimensions have been calculated using EZNEC for a non-critical design to give a free-space gain around 7.5Bi and a front-to-back ratio greater than 15dB. ES is the length of one element support measured from the beam to the point where the element is fixed.

* Note that these dimensions are for one side of the quad. The total length of the element is four times this figure.

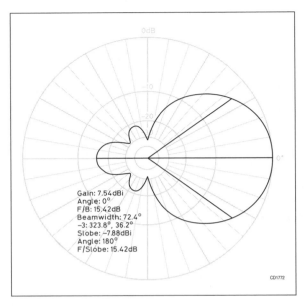

Fig 6.8. Computer analysis of a two-element wire element quad with 0.14λ element spacing

Fig 6.9. Computer analysis of a two-element wire element quad, (a) using 0.2λ spacing; (b) using 0.1λ spacing

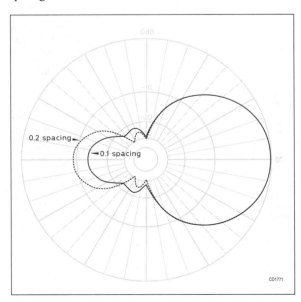

The parasitic element is normally tuned as a reflector. It can be tuned as a director but the gain and front-to-back ratio is inferior. Additionally, the optimum settings are more critical.

The reflector can be constructed using the same dimensions as L; a tuneable stub is then used to lower the frequency of the reflector. This stub can be used to tune the reflector for the greatest front-to-back ratio of the beam. When the adjustments are complete, cover the connecting blocks with grease to prevent corrosion. The stubs on the element corner supports can also be used reduce the overall size of the element and can be used with the driven element and the reflector. However, the lengths will have to be determined by experiment. The easiest way to construct these stubs is to use plastic-insulated wire elements and then to tape the stub along the element support, as shown in the right-hand detail of Fig 6.7.

The dimensions given in Table 6.3 are for a quad using an element spacing of 0.14λ and the computed free-space performance is shown in Fig 6.8. In addition the lengths of the element supports are given. The lengths of the supports could be longer than this; the length dimension is the point where the element is connected to the support.

The feed impedance of the quad using the dimensions shown in Table 6.3 is around 65Ω so the driven element can normally be connected directly to 50Ω feedline with only minimal mismatch. The 0.14λ spacing (S), given in Table 6.3, was chosen because it is the most prevalent in antenna literature. However, the spacing for a two-element quad can be reduced down to 0.1λ without any noticeable deterioration in performance – see Fig 6.9. Reduced spacing lowers the feed-point impedance and can give an improved match to 50Ω coaxial cable.

The quad can be made into a multi-band antenna by interlacing quad loops for the different bands on to a common support structure. In this case the element support length ER and ED should be the length for the lowest-frequency band. The disadvantage of this arrangement is that the wavelength spacing (S) between the driven element and the parasitic element is different on each band. This problem can be overcome by using an element support structure with a modified geometry as shown in Fig 6.10.

A multi-band quad using this type of geometry is often referred to as a 'boomless' quad for obvious reasons. The structure which holds the element supports in place at the correct angles is often referred to as a 'spider'. An example, obtained a club junk sale, is shown in Fig 6.11.

Dimensions *ER* and *ED* will have to be increased by around 5% with the boomless quad.

All the driven elements can be fed in parallel, as shown in Fig 6.10, without any compromise in performance.

Methods of fixing cane or glass-fibre element supports to booms are given in Chapter 8.

Design of an all-metal quad

This all-metal version of the quad evolved as an attempt to make a more simple, weatherproof version. The metal quad antenna for 14MHz looks like two 28MHz two-element beams stacked at half a wavelength. The tips of the elements of the bays are joined by 14SWG stranded copper wire, making full wavelength loops for 14MHz.

The lengths of the elements and the distance between the booms were initially set at approximately 5.5m (18ft); this dimension being determined by the quad formula:

$$L \text{ (total element length in metres)} = 306.3/f(\text{MHz})$$

or

$$L \text{ (total element length in feet)} = 1005/f(\text{MHz})$$

With these dimensions the resonant frequency of each metal quad loop was around 15.4MHz; this is probably due to the construction. When wire is added to the end of an aluminium tube it represents an extreme diameter taper, which causes the above formula to be inappropriate.

When the spacing between the bays and the vertical sections of the elements are increased to 6m (20ft) the quad element resonances move down into the 14MHz band.

The dimensions for a 14MHz quad are shown in Fig 6.12.

The reflector element can only be made longer by increasing the length of the aluminium tube horizontal sections; the final dimensions for 14MHz are 5.5m (18ft) for the driven element and 5.94m (19ft 6in) for the reflector. The driven element can be fed directly in the centre with 50Ω coaxial cable or via a matching system such as a gamma match.

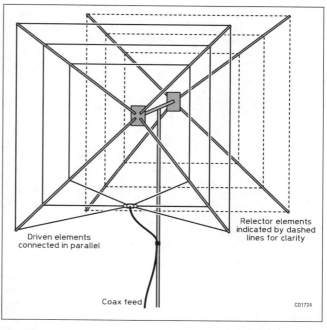

Fig 6.10. General view of a multi-band variant of the quad using optimum driven element/reflector spacing for each band

Fig 6.11. Construction of a commercial 'spider' for a multi-band quad, which allows optimum spacing on all bands

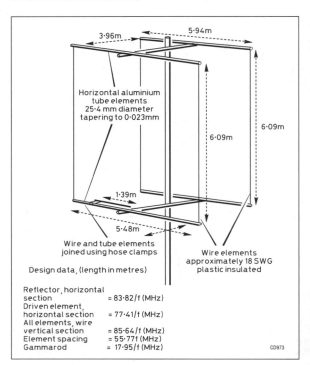

Horizontal aluminium
tube elements
25·4 mm diameter
tapering to 0·023mm

Wire and tube elements
joined using hose clamps

Wire elements
approximately 18 SWG
plastic insulated

Design data, (length in metres)

Reflector, horizontal section	= 83·82/f (MHz)
Driven element, horizontal section	= 77·41/f (MHz)
All elements, wire vertical section	= 85·64/f (MHz)
Element spacing	= 55·77f (MHz)
Gammarod	= 17·95/f (MHz)

CD973

Above: **Fig 6.12. Construction of a two-element all metal quad for 14MHz with design formula for other frequencies**

Above right: **Fig 6.13. 14MHz two-element, all-metal quad**

All measurements indicate that the gain is greater than that of a conventional quad [2].

This structure is neater, and has a smaller windage than the conventional wire quad on spreaders – see Fig 6.13. Its main disadvantage is that it requires a section of unguyed mast above the rotator. The unguyed rotating mast described in Chapter 8 is the most suitable support for this antenna.

BEAMS WITH BENT ELEMENTS

The 10m 'wingspan' of a conventional Yagi for 14MHz can be a problem for many locations. So can the elements be bent as is done with a dipole when trying to fit it into a smaller space, and still retain the beam characteristics?

With antennas there is very little that is actually new and a two-element Yagi with bent elements is one of them. A configuration where the elements of a two-element beam were bent so that the 'wingspan' was halved was first suggested by John Reinartz, W1QP, way back in October 1937. Burton Simson, W8CPC, constructed such an antenna [3], the elements of which were supported on a wooden frame. This allowed the element ends to be folded towards each other. The 14MHz antenna was constructed from ¼in copper tubing with brass tuning rods that fitted snugly into the ends of the elements for tuning.

A wire version of the W1QP/W8CPC two-element antenna was described in 1973 by VK2ABQ [4]. In this configuration the tips of the parasitic and driven elements support each other in the horizontal plane. The insulators are constructed so that the tips of the elements are 6mm (¼in) apart.

According to VK2ABQ, this capacitive end couples the reflector from the driven element although the gap between the tips of the elements is described as "not critical". A computer model is shown in Fig 6.14.

The computer model of the W1QP/ W8CPC/VK2ABQ arrangement suggests that the driven element/parasitic element coupling is the same as for a wide-spaced two-element Yagi and its performance is shown in Fig 6.15.

The Moxon Rectangle

Les Moxon, G6XN, did a lot of experimental work with the two-element Yagi with bent elements [5], particularly in optimising the element spacing. However, some of these structures are complex and difficult to reproduce. A simplified structure has been devised by L B Cebik, W4RNL, which he has named the 'Moxon Rectangle' [6], and this is shown in Fig 6.16.

The remarkable characteristic of this arrangement is its very high front-to-back ratio. It also has a feed impedance which is close to 50Ω. The dimensions for the Moxon rectangle for 7 to 28MHz are given in Table 6.4. The dimensions are not perfect scaling because the length-to-wire-diameter ratio changes for each band.

The antenna has a feed-point impedance between about 56 and 58Ω, a close match to the standard amateur 50Ω coaxial cable. Free-space gain and front-to-back ratio are consistent for all the models, averaging 5.8dBi and greater than 30dB in free space, respectively. A typical free-space azimuth pattern for the antenna is shown in Fig 6.17.

The Moxon Rectangle can be made into a multi-band antenna by interlacing the elements for the different bands on to a common support structure – see Fig 6.18. Unlike the quad, the geometry of the support system ensures optimum spacing on all bands. The dimensions of this antenna are given in Table 6.4, which is read in conjunction with Fig 6.18.

The Double-D antenna

If you want to make the bent-element Yagi even smaller, the ends of the elements can be folded back towards the mast in the vertical plane to accommodate the length of the element in a smaller area. This results in a pymamid configuration, which I have christened the 'Double-D' [2, 7] and

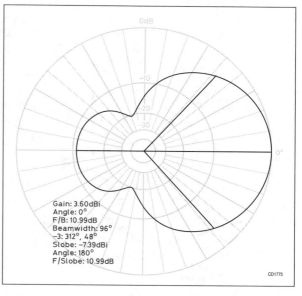

Gain: 3.60dBi
Angle: 0°
F/B: 10.99dB
Beamwidth: 96°
–3: 312°, 48°
Slobe: –7.39dBi
Angle: 180°
F/Slobe: 10.99dB

CD1773

Fig 6.14. VK2ABQ improved version by G5LZR

Fig 6.15. Computer analysis of a W1QP/ W8CPC/VK2ABQ configuration

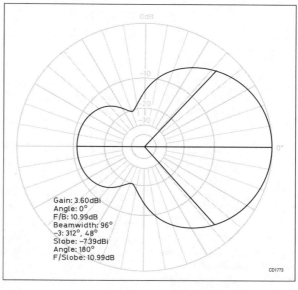

Gain: 3.60dBi
Angle: 0°
F/B: 10.99dB
Beamwidth: 96°
–3: 312°, 48°
Slobe: –7.39dBi
Angle: 180°
F/Slobe: 10.99dB

CD1773

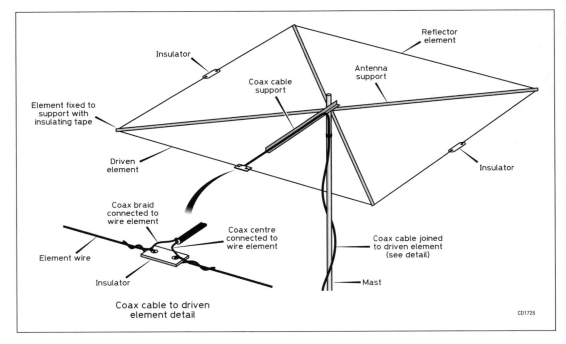

Fig 6.16. Perspective view of the Moxon Rectangle showing the general construction. The element supports can be made from weather-treated cane or glassfibre. Details of fixing the supports to the mast are shown in Chapter 8

its construction is shown in Fig 6.19. Use plastic tape to fix the wire to the canes; I have never noticed any detuning using this method.

This antenna will provide 3 to 4dB of gain over a dipole and a front-to-back ratio better than 14dB, which is not as good as the Moxon Rectangle but then this is a very compact antenna. The ends of the elements, with its 'guy' supports, provide a strong, lightweight structure.

Use the formula in Fig 6.20 to obtain the approximate wire lengths. In practice it is difficult to optimise the element lengths in a formula because of the geometry of the antenna. My suggestion is to make the ends of the elements (where they connect to the insulator) variable, as shown for the antennas in Fig 2.2 and 2.4 (Chapter 2). Then adjust reflector for maximum F/B and the driven element for minimum SWR. If you in the mood to experiment you should be able to increase the gain and improve the SWR by reducing dimension B.

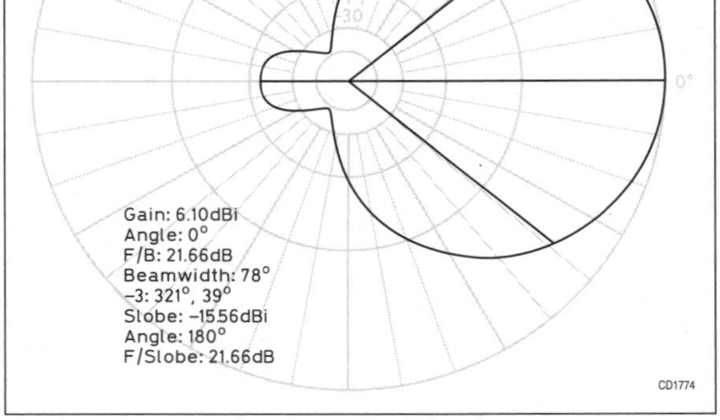

Gain: 6.10dBi
Angle: 0°
F/B: 21.66dB
Beamwidth: 78°
−3: 321°, 39°
Slobe: −15.56dBi
Angle: 180°
F/Slobe: 21.66dB

Fig 6.17. Computer analysis of the Moxon Rectangle

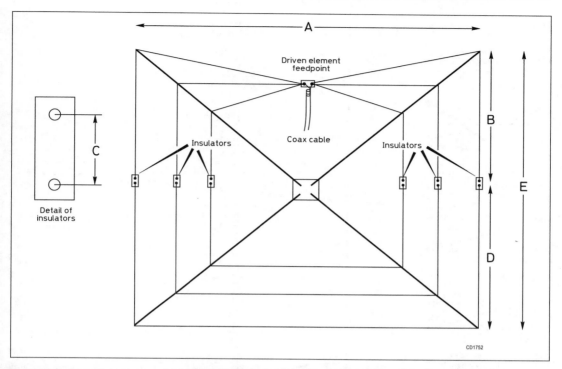

Fig 6.18. The Moxon Rectangle, multi-band variant with dimension data

Table 6.4. Dimensions for the W4RNL-designed Moxon Rectangle beam					
Design frequency (MHz)	**Dimensions, metres (*mm)**				
	A	**B**	**C**	**D**	**E**
29.50	3.79	0.59	125*	0.74	1.45
24.94	4.33	0.67	140*	0.84	1.66
21.20	5.00	0.80	158*	0.99	1.95
18.12	5.96	0.94	180*	1.16	2.28
14.17	7.62	1.22	219*	1.48	2.92
10.12	10.66	1.71	305*	2.07	4.08
7.15	15.10	2.75	405*	2.93	5.73
Design frequency (MHz)	**Dimensions in feet**				
	A	**B**	**C**	**D**	**E**
29.50	12.44	1.94	0.41	2.41	4.76
24.94	14.22	2.22	0.46	2.76	5.44
21.20	16.72	2.63	0.52	3.25	6.40
18.12	19.56	3.10	0.59	3.80	7.49
14.17	25.00	4.00	0.72	4.85	9.57
10.12	35.00	5.60	1.00	6.80	13.40
7.15	49.56	9.01	1.33	9.63	18.97

Refer to Fig 6.18 for dimensions A, B, C and D. These dimensions have been calculated using EZNEC for a non-critical design to give a free-space gain around 5.8dBi and a front-to-back ratio greater than 30dB. The elements are constructed from 1.6mm diameter copper wire

The Double-D is also amenable to multi-banding. A number of these antennas, for different bands, can be mounted on the same support as shown in Fig 6.21.

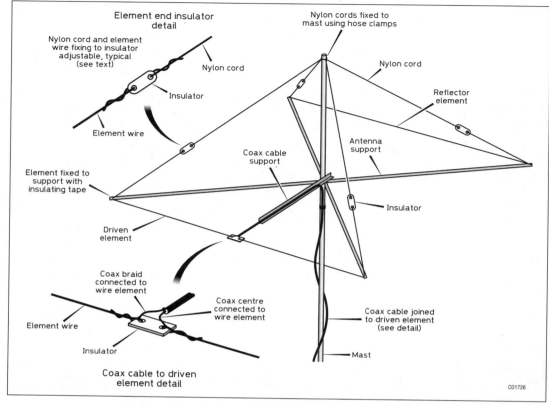

Element end insulator detail

Nylon cord and element wire fixing to insulator adjustable, typical (see text)

Nylon cord

Insulator

Element wire

Element fixed to support with insulating tape

Driven element

Coax braid connected to wire element

Element wire

Insulator

Coax cable to driven element detail

Nylon cords fixed to mast using hose clamps

Nylon cord

Reflector element

Antenna support

Coax cable support

Insulator

Coax centre connected to wire element

Coax cable joined to driven element (see detail)

Mast

CD1726

Fig 6.19. Perspective view of the Double-D antenna, showing the general construction. The element supports can be made from weather-treated cane or glassfibre. Details of fixing the supports to the mast are shown in Chapter 8

The simplest method of feeding turned out to be the best; paralleling the driven elements and feeding them with the one coaxial line as shown in Fig 6.21.

THE GAMMA MATCH

All the metal antennas described above can be matched to the coaxial feeder using the gamma match. It is not everyone's favourite but I like it because of its simplicity. The big advantage of this matching arrangement is that you don't have to make a centre insulator for the element: it can be clamped directly to the boom like the parasitic elements.

The gamma rod can be made out of thick aluminium wire, or even hard drawn copper wire as shown in Fig 6.22. It is fixed to the driven element a short distance from the centre. The other end of the rod is connected to the centre of the coaxial feeder via a capacitor. The approximate length of the gamma rod and spacing from the element (g and gs in Figs 6.1 and 6.5) and the value of the capacitor is given in Table 6.5. The gamma rod length is determined by experiment as described in Chapter 10.

COMMERCIAL ANTENNAS

This chapter would be incomplete without a description of a couple of the commercial minibeams that are available.

The MQ-2 antenna

I have reviewed this antenna [8] so I am fairly conversant with its performance and limitations.

The MQ-2 antenna is a compact two-element beam for the 14, 18, 21, 24 and 28MHz bands. It will also operate on the 50MHz band with limited performance. It uses end loading, comprising an inductance and capacitance 'spokes' at the ends of each element; a separate set of inductors and spokes are used for each of the HF bands. The parasitic element is a reflector, which uses a diamond configuration. The MQ-2 is shown in Fig 6.23.

One of the spokes in each set is constructed so that its length can be varied. This is achieved using an adjuster, comprising a sleeve with small clamping screws, and allows the resonant frequency to be set at a specific part of the band.

The MQ-2 appears to have been derived from the G4MH minibeam, designed many years ago. This antenna is also uses two elements and employs inductive and capacitive end loading to reduce the element lengths to 3.4m. The G4MH minibeam was designed for the 14, 21 and 28MHz amateur bands and the parasitic element is tuned as a director.

In spite of some of limitations of the MQ-2, I felt that this configuration had promise so I bought the review model with a view to modifying it.

While commenting on its small size – the element lengths are 3.6m (11ft 9in) and the boom length 1.37m (4ft 6in) – I did mention its lack of directivity on 14MHz and the difficulties in trying to match the antenna to the feeder on all the bands. These deficiencies can be rectified by making the antenna just a little bit larger.

Modifying the MQ-2

The element lengths were changed from 3.6m (11ft 9in) to 4.49m (4ft 8in) and the boom length from

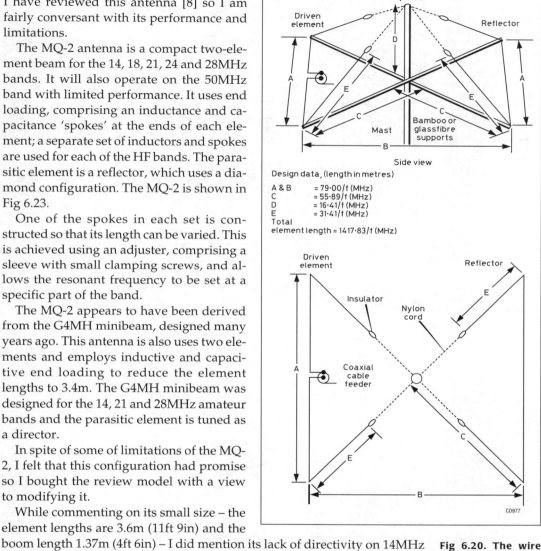

Design data, (length in metres)

A & B	= 79·00/f (MHz)
C	= 55·89/f (MHz)
D	= 16·41/f (MHz)
E	= 31·41/f (MHz)
Total element length	= 1417·83/f (MHz)

Fig 6.20. The wire Double-D antenna with approximate design data

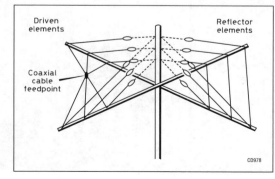

Fig 6.21. The multi-band Double-D antenna

Fig 6.22. The gamma match arrangement shown uses a fixed capacitor whose value is determined by experiment with a variable capacitor. The value of the variable capacitor is then measured and a fixed capacitor substituted. The gamma rod is made from hard drawn copper wire, which allows screw type electrical connectors to be used, making the matching unit easy to adjust. All connections should be well protected with a coating of grease after the adjustment is complete

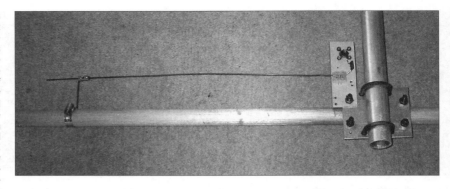

Table 6.5. Gamma match dimensions and capacitor values

Frequency (MHz)	Gamma rod length (g) (m)	Spacing (gs) (mm)	Capacitor value (pF)
14	1.22 (48in)	152 (6in)	150
18.1	1.0 (39in)	140 (5.5in)	125
21	0.92 (36in)	128 (5in)	100
24.9	0.75 (30in)	114 (4.5in)	87
28	0.60 (24in)	100 (4in)	75

See Figs 6.1 and 6.5 for g and gs. The capacitor values relate to the maximum value of a variable capacitor; in practice the final value after adjustment will be lower.

1.37m (4ft 6in) to 2.1m (6ft 10in). In practice this means replacing most of the metalwork in the antenna. The original element tubing diameter is 25.4mm (1.0in) outside diameter; the loading assembly at the ends of the elements have been machined to 22mm to fit inside this tubing. The electrical diagram of the modified antenna is shown in Fig 6.24.

Fig 6.23. MQ-2 multiband antenna

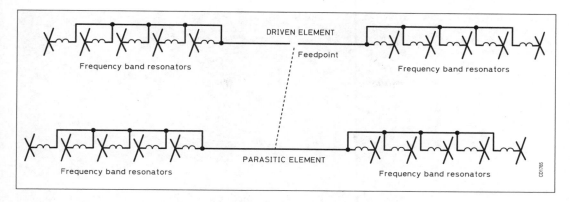

The reflector and driven elements are the same length but the driven element is cut in the centre so that it can be fed directly with coaxial cable.

The inductance of each of the loading assemblies needs to be reduced to compensate for the extra element length. This is achieved by removing one turn from each of the five coils on each of the loading assemblies.

The modification to the MQ-2 has made a big improvement to the 14 and 18MHz bands. In the higher frequencies there is no noticeable improvement in gain or front-to-back ratio but the improvement in the impedance bandwidth on all bands is most marked. In fact the performances on the various bands are similar to those predicted by EZNEC.

The antenna, shown in Fig 6.25, has been in use for several months now and has weathered several storms without any problem; there has also not been any noticeable deterioration in performance in wet weather.

Fig 6.24. Electrical diagram of the modified antenna MQ-2

Butternut HF5B

The HF5B is probably the best known of the very-compact, multi-band beams. L B Cebik, W4RNL, has used a Butternut HF5B for about 12 years or so with very good results. At his previous QTH the antenna was located 12m (40ft) high and at his present QTH (on a small hill) it is about 10.7m (35ft) high.

Fig 6.25. The compact multi-band antenna is fixed to the chimney using a double clamp. Even though the modification has resulted in a larger antenna it is still a very compact multi-band beam, as can be seen by comparison with the UHF TV antenna

Fig 6.26. Butternut
HF5B compact beam
antenna *(photo cour-
tesy Bencher Inc)*

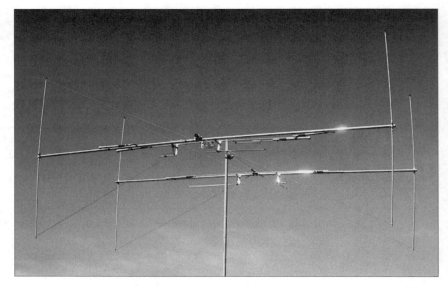

The fan dipoles making up each of the two elements are self-resonant at about 25MHz. The complex assemblies on each element are matching and resonating networks. The structure of the antenna is shown in Fig 6.26.

The antenna is at its best on 21 and 28MHz, where it gives performance equal to a two-element Yagi, with a similar back lobe that is down about two S-units. W4RNL prefers the lower F/B ratio for nets, so he can hear (but not at full strength) some who might want to check in off the rear.

On the 24MHz band, the antenna is also a two-element Yagi, but in the reverse direction, since it forms a driver-director. On 18MHz, the antenna is essentially a dipole, and on 14MHz, there is little or no gain over a 14MHz dipole, but there is directivity.

These performance evaluations are consistent with the Butternut specifications in Table 6.6.

The antenna requires very patient and careful setting-up and the tuning was done with the antenna pointed upward about 3m off the ground. The settings held very well and no tower-top adjustments were necessary. Be prepared to repeat some of the adjustments, since it is easy to overrun the setting correct points.

Once set, the antenna has held its settings without need for further adjustment. W4RNL maintains his antenna by tilting the tower and checking all mechanical connections every once in a while. Other than cleaning the elements (birds love to sit on the elements) and checking nut/bolt tightness, he has never had to make a readjustment. This includes having the elements laid on top of belongings when during the move to the present QTH. Re-assembly of the elements to the boom and mast turned out to be 'plug-'n'-play', with no readjustment necessary. The antenna slips the wind very well and has held up in some gales from big storms.

W4RNL is of the impression that those who have disliked the antenna have not had the patience to get it set up precisely in the first place. A few have had the wrong expectations: an antenna that is 3.8m (12ft 6in)

CHAPTER 6: SMALL ROTARY BEAM ANTENNAS FOR HF

Table 6.6. Specification of the HF5B five-band butterfly beam antenna. Five popular HF bands (20, 17, 15, 12 and 10m) in a rotatable, two-element beam. The antenna is light enough to be turned with a TV rotator	
Wingspan	3.8m (12ft 6in)
Boom length	1.8m (6ft)
Turning radius	2.1m (6ft 11in)
Vertical spreaders	1.8m (6ft)
Shipping weight	10kg (22lb)
Feed-point impedance	Nominal 50Ω. Includes RF connector for direct connection to any length feed line terminated in PL259
VSWR at resonance	1.5:1 or less
Power rating	500W CW/1200W PEP SSB input to the final
Unguyed wind survival	129kph (80mph)
Bandwidth for VSWR of 2:1 or less	10m – 0.5MHz, 12m – entire band, 15m – entire band, 17m – entire band, 20m – 200kHz
Gain	3+ dBd 20m, up to 5dBd on all other bands except 17m where it acts as a rotary dipole
Front-to-back	Up to 20dB
Front-to-side	Up to 30dB
Minimum height above ground	9.1m (30ft)
Mast	Accepts up to a 38.1mm (1½in) mast

side-to-side, 1.8m (6ft) high, and on a 1.8m (6ft) boom will not equal a beam with full-size elements on all bands (10.7m or so on the 14MHz band). However, it is a pretty fair choice for a backyard QTH where a full-size beam will not fit. It is considerably smaller than a quad, 5.5m (18ft) side-to-side for three- or five-band versions, and it is lighter. W4RNL has used this antenna with a CD-45 and a HD-73 rotator with no mechanical problems.

REFERENCES

[1] *W6SAI Quad Antenna Book.*
[2] *The Antenna Experimenter's Guide*, 2nd edn, Peter Dodd, G3LDO, RSGB.
[3] 'Concentrated directional antennas for transmission and reception', John Reinartz, W1QP, and Burton Simson, W8CPC, *QST* October 1937.
[4] 'VK2ABQ antenna', Fred Caton, VK2ABQ, *Electronics Australia* October 1973.
[5] *HF Antennas for all Locations*, 2nd edn, Les Moxon, G6XN, RSGB.
[6] L B Cebik, W4RNL, on Internet at http://funnelweb.utcc.utc.edu/.
[7] 'Wire beam antennas and the evolution of the Double-D', Peter Dodd, G3LDO, *QST* October 1984, also *Radio Communication* June/July 1980.
[8] 'Review of the MQ2 Mini-Beam Antenna', Peter Dodd, G3LDO, *Practical Wireless* August 1999.

7 | VHF and UHF antennas

THIS chapter contains constructional information for making VHF and UHF antennas for the 50 to 430MHz bands. Some are very simple and can be constructed in an hour or so. Others are better engineered to stand up to the weather in a more exposed site.

For the backyard antenna constructor the limitations posed by a small site are considerably less than that for HF, and fairly large VHF/UHF antennas are physically small compared with the HF antenna.

OMNIDIRECTIONAL ANTENNAS
The dipole

Fig 7.1. Simple dipole constructed from hard-drawn copper wire, fixed to a wooden support using staples. This construction is suitable for the 2m or 70cm bands and can be used as a vertical or horizontal polarised antenna

The simplest method of construction of a dipole is to fix 14SWG (2mm) hard-drawn copper wire elements to a wooden boom using netting staples, as shown in Fig 7.1. This method of construction is only suitable for the 144 and 432MHz bands because 2mm copper wire is unsuited for the unsupported longer elements required for the 70MHz and 50MHz bands.

- For 145MHz the total element length is 992mm (39in).
- For 432MHz the element length is 330mm (13in). For 438MHz the element length is 323mm (12.7in). In practice a total element length of 326mm will allow coverage of the whole band.

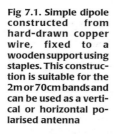

The element can be cut at the centre and fed directly with coaxial cable. The total length of the element includes the gap in the centre where the cable is fed to the element.

Dipoles for the lower VHF bands can be constructed using material from antenna suppliers or at rallies. Centre insulators and element-to-boom clamps are easily available and one is shown in Fig 7.2. The standard element diameter appears to be 12mm.

The feed impedance of a centre fed dipole is nominally 75Ω in free space, which is why all coaxial cable for television and FM radio is 75Ω. Most VHF antennas are more than two wavelengths

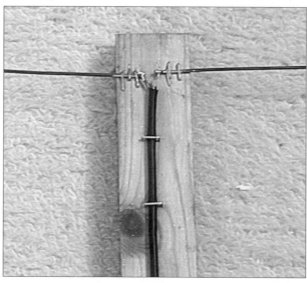

high so the feed impedance will be around 70Ω, giving an SWR of around 1.4:1 on 50Ω cable. The SWR at the transceiver will be less than that due to coaxial cable losses so it should match into the transceiver without any problem.

Fig 7.2. A FM VHF radio antenna centre insulator can be used for constructing dipoles for the 50, 70 and 144MHz bands. Dipole lengths using 12mm aluminium tubing are: 145MHz = 962mm (37.9in), 70.25MHz = 1.99m (78.4in), 50.5MHz = 2.79m (109.8in)

A dipole can be constructed without any insulators at all, as shown in Fig 7.3. In this case the element is coupled to the coaxial feeder with a simple gamma match. The length of the gamma rod and the value of the capacitor can be adjusted for a very low SWR.

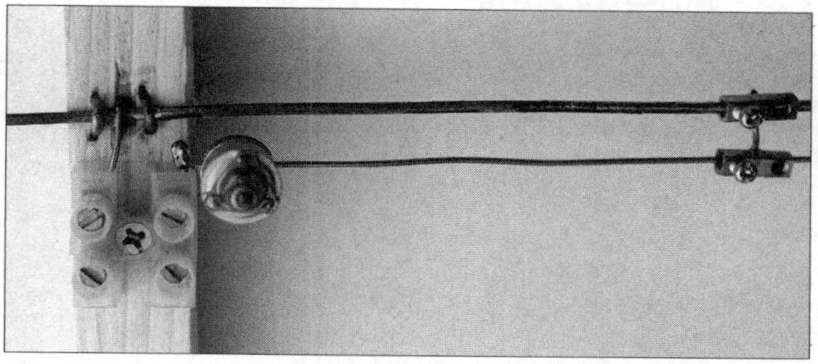

The G4LQI multi-band vertical

This rather interesting antenna [1] uses the G5RV principle (described in Chapter 2) to cover 29.6, 51.5 and 70MHz. The antenna is shown in Fig 7.4. The impedances of the dipole on the three different bands vary widely but G4LQI has found a length of open-wire tuned feeder that presents a reasonable impedance, resulting in an SWR of less than 3:1 on all three bands.

Fig 7.3. A 145MHz dipole constructed from 2mm hard-drawn copper wire. The capacitor and wire conductor form a gamma match. The length of the gamma rod and the value of the 20pF variable capacitor are adjusted for minimum SWR

The twin-line matching section is constructed from 1mm diameter wire; the spacing is 25mm with plastic spacers every 15cm. The end of the twin-line matching section is connected directly to RG58 cable. The coaxial-to-open-line junction was moisture sealed and strain relieved. The feed line could be made from 75Ω satellite cable, which would give less loss and a better match. Just below the junction, a choke balun is made by coiling the cable into three 8cm-diameter turns.

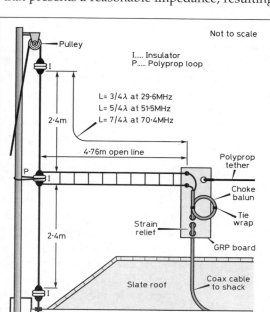

Not to scale

Pulley

I..... Insulator
P..... Polyprop loop

L= 3/4λ at 29·6MHz
L= 5/4λ at 51·5MHz
L= 7/4λ at 70·4MHz

2·4m

4·76m open line

Polyprop tether

P

Choke balun

Tie wrap

Strain relief

2·4m

GRP board

Slate roof

Coax cable to shack

Wooden pole

Gutter

CD1727

Fig 7.4. The G4LQI multi-band vertical for 29.6, 51.5 and 70MHz using the G5RV matching principle

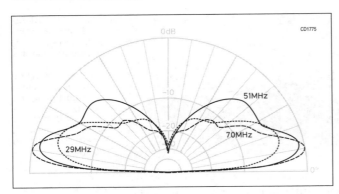

51MHz

70MHz

29MHz

Fig 7.5. Elevation polar diagrams of the G4LQI multi-band vertical

The antenna works well on all three bands. An elevation plot of the antenna, see Fig 7.5, shows it to be a useful antenna for local VHF working and even DX.

On the 28MHz band, the frequency of best SWR, 1.6:1, is at 29.3MHz. The automatic ATU used with the transceiver will handle SWRs of up to 3:1, permitting good matching anywhere from 28.0 to 29.7MHz. On the 50MHz band, the SWR is 2.8:1, and a small box with an L-match is used for matching. On the 70MHz band the antenna is used with a modified PMR, whose PA tuning can be adjusted to match the 2.3:1 SWR on that band.

A vertically polarised antenna for 145 and 435MHz

This is an omnidirectional vertically polarised antenna, which is an end-fed half-wave radiator on 145MHz and two stacked $5\lambda/8$ radiators on 435MHz. On 145MHz it has a gain of 0dBd and on 435MHz a gain approaching 5dBd. It was designed and built by Bert Veuskens, PA0HMV [2].

The high-impedance feed point of the antenna is matched to the coaxial cable on both bands by the circuit arrangement shown in Fig 7.6. On 435MHz, resonant radials are required; these are insignificant on 145MHz.

The phasing of the stacked sections is achieved by the phasing, as shown in Fig 7.7.

Construction

The antenna is built on to an N-type 50Ω coaxial socket (PTFE insulation) with square flange and the complete assembly fitted onto 28mm OD copper or brass mounting tube.

First, saw and file the corners of the coaxial socket flange to ensure a snug fit into the 28mm mounting tube as shown in Fig 7.6. Drill a hole for the earthed end of the coil, as shown in Fig 7.8.

Cut two 360mm long sections of 3mm brass rod or tubing for the radials and pre-bend them at the centre as shown in Fig 7.8.

The radials are soldered to the socket with the aid of a jig, which is constructed by drilling a 16mm diameter hole in the centre of a 25cm square piece of chipboard. The socket is inserted, barrel-down, into the hole, with the two sets of radials placed as shown in Fig 7.6 and Fig 7.8 fixed to the chipboard with staples. The radials are now soldered into place with a 50W or larger soldering iron. If you have used a professional-grade coaxial connector, its insulation will be PTFE and will not melt in the process. The radials are then cut to 173mm, measured from the centre of the socket.

Solder the 'cold' terminal of the tubular trim-capacitor to the connector.

Fig 7.6. The PA0HMV dual-band vertical, matching section

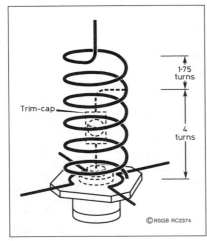

1·75 turns

Trim-cap

4 turns

Unroll and stretch the antenna wire to straighten it. Cut off 60cm, and, starting at one end, tightly wind six turns on a 19mm (¾in) tube, rod or dowel. Stretch the coil and fashion its ends to the shape and dimensions of Fig 7.7. Solder the short end of the coil into the hole drilled in the flange of the socket and connect the other terminal of the trim-capacitor to the coil, four turns above the earthed end. Approximately half of the lower radiator section should now point straight up, coaxially with the coil.

With the remaining wire, shape the phasing section as in Fig 7.9 using a 9.5mm (³⁄₈in) drill bit as a former. Trim the lower wire end so that it, when butt-spliced to the top of the wire on the coil, makes up the 450mm shown in Fig 7.9. Slide a polystyrene foam centring disk onto the wire below the phasing stub. Butt-splice the two sections together by soldering them into a short sleeve of copper tubing.

Cut the top wire to 460mm (this leaves some for later pruning to frequency). Slide the second centring disk onto the top wire. Saw and/or file into one end of the 28mm copper pipe four slots, 90° apart and each 4mm wide by 7mm deep, as shown in Fig 7.10. Do the same with one end of the PVC tubing but make the slots 70mm deep.

After assembly and tuning, the 28mm mounting tube will be clamped to the top of the mast using commercial hardware, eg two U-bolts, each with three saddles.

Tune-up

Tune the antenna on the 432MHz band for the lowest SWR. Note that this point should be 3MHz above the required frequency because the PVC weather shield lowers the resonance frequency on this band by approximately 3MHz when fitted.

Remove the antenna assembly from the chipboard and inspect all solder work. Feed a short coaxial cable through the 28mm copper pipe and connect it to the N-socket. Push the socket into the copper pipe until each radial touches the bottom of a slot. Place the assembly well clear of other conductors, but low enough to be accessible. Connect a 432MHz band signal source, eg a hand-held transceiver, through an SWR meter.

If the frequency of lowest SWR is lower than intended, bring the resonant frequency up by snipping bits off the top of the antenna, eg to 438MHz.

Fix the two centring discs with a drop of epoxy glue to the radiator at the voltage nodes, 170mm

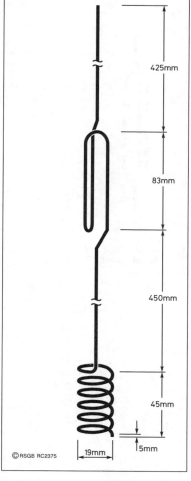

Fig 7.7. The PA0HMV dual-band vertical, shape and dimensions of the elements

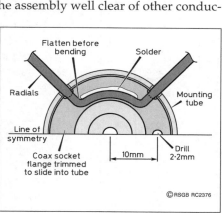

Fig 7.8. Coaxial socket and radials of the PA0HMV antenna. The radials are cut to 173mm, measured from the centre of the coaxial socket after being fixed in place

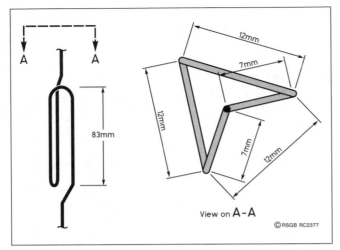

12mm

7mm

12mm

83mm

7mm

12mm

View on **A-A**

©RSGB RC2377

Fig 7.9. The PA0HMV dual-band vertical, phasing stub

below the top and halfway between the top of the coil and the bottom of the phasing stub. Slide the PVC pipe down on the antenna until each radial is squeezed between the bottom of its slot in the copper pipe and the top of its slot in the PVC tube. Verify that the best SWR now is where you want it and that it is below 1.5:1.

Connect a 144MHz band signal source, raise the PVC tube just enough to gain access to the trim-capacitor and adjust it for best SWR on 145MHz.

It was found that a capacitor fashioned from a piece of RG58 coaxial cable as shown in Fig 7.11 performed well but some adjustment of the braid length may be necessary.

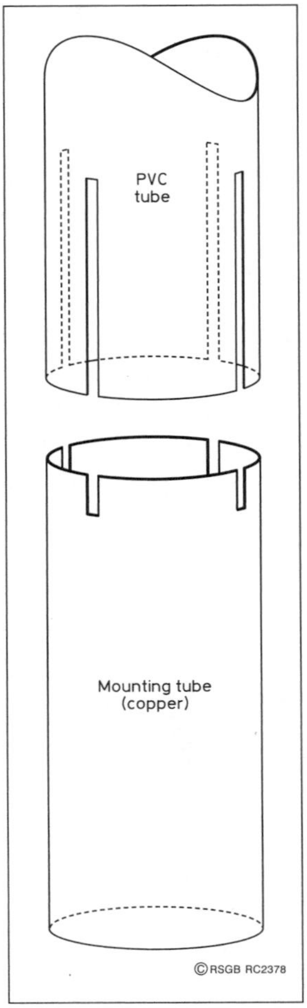

This completes the adjustment. Push the PVC tube down again and fix it in that position with a stainless-steel jubilee clip below the radials. Place the cap on top and weatherproof the assembly by applying sealing compound to the gaps in the PVC around the radials, making sure that rain cannot reach the capacitor but that condensation has a way out.

Materials

The materials used to make this antenna, listed below, are those which PA0HMV bought and used in Holland. The italicised notes give some idea as to what is available in the UK.

- Copper or brass mounting tube, 28mm OD, 220mm long. *28mm copper tubing is available from plumbers' supplies distributors in 3m lengths.*
- PVC tube, 32mm OD, 28mm ID, 1.2m long. *32mm OD white PVC tubing is sold in 2m lengths at DIY stores.*
- Jubilee clip, 32mm, preferably stainless steel.
- N-type (preferred) 50Ω coaxial socket with square flange.
- Brass rod or tubing, 3mm OD, for 4 radials, 720mm required. *1/8in OD copper tubing is suitable from old central heating pilot thermostats.*
- Bare copper wire, single strand, 2.25mm diameter, 1.6m required. *Wire of 2.25mm diameter is not available in the UK – the nearest is 14SWG, 2.03mm.*

PVC tube

Mounting tube (copper)

©RSGB RC2378

Fig 7.10. Mounting tube and PVC cover

- Trim-cap, tubular, 10pF max (or RG58 per Fig 7.11).
- Centring discs, polystyrene foam, sliding in PVC tube, 2 required.
- Sealing compound [6]. *Professional silicone rubber (Maplin YJ91Y or ES 035168G) is ideal, but bathtub sealant will do.*

BEAM ANTENNAS
Simple three-element beam

This antenna was originally built as a standard for VHF modelling of HF antennas [2]. The antenna is constructed using 2mm hard-drawn copper for the elements. These are fixed to a wooden boom using wire netting staples as shown in Fig 7.12.

Copper tubing can also be used for an antenna boom. The elements can be fixed to the boom by soldering them directly onto the surface, see Fig 7.13. A small groove is cut into the boom and tinned with solder before fixing the element. The only disadvantage of this construction is that it anneals the hard-drawn copper at the point where it is heated so that the elements are not as strong. A better solution would be to use thin copper tubing with an inside diameter of 2mm for the centre of the elements and to use the hard-drawn copper wire, soldered to the inner tube section, for the ends of the elements. This arrangement allows the lengths of the elements to be made variable. All you have to do is apply heat at the join and move the end section of the wire to the required length.

Elements can also be attached to the boom using copper pipe-to-wall plastic fixings and held in position with a self-tapping screw as shown in Fig

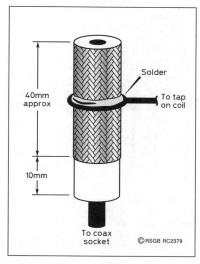

Fig 7.11. The 145MHz tuning capacitor can be made from RG58 cable

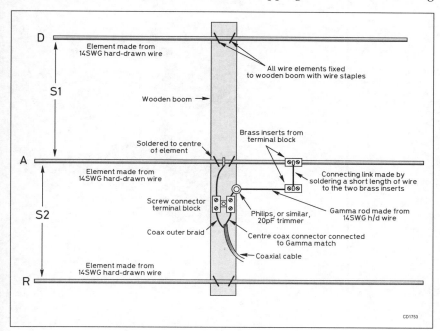

Fig 7.12. A three-element Yagi antenna construction using copper wire elements fixed to a wooden boom. The dimensions in millimetres and inches, using 2mm H/D copper wire for the elements, are as follows. 145MHz: *D* = 940mm (37in), *A* = 990mm (38.9in), *R* = 1072mm (42in), *S1* = 250mm (9.8in), *S2* = 313mm(12.3in). 430MHz: *D* = 310mm (12.22in), *A* = 322mm (12.7in), *R* = 352mm (13.86in), *S1* =103mm (4in), *S2*=103mm (4in)

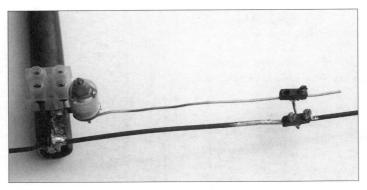 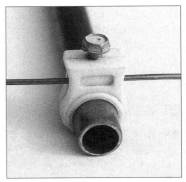

Above: **Fig 7.13. VHF/UHF antenna construction, using a copper wire element soldered to a copper tube boom**

Above right: **Fig 7.14. Alternative construction, using a plastic pipe-to-wall fitting for element-to-boom fixing**

7.14. The advantage of this method is that element spacing can be adjusted very easily.

VHF/UHF quad antenna

The quad is an excellent antenna for home construction. The example shown in Fig 7.15 was used for various experiments and incorporates features which allow variations in element spacing and parasitic element tuning.

The boom is made from 15mm copper tubing with a T-piece in the centre for fixing the mast. The element supports are made from square 10 or 12mm thick wooden doweling fixed to square pieces of plywood using nuts and bolts. The plywood centres are fixed to the copper boom using L-brackets and hose clamps.

Although the quad shown in Fig 7.15 is for the 145MHz band the

Fig 7.15. Wire quad antenna for the 145MHz band. The same construction can be applied to all the VHF bands. The dimensions are shown in Table 7.1. In this model the reflector is made the same size as the driven element and brought to the correct resonance using a stub

Table 7.1. Dimensions for a two-element VHF quad antenna. The reflector could be made the same size as the driven element and tuned with a stub, as shown in Fig 7.15			
Band	**Element spacing**	**Reflector**	**Driven element**
145MHz	294mm (11.58in)	548mm (21.6in)	524mm (20.67in)
71.1MHz	600mm (23.6in)	1210mm (44.5in)	1080mm (42.5in)
51MHz	0.84m (33in)	1.56m (62in)	1.5m (59in)

construction can be used for all the VHF bands. The dimensions are shown in Table 7.1.

Quads on different VHF bands can be nested within each other as on the HF bands. The same problem exists of getting the correct element spacing. The options are to go for a compromise spacing using the support structure shown in Fig 7.15, or use the optimum spacing method on all bands shown in Chapter 6, Fig 6.11.

UHF quad

Elements can be fixed to a tubular metal boom using hose clamps. A UHF quad antenna (with circular elements) is shown in Fig 7.16 using this method of construction.

The antenna elements are made from 14SWG enamelled covered copper wire. All the separate parts of this antenna are fixed together using hose clips (jubilee clips).

The driven element is fixed to the boom using a hose clamp; a white plastic connector block with three terminals is used to enable the coaxial cable

Fig 7.16. A UHF four-element quad constructed by fixing elements to the boom, and the boom to the mast, using hard drawn copper wire and hose clamps

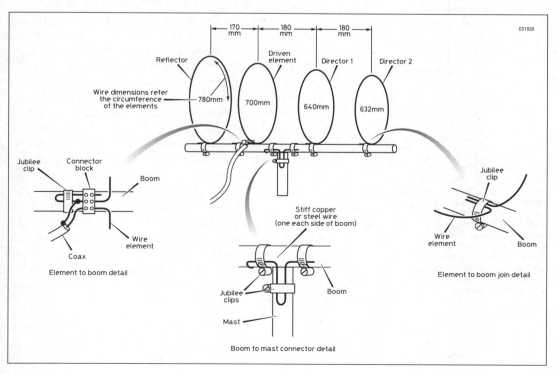

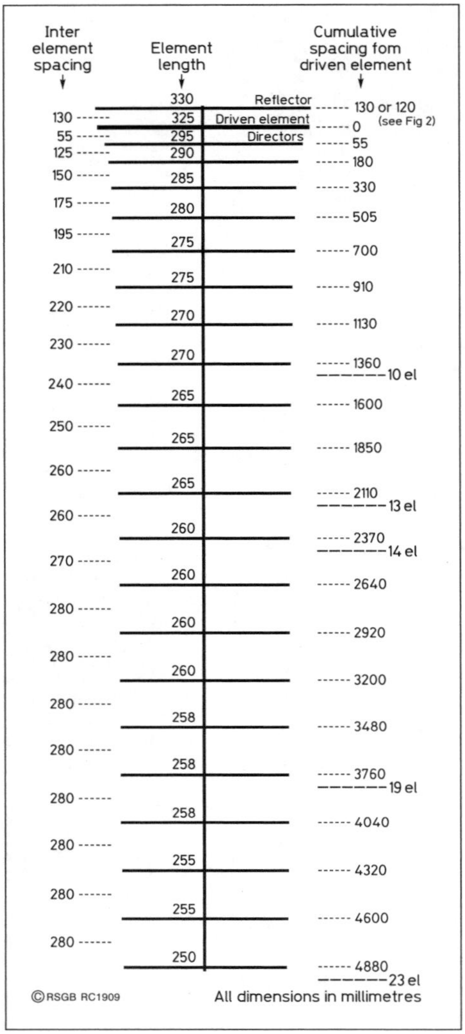

Fig 7.17 table:

Inter element spacing	Element length		Cumulative spacing from driven element
	330	Reflector	130 or 120 (see Fig 2)
130	325	Driven element	0
55	295	Directors	55
125	290		180
150	285		330
175	280		505
195	275		700
210	275		910
220	270		1130
230	270		1360 — 10 el
240	265		1600
250	265		1850
260	265		2110 — 13 el
260	260		2370 — 14 el
270	260		2640
280	260		2920
280	260		3200
280	258		3480
280	258		3760 — 19 el
280	258		4040
280	255		4320
280	255		4600
280	250		4880 — 23 el

© RSGB RC1909 — All dimensions in millimetres

Fig 7.17. Element lengths and spacing for a 435MHz 23-element long Yagi. The beam is made from 20mm × 20mm square tubing, and the elements from 8mm-diameter tubing. The antenna can be cut to 10, 14, 13 or 10 elements, without disproportionate reduction of performance

to be connected to the elements. The enamel insulation is then cleaned from the ends of the elements to a distance of 20mm (0.8in) from one end and 50mm (2in) from the other. The ends of the elements are then bent at right-angles, the element formed into a loop, the ends pushed through the connector block and the screws tightened. The long 50mm (2in) end is formed into a loop and pushed back though the third connector. The loop formed by this is used to connect the driven element to the boom.

The parasitic elements should be made 40mm (1.6in) longer than the lengths shown in Fig 7.16. The enamel insulation is then cleaned from the ends of the elements to a distance of 20mm (0.8in) from the ends. Bend the ends of the wire at right-angles and then form the wire into a loop. It is preferable, but not essential, to solder the ends of the wires together. This makes it easier to assemble the antenna.

The hose clamp and wire type fixing can be used to fix the antenna to the as shown in Fig 7.16.

Long Yagis for 70cm

Long Yagis for 435MHz feature in most antenna books but few of them show how an amateur can build one which rivals the best commercial beams. The following designs [3] are by Noel Hunkeler, F5JIO.

Dimensions for the famous DL6WU designs can be found in Rothammel's book, the German antenna 'bible' [4]. It also contains suggestions for the mechanics and details of the corrections to element lengths as a function of the round or square boom diameter and element-to-boom fixing, ie through the boom, on the boom or above and insulated from the boom. Two of the designs selected by F5JIO are shown below.

The method of mounting of horizontally polarised 435MHz beams is also discussed in Rothammel's book. The construction method of clamping the boom to the side of a metallic mast is fine for the lower-frequency bands but introduces sufficient asymmetry at UHF to spoil a carefully optimised pattern. This problem can be overcome by mounting the boom on top of the stub mast and fastened by sheet metal triangles. If a non-conducting stub mast is used, the outer of the coaxial downlead must be connected to the top of the earthed metallic mast or tower for lightning protection. In all cases, the coaxial feeder should be run in the beam's plane of symmetry, unless well behind the reflector. The same caveats apply to vertically polarised 435MHz beams, mounted on side arms.

Two designs

Dimension for a husky model of similar construction to one which has served F5JIO at a hilltop digipeater for over two years are shown in Fig 7.17. It has a square boom, a folded dipole driven element earthed to the boom at its centre, and parasitic elements insulated from the boom.

An interesting feature is that the full 23-element version on a 5010mm boom can be cut to 19, 14, 13 or 10 elements, with a corresponding reduction in boom length, without appreciably changing the feed-point impedance. An extra gain of 0.2dB and some reduction of back lobes can be obtained using twin reflectors, as shown in Fig 7.18.

Fig 7.19 shows a 12-element lightweight model, said to give a gain of 13.2dBd. It uses a 15mm square boom and the same driven element and balun as the beam in Fig 7.17. The parasitic elements are made of 2mm-diameter stainless steel rod forced through tight-fitting holes in the boom; each one is additionally held by a push nut and 10mm of shrink tubing on either side of the boom. Cutting element ends to their exact length is best done after fixing them to the boom.

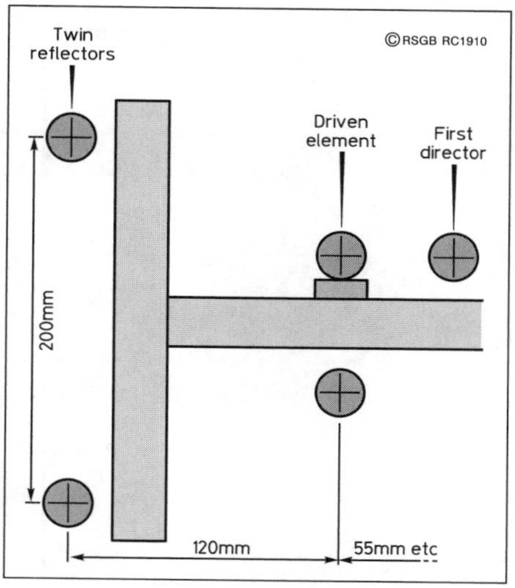

Fig 7.18. Twin reflectors provide extra gain of 0.2dB and some reduction of back lobes, but note that the spacing is altered

The balun

All models shown in Fig 7.17 and 19 have a balanced feed point of 200Ω. A 4:1 balun is required for feeding with 50Ω coaxial cable. A half-wave re-entrant line made of coaxial cable is suitable but again most handbooks are vague about the mechanics. F5JIO made his from small PTFE-insulated cable which can be coiled up in a small weatherproof box. Its higher loss compared with larger cable is trivial for such a short length. Fig 7.20 shows the termination for 75Ω URM111.

Mechanical details

Bending alloy tubing into a folded dipole, aptly named 'trombone' in French, is the most difficult job. This is detailed in G3SEK's VHF/UHF antenna construction practice, described later.

It is much easier to bend and drill flat 9.5 × 1.6mm alloy bar. Overall the dimensions of the folded dipole would be the same.

Increasing VHF/UHF antenna gain

As already mentioned just lengthening the boom and adding more directors can increase

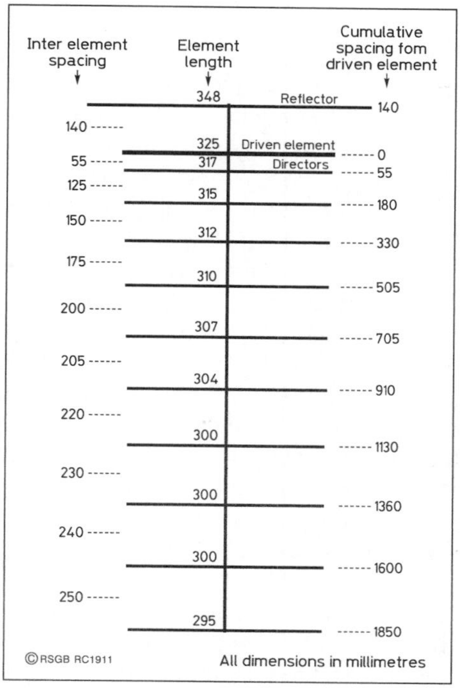

Fig 7.19. Element lengths and spacing for a 435MHz Yagi antenna. The boom is made from 15mm × 15mm square tubing, the driven element from 8mm-diameter tubing and the parasitic elements from 2mm stainless steel rod installed through the boom without insulation

117

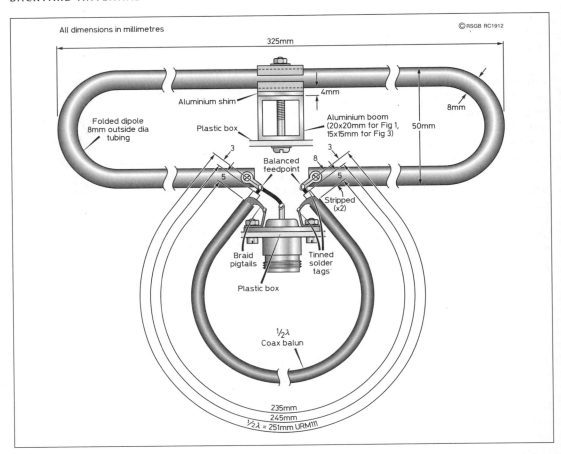

All dimensions in millimetres © RSGB RC1912

325mm

Folded dipole 8mm outside dia tubing

Aluminium shim

4mm

8mm

Plastic box

Aluminium boom (20x20mm for Fig 1, 15x15mm for Fig 3)

50mm

Balanced feedpoint

Stripped (x2)

Braid pigtails

Tinned solder tags

Plastic box

½λ Coax balun

235mm
245mm
½λ = 251mm URM111

Fig 7.20. A half-wave 435MHz 4:1 balun made from PTFE co-axial cable

the gain of a Yagi. However, to get an extra 3dB of gain you have to double the size of the antenna, ie double the length of the boom. A preferred method of obtaining high gain for moonbounce, meteor scatter or contest work is to 'stack' two or more antennas as shown in Fig 7.21. This can provide better performance than one long Yagi with the same theoretical or measured gain.

Any number of antennas, within reason, may be stacked but the problem of feeding all of them in the correct phase with equal levels of power becomes more difficult with larger arrays. The optimum stacking distance between them is optimum where their apertures just touch. A simple rule of thumb regarding the stacking of Yagis or quads is that the stacking distance (distance between the antennas in the stack) should be three-quarters of the length of the antenna booms.

The power applied to the array must be divided equally among the antennas and be in the proper phase to permit the individual fields to add vectorially. This is achieved using a harness of open-wire line or coaxial cable as shown in Fig 7.22. The antennas must be identical and well matched to the impedance of the interconnecting phasing line. In this example, each driven element is adjusted to provide a 50Ω feed point. Typically, this may be done with a gamma match or a folded dipole having the proper balun and transformation ratio as already described in 'Yagi design'.

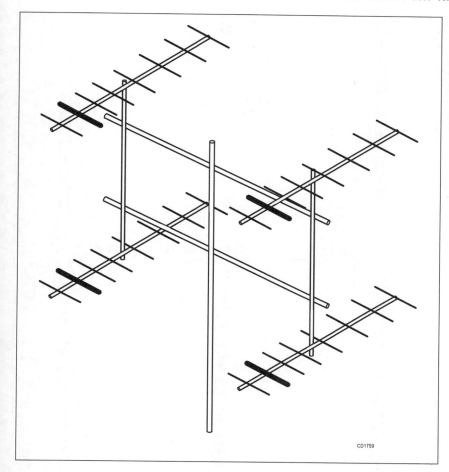

Fig 7.21. Method of stacking four Yagis to obtain increased gain. The method could also be used with quad antennas. The distance between the antennas in the stack should be at least three-quarters the length of the antenna booms

CD1759

The way that this works is the 50Ω feeders in parallel present 25Ω at point A of Fig 7.22. This is transformed to 100Ω by the odd quarter-wave section between A and B. The two 100Ω impedances in parallel at B equal 50Ω, matching the feeder to the transceiver.

The cable connections at A and B could be done with coaxial cable splices to save on the cost of expensive connectors.

For the larger, more complicated arrays, many VHF experimenters use balanced, open-wire line in preference to coaxial line.

G3SEK's VHF/UHF antenna construction practice

The following information is from G3SEK's column [5]. It gives practical constructional details of the mechanical aspects of building VHF/UHF Yagis. The first item deals with the problem of fixing a folded dipole to the support boom of a Yagi. This is followed by methods of making folded dipole elements from aluminium tubing, detailing which dimensions are critical.

Using junction boxes

When VHF TV antennas were common, it wasn't too difficult to find suitable plastic mouldings. These can still be obtained from suppliers of antennas but

119

Fig 7.22. A coaxial harness for feeding a stack of four antennas as shown in Fig 7.24. They are fed from a central feed point (B). Each branch feeds two other antennas at the secondary feed point (A). Each antenna must present an unbalanced 50Ω feed point to the harness. The lengths L1 to L4 are unimportant as long as they are equal. L5 and L6 are an odd multiple of quarter-wavelength multiplied by the velocity factor of the coaxial cable

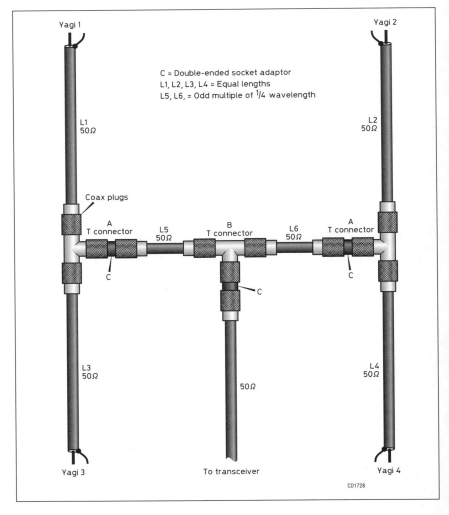

Fig 7.22. A coaxial harness for feeding a stack of four antennas as shown in Fig 7.24. They are fed from a central feed point (B). Each branch feeds two other antennas at the secondary feed point (A). Each antenna must present an unbalanced 50Ω feed point to the harness. The lengths L1 to L4 are unimportant as long as they are equal. L5 and L6 are an odd multiple of quarter-wavelength multiplied by the velocity factor of the coaxial cable

they won't necessarily fit your size of tubing and may not have enough internal space to connect a balun. One solution devised by PE1DAB is to use a strong, thick-walled plastic conduit box, with plastic cable glands to support the ends of the dipole. The method is shown in Fig 7.23 is almost self-explanatory, and also shows the coaxial half-wave balun that is commonly used with a folded dipole. The centre of a dipole is a relatively low-impedance area, so the grade of plastic is not critical.

It isn't always necessary to support the opposite side of the folded dipole, because cable glands of the right size will grip the tubing tightly when tightened and will probably support a 430–440MHz folded dipole firmly enough on its own. If you do need to support the opposite side of a longer folded dipole, do not drill through the relatively thin tubing – the hole makes the whole thing weaker, not stronger. Instead, use some form of clamps onto a plastic plate that is screwed to the opposite side of the boom, as suggested in Fig 7.24. Do not attempt to 'ground' the middle of a folded dipole to the boom, because that will almost inevitably result in unwanted RF currents running along the boom. The only connection to the boom should be through the balun, allowing the opposite side of the folded dipole to find its own electrical centre.

Note that Fig 7.24 shows the boom running through the middle of the folded dipole. This doesn't seem to detune the dipole significantly. You'll also notice that some Yagi designs have the parasitic elements level with the driven side of the folded dipole, others level with the continuous side, and yet others split the difference. Once

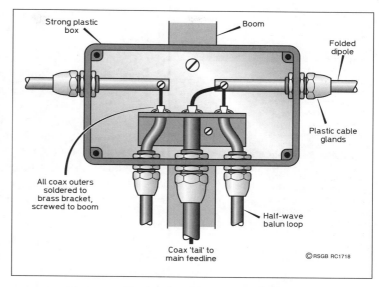

Fig 7.23. PE1DAB's mounting box for a folded dipole

again, this doesn't seem to have any significant effect on the performance. This relaxed approach may come unstuck if the first director is very close to the driven element, as in most of the modern Yagis that have been influenced by the DL6WU design approach. With such antennas you can easily adjust the SWR to compensate for minor differences in driven element mounting by bending the ends of the first director either to the driven element or farther away.

Waterproofing of the driven element is controversial. Either you can attempt to keep the whole system completely sealed, or else drill a vent hole in the bottom of the box to allow it to 'breathe'. The sealed system is fine if it truly is sealed for life but, if there is even the slightest leak, the repeated daily temperature cycles will quickly pump in disastrous quantities of condensation, which cannot run out. The vented system avoids the accumulation problem but it allows slow atmospheric corrosion because moisture and dissimilar metals are always present. As basic precautions you should waterproof the open ends of the coaxial cable using hot-melt glue or some other sealant, and spray the exposed metalwork with polyurethane or

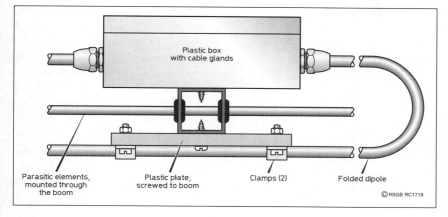

Fig 7.24. One way of clamping the middle of the folded dipole to the boom for additional support. Do not drill through the dipole element, or attempt to 'ground' it to the boom

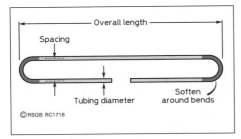

Fig 7.25. Folded dipole dimensions for frequencies 50 to 440MHz. Note the zones that have to be softened for DIY bending

similar lacquer. If the folded dipole is mounted vertically, you will also need to drill a small hole in the bottom end of the U-bend to allow condensation to drain out. Otherwise water can accumulate in the bend, and may split the tubing when it freezes.

G3SEK strongly recommends that a flange-mounting coaxial socket directly on the wall of the box is not used for connecting main coaxial feed line to the driven element. It is almost impossible to reliably waterproof such a socket. Instead, use another cable gland as shown in Fig 7.20, and bring out a 'tail' of coaxial cable with a line socket. The in-line connection to your main coaxial cable then becomes a very easy shape to waterproof with a wrap of self-amalgamating tape, followed by ordinary PVC tape.

DIY folded dipoles

Surprisingly, the only critical dimension of a folded dipole element seems to be the overall length (Fig 7.25). The second most important dimension is probably the tubing diameter, but both of these are less critical for a folded dipole than for a plain rod dipole and certainly less than for parasitic elements.

The spacing between the two arms of the 'trombone' can vary between quite wide limits, which is a great comfort for DIYers. Having said that, you should obviously try to reproduce the dimensions given in the antenna design details as closely as possible. Typical tubing diameters for the 2m and 70cm bands are 0.25in (6mm) up to $3/8$in (8–9mm).

The key to good results is to invest a little time in building a bending jig. As Fig 7.26 shows, this can be very simple and can be made out of scrap wood. The diameter of the round former needs to be about 5mm less than the inside diameter of the bend you're aiming for, to allow for some 'spring' when bending the tubing by hand. A former diameter of 35–45mm is usually about right; 50mm is possibly too big for a 144MHz dipole and definitely too big for 432MHz. A good candidate for the former would be a metal pulley (or a wheel with the rubber tyre removed), because the groove will help to locate the tubing as you bend it. However, the former could be nothing more elaborate than a short, sawn-off length of antenna mast, secured to the wooden base of the jig by a few strong nails down the inside.

The purpose of the back rail is to support the straight part of the tubing and to make sure the bend starts with the tubing held tightly on the former. If a grooved former is used, you will also have to provide a packing strip to make the tubing enter the groove at the

Fig 7.26. A DIY bending jig for folded dipoles

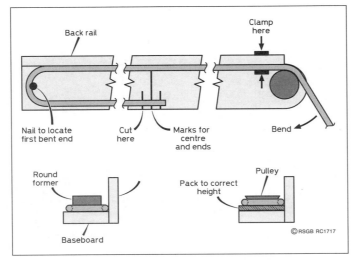

right height. It is also useful to round off the end of the base in case a mallet is required to persuade the tubing to go round the former

Some grades of aluminium alloy tubing may be soft enough to bend without collapsing but then the straight parts of the dipole may not be as strong as they should be. If you have a choice, buy a hard, stiff grade of tubing and soften it only where it needs to be bent. If you try to bend a hard grade of tubing without softening it first, it will either break or collapse. If the tubing is packed with sand to prevent it from collapsing, that will only make it stiffer and even more likely to break the jig. The answer is to soften the parts of the tubing that will need to be bent, shown shaded in Fig 7.25, leaving the straight parts at full hardness for mechanical strength. Begin by measuring out or calculating which parts of the original straight length will need to be softened and mark these clearly. Make the softening zone longer than the theoretical limits of the bends. Then heat each of those zones in a blowlamp flame until they're softened. This is not as easy as it sounds, because all the metal has to be heated uniformly to the right temperature. One time-honoured method of indicating the temperature is to rub soap on the metal and note the darkening colour as the metal is heated up, a process that can only be determined by experiment. If the temperature is not high enough, the metal will still be too hard to bend successfully; if overheated, the end will drop off!

To bring all metal up to temperature without melting it, use the flame-gun with a big, bushy flame. Keep it moving up and down the tubing while at the same time rotating the tubing. Allow the tubing to cool naturally in air.

To make the first bend, calculate and mark exactly where the bend should begin, and locate the tubing in the jig. Clamp the straight part in the jig and pull the free end tightly around the former. After it has been softened, normal tubing of 16SWG wall thickness should bend quite easily without collapsing significantly. If necessary you can use a soft mallet to encourage the tubing to follow tightly around the former, especially towards the finish of the bend.

There is a tendency for the trombone bend to spring off the former. Because of this it is necessary to make an allowance for this when the element is marked out for the bend at the opposite end, in order to finish with a folded dipole of the correct overall length. This cannot be done by guesswork, only by measurement and careful marking-out. Take care to get this right, because it's very difficult to change a bend once it has been formed. Once you have the correct dimensions, a nail at the far end of the jig will locate the inside of the first bend and ensure that all subsequent dipoles will be the same overall length. When you make the second bend, also make sure that the two ends of the folded dipole will be in the same plane – it's easy to make small corrections by twisting.

Because the DIY bending process isn't completely reproducible, it is best to leave some extra length so that the ends of the tube overlap in the centre when the dipole is folded. The exact centre can then be found and the ends trimmed correctly, using marks on the jig. After a few initial trials you should be able to make folded dipoles with an overall length that is repeatable too less than 3mm. That's accurate enough for any frequency up to 440MHz.

REFERENCES

[1] 'Eurotek', Erwin David, G4LQI, *Radio Communication* December 1993.

[2] 'Eurotek', Erwin David, G4LQI, *RadCom* September 1999.

[3] 'Long Yagis for 435MHz', Noel Hunkeler, F5JIO, *Radio-REF* 3/98. Reported in 'Eurotek', *RadCom* September 1998.

[4] *Antennenbuch*, Karl Rothammel, Y21BK, SK 1987, updated and enlarged by Alois Krischke.

[5] 'In Practice', Ian White, G3SEK, *RadCom* April 1998.

8 Antenna materials, construction and supports

INTRODUCTION

This chapter contains information on materials for constructing antennas and antenna supports, and discusses construction techniques for antennas and masts. It also gives advice on how to fix antennas to a house and how to estimate the wind loading of the antenna structure.

In addition to the antenna elements themselves, an antenna system must also include some means to support those conductors and maintain their relative positions – the boom for a Yagi antenna or the halyards for a wire dipole. This chapter also considers materials for those applications. Structural supports such as masts, poles and methods of fixing antennas to buildings are also discussed.

MATERIALS

There are two main types of material used for antenna conductors: wire and tubing. Wire antennas are generally simple and therefore easier to construct, although some arrays of wire elements can become more complex. When tubing is required, aluminium tubing is used most often because of its light weight.

Antenna wire

Wire antennas can be made from any copper wire. The RF resistance of copper wire increases as the size of the wire decreases. However, in most types of antennas that are commonly constructed of wire (even quite small wire), the radiation resistance will be much higher than the RF resistance, and the efficiency of the antenna will still be adequate. Wire sizes as small as 0.3mm have been used quite successfully in the construction of 'invisible' antennas in areas where more conventional antennas cannot be erected. In most cases, the selection of wire for an antenna will be based primarily on the physical properties of the wire. For long wire antennas the best material is 14SWG hard-drawn copper wire, which is ideal for applications where significant stretch cannot be tolerated. Care is required when handling this wire because it has a tendency to spiral when it is unrolled. Make sure that kinks do not develop – wire has a far greater tendency to break at a kink.

For wire beams, insulated 14 to 16SWG multi-strand flexible tinned copper wire is my first choice. Wire having an enamel coating is also useful and preferable to bare wire, since the coating resists oxidation and corrosion.

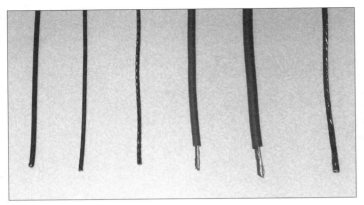

Fig 8.1. Various types of antenna wire. From the left to right: (1) 16SWG hard drawn single strand, (2) 14SWG hard drawn single strand, (3) 14SWG multi-strand, (4) plastic covered 1.5mm multi-strand, (5) plastic covered 2mm multi-strand, (6) multi-strand FLEXWEAVE antenna wire *(wire samples supplied by W H Westlake Electronics)*

Wire antennas should preferably be made with unbroken lengths of wire. In instances where this is not feasible, wire sections should be spliced. The coating should be removed for a distance of about 100mm from the end of each section by scraping with a knife or rubbing with sandpaper until the copper underneath is bright. The ends of the wire should be wrapped tightly around each other and the crevices formed by the wire should be completely filled with rosin-core solder. A large-wattage soldering iron will be required to melt solder outdoors or a propane torch can be used. The joint should be heated sufficiently so the solder flows freely into the joint when the source of heat is removed momentarily. After the joint has cooled completely, it should be wiped clean with a cloth, and then sprayed generously with acrylic to prevent corrosion.

Most antenna material dealers sell various types of antenna wire as shown in Fig 8.1. Antenna wire can often be obtained from scrap yards. Scrap electrical wire is usually heavily insulated and therefore too heavy for antenna elements but is fine for radials.

A cheap source of hard-drawn material is scrap outdoor telephone twin, insulated wire, used (in the UK) to distribute underground cable to subscribers via a telegraph pole.

Aluminium tubing

Many of the beam antennas described in this book are constructed from aluminium tubing.

Self-supporting horizontal HF beam elements require careful mechanical design to arrive at the best compromise between storm survival, sag and weight. This is done by 'tapering' the elements, ie assembling the elements from telescoping tubes, thick in the centre and thinner, in several steps, towards the tips as shown in Fig 8.2. G4LQI has investigated the availability of aluminium tubing and what follows is the result of his work [1].

The most common range of American tubing comes in OD steps of $^1/_8$in (3.18mm) and with a wall thickness of 0.058in (1.47mm). This means that each size neatly slides into the next larger size.

British amateurs who have tried to copy proven American designs have found that this could not be done with alloy tubing available in the UK. The only tubing sizes easily obtainable in the UK are imperial, regardless whether designated in inches or millimetres. They come in outside diameter steps of $^1/_8$in (3.18mm) but with a wall thickness of 0.064in (1.63mm), so the next smaller size does not fit into the larger one. This means that the smallest taper step is ¼in (6.35mm), requiring the filling of the 1.55mm gap with aluminium shims. This method of construction is described later.

American-size tubing is perfect; each size just fits into the $^1/_8$in larger size. With the imperial sizes available in the UK, the minimum step is ¼in.

Metric sizes are a compromise but they fit with an easily shimmed gap. Metric size tubing (all inside and outside diameters in whole millimetres), standard on the Continent, are shown in Table 8.1.

Aluminium tubing is also available from scrap yards. However, with the exception of scaffolding poles, aluminium tubing is the scarcest material to find. This is because there are not many commodities in our society using this material, and where it is available it only comes in one-off items such as tent poles. Aluminium is normally stored in skips at a scrap metal yard so any aluminium tubing that arrives is quickly chopped up into short lengths. For this reason I usually buy any sensible lengths of lightweight tubing that becomes available.

There is a further type of material called *duralumin*, commonly used for aircraft construction and boat masts. It has the advantage of being lighter and stronger than aluminium but is more brittle. In fact almost all aluminium tube is an alloy of some sort because pure aluminium is rather malleable.

Aluminium or duralumin tubing is useful for making lightweight masts. Lightweight sections of thin-wall tubing can be joined together using a short joining section, which is sliced longitudinally with a hacksaw and sprung open using a screwdriver – see Fig 8.3. The two sections to be joined are forced into the joining section and clamped tight using hose clamps.

Aluminium scaffolding poles are useful for masts and booms of larger HF beams. This material is thick walled, strong and has the advantage of having clips, clamps and extension sleeves (see Fig 8.4) used in the process of building scaffolding platforms. Its use in the construction of a fold-over mast is described later in the chapter.

Steel tubing

Steel tubing is an excellent material for constructing antenna masts and is usually available in scrap metal yards. Tubing used for antenna masts should be free from damage and excessive corrosion.

The lower sections of a 12m (40ft) high steel self-supporting mast should be at least 10cm (4in) in diameter, with a wall thickness of 5mm.

Steel tubing is often available, threaded, with screw couplers. These couplers are fine for the purpose for which the tubing was designed, ie piping liquid or gas. When tubing is used for antenna supports it is often under some bending stress.

Couplers only have a short length of screw thread and will be a source of weakness when tubing is employed as an antenna mast, so do NOT be tempted into making a mast using these couplers.

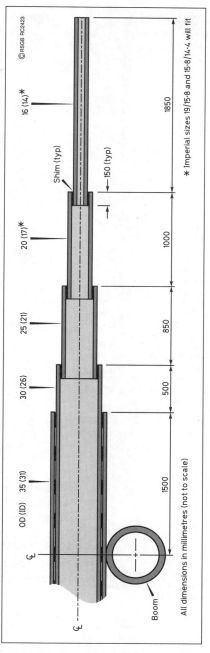

Fig 8.2. A 14MHz reflector designed to survive wind speeds of up to 159km/h, sagging 16cm and weighing 5.6kg

Table 8.1. Metric-size alloy tubing available in continental Europe

OD (mm)	Wall	Weight (g/m)
6	1	42
8	1	60
10	1	76
12	1	93
13	1	103
14	1	110
16	1	127
19	1.5	227
20	2	–
20	1.5	235
22	2	339
22	1.5	261
25	2.5	477
25	2	398
25	1.5	298
28	1.5	336
30	3	687
30	2	484
32	1.5	387
35	2	564
36	1.5	438
40	5	1495
40	2	644
40	1.5	489
44	1.5	541
45	2	–
48	1.5	603
50	5	1923
50	2	820

Material F22 (AlMgSo 0.5%). Tensile strength 22kg/mm². Standard lengths are 6m.

Steel tubes should only be joined by employing lengths that telescope into each other, with at least 30cm (12in) of overlap and secured with a nut and bolt. Do not weld the sections together – a 12m section of steel tubing is very heavy and difficult to manage. It is much easier to assemble a mast in sections. Details on how to construct a steel mast are described later.

Ensure the tubing lengths will fit into each other. I once bought a length of tube for a section of an antenna mast. The smaller-diameter tubing would not fit into this new section because the inside wall was partially furred with a hard calcite deposit caused by its previous use.

When a small-diameter pole is joined to larger-diameter pipe, eg scaffolding pole into 8cm (3in) pipe, metal strip or angle iron shims can be used to pack any space between the differing diameters before securing with a nut and bolt.

Copper tubing

Copper has a very good conductivity but is rather heavy so is not suitable for large HF antennas. Copper is suitable for small compact HF antennas, mobile and VHF antennas. A further advantage of copper for the antenna constructor is that there is a good selection of couplings available.

Copper tubing is also relatively plentiful at metal scrap yards because of changes to central heating systems. In the UK the most common copper tubing diameters available are 16 and 22mm. However, some old scrap tubing may have imperial dimensions so check these if the tubing is to be integrated with an existing structure.

Metal plates

Aluminium plates are particularly useful for making mast-to-boom and boom-to-element fixings as shown in Fig 8.5.

A scrapyard as a source of material

Fig 8.3. Method of joining lightweight tube of equal diameters

I generally buy antenna material from scrap metal yards. Antenna construction and experimenting costs can be reduced considerably by using materials from these sources because they are sold at scrap weight values. If you are really into antenna building and experimenting then it pays to visit the scrap metal yard regularly because specific items are rarely found during one visit. The policy of some scrap metal dealers is to reduce tubing and pipes to short lengths when it arrives on site so as to make it more manageable. Others keep

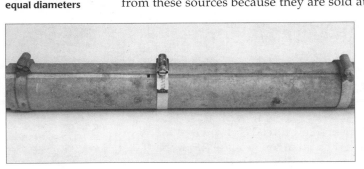

long lengths because they consider it as a more marketable commodity in this form.

The best scrap metal yards are those located near an industrial estate. These contain a much more useful selection of material for antenna constructors. Materials obtainable from scrap metal yards which are useful for antenna work construction are listed below:

- Steel tubing (for antenna masts)
- Steel casing (for mast foundations)
- Steel angle material (for ginpoles, clamps and guy rope anchors)
- Copper and aluminium tubing (for elements and booms)
- Paxolin, Bakelite or plastic sheet (insulators)
- Electrical wire (antenna elements)
- Electric motors and gear-boxes (for rotators)
- Aluminium angle stock (quad and Double-D spreaders)
- Aluminium plate (couplers for joining elements to booms and booms to masts – see Fig 8.5)

Other materials

The following materials are very useful for antenna construction.

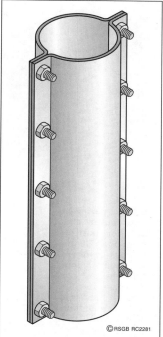

Fig 8.4. Two-piece steel sleeves of the type used to join scaffolding tubes together

- *Hose clamps* (jubilee clips), the antenna experimenter's friend. They can be used for joining different-diameter sections of elements, joining sections of mast, joining wire-to-metal elements, joining quad spreaders to angle stock – the list is endless. They are readily available at all hardware, DIY and car (auto) part stores. When a clamp is used as part of an outdoor antenna structure always coat it with a film of grease to prevent corrosion. Never use paint or varnish because this will make it very difficult to dismantle.

- *Insulators.* Antenna insulators should be made of material that will not absorb moisture. The best insulators for antenna use are made of glass or glazed porcelain. Depending on the type of a wire antenna they must also be capable of taking the same strain as the antenna wire and insulators.

- *Pulleys.* Several types of pulleys are readily available at almost any hardware store. Among these are small galvanised pulleys designed for awnings and several styles and sizes of clothes-line pulleys. Heavier and stronger pulleys include those used in marine work. The factors that determine how much stress a pulley will handle include the diameter of the shaft, how securely the shaft is fitted into the sheath and the size and material that the frame is made of. Another important factor to be considered in the selection of a pulley is its ability to resist corrosion. Most good-quality clothesline pulleys are made of alloys that do not corrode readily. Since they are

Fig 8.5. Method of fixing the mast-to-boom and boom-to-element using aluminium plate and U-clamps

Fig 8.6. *Above left:* Mast top guy ring bearing suitable for mast diameters up to 50mm (2in). (Upside-down view to show guy connection holes). *Above right:* Bearing suitable for base or mast top, for mast diameters up to 9cm (3.5in). Supplied with fittings (not shown) to connect guys

designed to carry at least 50ft of line loaded with wet clothing in stiff winds, they should be adequate for normal spans of 100 to 150ft between stable supports. Chose a pulley to suit the line. The worse situation that can happen with a pulley is when a thin line gets trapped between the pulley wheel and the sheath.

- *Exhaust pipe clamps* (in the USA called *muffler clamps*). Used to construct boom-to-mast and element-to-boom fittings.
- *Spreaders for wire beams.* Cane (lightweight bamboo) or glassfibre rod – glassfibre rods are preferred because they are lightweight and weather well. In addition they have excellent insulating properties.
- *Polypropylene rope.* Used as halyards and guys for pulling up, and keeping up, mast and antenna structures.

Specialised antenna fittings

The importance of guying masts correctly is discussed later. The problem of how to guy a rotating mast can be overcome with appropriate fittings. There are a number of specialised commercial fittings available for antenna constructors.

Mast top guy ring bearings suitable for mast diameters up to 50mm (2in) and 90mm (3.5in) are shown in Fig 8.6. These bearings are supplied with fittings to connect the guys.

Fig 8.7. Selection of commercial antenna fittings

There are a number of fittings that are used by the TV antenna industry that can be pressed into amateur radio antenna service. These are mainly clips for fitting a small antenna to a boom, as shown in Fig 8.7. They can be

used for fixing elements to booms of HF antennas of VHF antennas to masts.

ANTENNA CONSTRUCTION

Antennas can be built using all-metal construction or with wire elements supported on spreaders.

All-metal antenna construction

The boom can be fixed to a tubular mast with a metal plate and car exhaust

U-clamps as shown in Fig 8.5. Elements can be connected to booms in a similar manner.

Tapered elements can be constructed from lengths of aluminium alloy tubing with different diameters so that the lengths can be telescoped into each other. I rarely find that sections fit snugly and the ends of joining sections need to be modified as shown in Fig 8.8.

Additionally, if there is a relatively large difference between the two joining sections, a shim can be made from a short section of tubing slit longitudinally. Any corrosion on any of the metal surfaces that make up the join should be removed with fine sandpaper. The surfaces are then wiped with a cloth and coated with a thin film of grease to prevent corrosion.

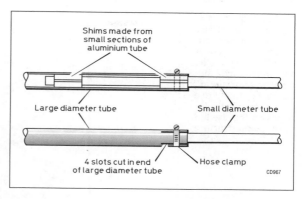

Fig 8.8. Method of joining sections of aluminium tube where the tube diameters present a poor fit. (Top drawing depicts cross section of joint)

The join is then clamped tight using a hose clamp. This method is far superior to using a nut and bolt where a new set of holes has to be drilled every time an adjustment to length is made. The hose clamp method also gives the joint a lower contact resistance.

If the antenna elements are constructed from tubing and insulated copper wire (such as the all-metal quad – see Chapter 6), then a short length of the plastic insulation is stripped from the wire element extensions. These ends are then fixed with hose clamps to the end of the metal elements.

It is particularly important that these copper wire/aluminium tube joins are protected with grease to prevent corrosion. I have not found these sorts of joints to be a problem, possibly because my antennas are in a constant state of change and all connections are protected with grease so that parts can be re-used. However, one authority [2] even goes as far as to state that contact between aluminium and copper should be avoided at all costs and that a small stainless-steel washer should be used to provide isolation.

Wire beam construction

Insulating spreaders for wire beam antennas or helically wound elements can be constructed using cane (lightweight bamboo) or glassfibre rod. The main disadvantage of these materials is that they can easily damaged by crushing at the support point. Special support is required to avoid damaging the ends and aluminium angle stock can be used. The length of this aluminium section depends on the size and the frequency range of the antennas to be supported, and for a conventional multi-band quad or Double-D a 3ft length is suitable. Two sections are required for a Double-D or four for a quad. Two holes are drilled at the centre of each section – the distance apart will depend on the size of the mast or boom and hence the size of the U-bolts.

The canes or glassfibre rods are fixed to the ends of the aluminium angle using hose clamps as shown in Fig 8.9. Rubber or plastic tubing cushions can be used to prevent the clamps damaging in cane or glassfibre rod supports.

Fig 8.9. Method of fixing cane or glassfibre wire beam element supports to a boom or mast. The length of the aluminium angle material and the spacing between the hose clamp supports depends on the sized of the antenna structure

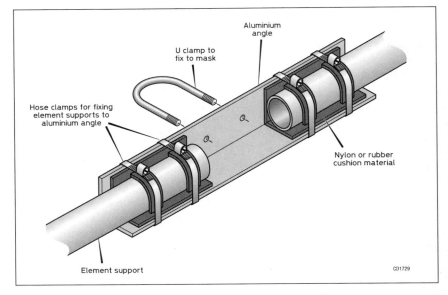

Aluminium angle

U clamp to fix to mask

Hose clamps for fixing element supports to aluminium angle

Nylon or rubber cushion material

Element support

CD1729

ANTENNA SUPPORTS
Using the house as a support for an antenna

Placing a large antenna 10 or 20m into the air, with access for adjustment and tuning, can be a minor civil engineering project. Backyard locations often do not have the space for a free-standing mast or tower. In this case the only solution is to fix the antenna to the house. The usual method of doing this is to fix it to the chimney (if you have one), using a chimney bracket, or to fix it to the side of the building with a wall bracket.

Wall brackets

The best description for fixing wall brackets that I have seen comes from Ian White, G3SEK, and his advice is given below [3].

Even a small antenna installation can generate considerable wind forces on the support structure.

Think about the directions in which the wind force could act. If the wind is pushing the bracket on to the wall, the force is spread over several bricks, and the fixing is as strong as the wall itself. If the wind is blowing parallel to the wall, and the bracket is strong enough, most kinds of wall fixings will be extremely secure against the sideways forces. The difficult situation is when the wind is blowing away from the wall and trying to pull the bolts straight out of the bricks . . . or the bricks straight out of the wall. This latter possibility is a serious one unless the wall is well built. Older houses with mortar that has weakened over the years, and bricks made before the era of factory-quality control, are simply not a good prospect for a mast bolted to the wall.

Assuming your house does have reasonably sound brickwork, the aim should be to mount the top bracket as high as possible to reduce the wind forces but always leave at least three courses of bricks between the ones you drill and the top of the wall. Also leave plenty of sideways clearance from upstairs window openings, which considerably weaken the brickwork.

The bracket itself is important. A cheap, poorly made wall bracket, intended for UHF TV antennas, is unsuitable. Go to an amateur radio dealer and get something substantial and well made, and preferably galvanised. A suitable bracket will look something like Fig 8.10, with a T-shaped piece that bolts to the wall and a well-braced arm for fixing the mast. All the component parts should be solidly double-seam welded, not just 'tacked' together. Typically there will be two or more bolt holes in the horizontal member of the 'T', and one or two more in the vertical member. The top row of fixings will bear almost the entire load, and Fig 8.11 shows a typical drilling pattern.

To fix the bracket, you must use some kind of expanding wall anchor. These come in several kinds, but they all work by expanding outwards and gripping the sides of the holes. The traditional Rawlbolts™ are best, which can give a very secure fixing. There are other anchor methods. The 'DIY' fixing using large plastic wall plugs and 'coach bolts' are not recommended.

This is a safety-critical application, so spend some money on properly engineered fixings that are designed to work together as a system, and follow the manufacturer's instructions exactly.

The holes for the Rawlbolt anchors should be drilled in the centre of the brick as shown in Fig 8.11. The optimum size for ordinary brickwork is M10, which requires a 16mm diameter hole. Three or four of these should be more than adequate to withstand the wind forces envisaged – but only if they are installed correctly.

Choose a sound set of bricks for drilling, free from any hairline cracks. If necessary, be prepared to move the mast a little from its planned location. Drill into the exact centre of each brick, not near the edges, and never into mortar. If necessary, make new mounting holes in the bracket to suit your own brickwork. The holes in the brackets should be 10mm diameter for M10 bolts, with some extra clearance to help the bolts line up. Hold the bracket to the wall, level it with a spirit level and mark the centres of the holes. Begin drilling with a small masonry bit. Before you use the electric drill, place the point of the bit exactly on your drilling mark and tap gently with a hammer to chip out a small dimple. This will prevent the point from wandering when you start drilling. If you're using a hammer-drill, start without the hammer action until you've made a deep enough hole to prevent the bit from wandering. Do the same at each change of bit as you open out the holes gradually, using progressively larger sizes. Use patience rather than brute force, and you're more likely to make good cylindrical holes, square to the wall and exactly where you want them. It's also kinder to the electric drill; and above all it's much safer for you on the ladder.

The final holes must be exactly the right diameter

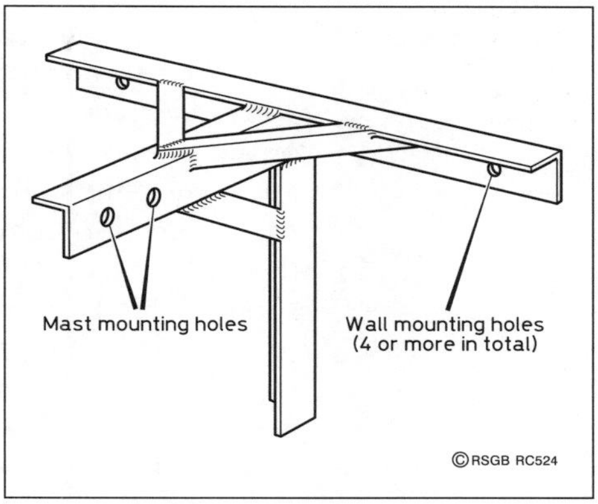

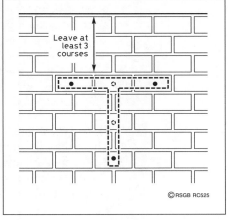

Fig 8.10. A typical well-braced wall bracket

Mast mounting holes

Wall mounting holes (4 or more in total)

©RSGB RC524

Fig 8.11. Typical drilling pattern for fixing a wall bracket. Patterns may vary, but always drill into the centres of the bricks

Leave at least 3 courses

©RSGB RC525

as specified by the manufacturer. For example, the hole for an M10 Rawlbolt must be 16mm diameter – not 15, not 17, but 16mm. This is very important because the entire strength of any type of wall fixing comes from the contact of the anchor sleeve against the inside of the hole. The sleeve should be a gentle tap fit, so that when the bolt is tightened the anchor will immediately start to grip hard.

Tap the anchor sleeve into place, just below the surface of the wall, so that when the bracket is bolted on it contacts the wall and not sitting on the end of the sleeve. Do this without the bolt inserted, and then fit the bracket. Leave the bolts slightly loose, level the bracket, and then tighten them. The tricky part is to tighten the bolts to the correct torque – enough to expand the anchor sleeve and develop the fixing strength, but not so much that it splits the brick and ruins the whole fixing.

Although G3SEK uses Rawlbolts, he notes that they can be very prone to split the bricks if over-tightened. You might consider alternative types, such as the Fischer bolts which use a softer plastic sleeve to grip the inside of the hole. In any case, use the type of anchor with a free bolt, which screws in, and not the type with a stud that takes a nut.

If your house is built using modern bricks that have holes right through the middle, conventional expanding anchors are no use and you'll need to investigate other systems. Wall anchors using a chemical adhesive fixing system are also available, and have the advantage of not stressing the bricks at all, while having higher claimed strengths than conventional expanding anchors. They can also be used for fixing into hollow bricks but the strength of the bricks themselves may become a factor. As with any adhesive bonding system, success depends on careful preparation and following the instructions *exactly*. One suggestion when using conventional Rawlbolts in ordinary brickwork is to use epoxy resin as well, to try and obtain the best of both worlds.

If you are fixing to a gable end wall, yet another possibility is to drill right through the whole wall and into the loft space, and then use long bolts or studs to secure the bracket to a steel plate that spreads the load over the inside wall.

The lower bracket is much simpler, because it bears much less load than the upper one. Its main purpose is to steady the mast and prevent it from bowing below the upper bracket. Mark out and drill for the lower bracket after fixing the upper one, lining them up with a plumb line.

In the longer term, wall anchors can work loose owing to either frost or thermal expansion/contraction cycles, and then the wind will work on them further. Check the fixings every spring and autumn.

If you are intending to mount a commercial mast or antenna against the wall, obtain specific advice from the manufacturer and follow it exactly.

House chimney

The house chimney can be used for an antenna support as shown in Fig 8.12. The main advantage of this method is that chimney-mounting brackets are easy to obtain. Some of these mounting brackets can be seen supporting some precariously tall TV antenna structures in fringe TV signal areas.

The chimney of an older house, where the mortar that has weakened over the years, needs to be examined, and if necessary repointed before fitting a chimney-mounted antenna.

The single-wire lashing kits used for TV antennas are totally unsuitable for amateur radio antennas. A double TV antenna chimney lashing kit is essential and will support a large VHF array or a small sized HF beam.

Routing cables into the house

While on the subject of modifying the house for amateur radio, this might be a good time to consider how to route cables into the house. You might have a multi-band beam with its coaxial cable and rotator control cable, plus a VHF antenna and a long-wire antenna for the lower frequency bands. And of course there is the earth connection.

Fig 8.12. Example of a double chimney lashing used to support a beam antenna and rotator

The time-honoured way of dealing with this problem is to drill lots of holes in the window frame – this is the method I have used for many years. I drill an extra hole as I need it and cover up the whole mess with the curtains and hope that the XYL won't notice.

However, modern houses (and a lot of older ones) use double-glazing, with its plastic and metal window frames. Using the window frame as a route for cables is not feasible and another method must be sought. G3SEK routed the cables by inserting a length of plastic drainpipe through the wall [4]. What follows is how he did it.

In a traditional British brick house with cavity outside walls, the job is well within the reach of a competent DIYer and it should make very little mess. Think of it as installing a waste pipe for the kitchen sink, because 40mm sink waste pipe is probably what you'll need – though it's always good to leave enough room for more antennas in the future! You'll also need a good electric hammer drill, at least one masonry bit of about 10mm diameter that is long enough to go right through the double wall, a shorter masonry bit of about the same size, a fairly large hammer and a long, narrow cold chisel.

Plan very carefully to find the best place to drill through. Leave at least one whole brick away from doors or window frames. Remember that the frame has a solid lintel across the top, extending outwards on both sides. Check both the inside and the outside of the wall with a live cable and metal detector to be sure that you won't meet any nasty surprises. If yours is a wooden-framed house with a brick outer skin, take great care to avoid structural timbers.

First you need a pilot hole, right through the wall, and then the hole is enlarged from each side by continuing around a circle. Start from the outside and drill through the mortar, halfway along a brick, as shown in Fig 8.13.

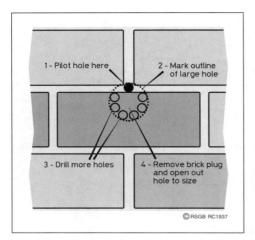

1 - Pilot hole here

2 - Mark outline of large hole

3 - Drill more holes

4 - Remove brick plug and open out hole to size

©RSGB RC1937

Fig 8.13. How to drill a 40mm hole through bricks. You can also use the same technique for larger holes

Use one of the shorter masonry bits to start the hole, and take care to drill it accurately at right-angles to the wall – the mortar joint will guide you. (It's just possible that you will hit a metal wall tie. If this happens move along to the next brick.) When you break through into the wall cavity, change to the longer bit and carry on drilling. To avoid pushing off a big patch of plaster from the inside wall, stop when you're within a few centimetres of breaking through. Switch off the hammer action of the drill, and continue with very gentle pressure until you're right through both walls.

Now mark out a circle on each side of the wall, rather larger than the diameter of the pipe, as shown in Fig 8.13. The pilot hole is at the top of each circle. Work separately from each side, using the shorter masonry bit. Drill a ring of holes as close together as possible, stopping when you're through to the cavity. Because it's important to start each hole in exactly the right place, it helps to begin with a smaller bit, using the drill at slow speed with the hammer action off. When the hole is well started into solid brickwork (or breeze block on the inside wall) it's safe to change to the larger bit with the faster hammer action. Next you need to open out the hole from each side, using the cold chisel and occasionally perhaps the electric drill, until the pipe will slide right through.

Chip away carefully without too much violence so as not to crack the outside brick or do any unnecessary damage to the interior plasterwork – and try to pull the central plugs out rather than pushing them into the cavity. With care you can make almost as good a hole as a professional using a big core drill. Make sure that the pipe will slide through horizontally, or sloping a few degrees upward from the outside so that rainwater won't run in. Set the end of the pipe just proud of the inside wall, and leave any overhang outside. Fill the gaps around the pipe with mortar or exterior filler on the outside and plaster or interior filler on the inside, and let it all set solid. The next day saw off the outside end of the pipe, a few centimetres away from the wall. Now you can start to thread the cables. A 45° right-angle pipe elbow, facing downwards, fixed to the pipe where it emerges on the outside wall, may be used to help keep the rainwater out. When all the cables are in place, stuff in plastic foam for draught proofing, or use aerosol-expanding foam.

This method of installing a pipe is quite easily reversible if you move house. The pipe will pull out from the outside with a bit of effort, and you can plug and plaster over the hole in the inside wall. On the outside, you'll only need to replace one brick if you have followed the drilling pattern in Fig 8.13.

Construction of fold-over antenna masts

I prefer home-made masts to the commercial ones. You can build it to fit your garden and the designs that follow are easy to raise and lower, which means they can be quickly folded over if gale force winds are forecast.

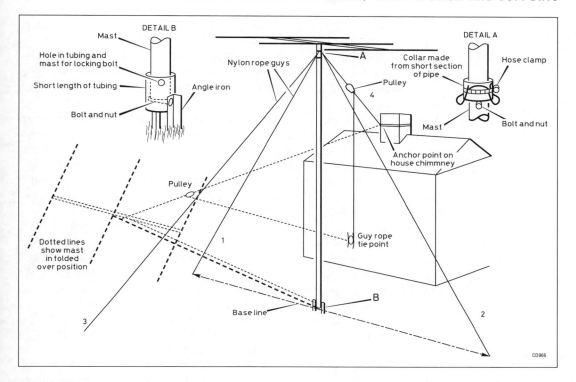

Fig 8.14. Construc-
tional details of the
G2XK type of light-
weight fold-over mast

Safety

Safety should be a primary consideration when erecting antenna masts. NEVER erect an antenna and mast that could possibly come in contact with electric power lines. Never rush this sort of work. Always stop to consider the implications of the next move, particularly when dealing with heavy sections of steel tubing.

Do not use an antenna support structure that requires the joint efforts of all members of the local radio club to raise and lower it, although help in the construction stages is always welcome. The following are two designs for fold-over masts for single-handed construction.

The G2XK lightweight fold-over mast

Eric Knowles, G2XK, used the method described below to support a 6-element 10m beam on a 11m (36ft) boom at a height of 12m (40ft), using only 80mm (3in) diameter thin-wall duralumin tubing – see Fig 8.14. This large structure weathered many a gale that swept across the Vale of York.

There is nothing new in this method of supporting, or raising and lowering, masts using guy ropes. The military have used the method for many years for supporting fixed wire antennas.

The description that follows is of a similar mast; suitable for supporting a medium-sized experimental beam antenna. No special tools or welding equipment are required to construct this structure and it is an excellent support for experimental antennas provided the space for the guys is available. Do not use steel tubing for the mast of this design because it is too heavy. Aluminium scaffolding pole is not really suitable for this design of mast because of the weight/length ratio, although it could be used for short masts of up to 8m (25ft) high.

The layout is illustrated in Fig 8.14. The structure can be used with a fixed mast and rotator, or the mast can be rotated. In this case provision has to be made to allow the mast to rotate and be folded over. A minimum of four guy ropes is used.

The anchor point for guy wire 4 must be above ground level; the chimney of a nearby house is suitable with a lightweight structure. Guy ropes 1 and 2 are anchored along the baseline so that they retain the same tension when the mast is being erected or folded over. The length of guy rope 3 is adjusted so that it is under tension when the mast is in the vertical position. The original G2XK version used two sets of guy ropes but only one set is illustrated in Fig 8.14 for clarity.

This structure gains all its strength from its guys, so it is important that the guy ropes are strong and are connected securely, both at the anchorage and the top of the mast. Polypropylene rope (6mm diameter) is a suitable material for the guys, which should ideally be at 45° to the mast. This angle can be reduced if space is limited but this increases the downward pressure on the mast in high winds and increases the chances of the mast buckling.

Commercial guy-rope-to-mast bearings are available for the top of the mast (see Fig 8.6) and are recommended for this sort of application. The guys should be connected to the bearings with D-clamps.

If a commercial rotatable guy-rope support bearing is unavailable, one can be constructed with a short length of steel tube, slightly larger in diameter than the mast. Very thick wire loops can be fixed to the tube using two hose clamps. The top of the mast is inserted into this tubing. A bolt and nut, through the appropriate point on the mast, holds the guy support collar in position. Detail A of Fig 8.14 illustrates this.

The guy anchorage can be constructed from a 1m (40in) or so length of angle iron, cut to a point one end and with a hole drilled in the other. This can be driven into the ground at 90° to the angle of pull. The guy anchorage may need to be more substantial for very large masts and/or if the soil is light and sandy. The guy rope should be connected to the guy anchorage with a D-clamp. A pulley is required for the halyard to enable the mast to be hauled up; a good-quality clothes-line pulley is suitable.

The base pivot point comprises two lengths of angle iron, cut to a point at one end and with a hole drilled at the other. The two angle-iron pieces are driven into the ground, with the holes aligned so that the pivot bolt can be fitted. If the design calls for a rotatable mast then a small section of tubing, whose internal diameter is slightly larger than the outside diameter of the mast, is pivoted to the angle iron. The mast fits inside this section of tubing and is free to rotate. Holes can be drilled through the base tubing and the mast to enable the structure to be locked on any particular heading. Detail B of Fig 8.14 shows how this is done. Lightweight sections of thin-wall tubing can be joined together using a short joining section – see Fig 8.3.

Counter-weighted fold-over mast

This type of support is heavier and requires more construction effort. Its main advantage is that guy ropes are not absolutely necessary. I have built several masts to the same basic design, which is based on a 18m (60ft) tilt-over support [5] designed by Alfred W Hubbard, K0OHM.

The original was designed to support a 3-element tri-band beam and a rotator. In this design all sections of steel tubing of the mast were welded together.

In the original design the fold-over mast was partially counterweighted by filling the lower half of the tilt-over section with concrete! A pulley is used to manage the remaining 160kg (350lb) pull.

The design of the base is interesting. It comprises a section of casing fixed in the ground with a concrete foundation.

The gap between the mast and the casing is filled with sand. This removes the high-stress point that normally exists if the mast is set directly into concrete. The sand acts as a buffer and allows the mast to flex within the base during high winds. The internal casing diameter should be around 5cm (2in) greater in diameter than the lowest section of the mast.

Of the masts I have built using this design, the largest was 18m (60ft) high and supported an all-metal quad. The mast and payload should not be fully counterweighted. A top weight imbalance of around 45kg (100lb), controlled with a winch will enable the momentum of the structure to be more easily managed.

Medium-size 12m (40ft) fold-over steel mast
The mast described above is too large for most backyard sites. The following is a description of a smaller version, but even this will require a garden at least 12m long. However, the design can be scaled down if required.

This mast is counterweighted with approximately 15kg (30lb) of top weight so a pulley is not required. It takes about 15 seconds to raise the antenna mast into the vertical position. The mast is relatively lightweight; the top third of its length is 5cm (2in) diameter scaffolding pole. The whole mast is rotated manually using a handle fixed to the bottom of the mast.

The sections of steel tubing that make up the mast are telescoped into each other for about 30cm (12in) and secured by a bolt and nut. This allows the mast to be assembled, modified or repositioned much more easily than if the section was welded.

The detail of this mast can be seen in Fig 8.15 and a more general view can be seen in Figs 8.16 and 8.17. At the time these photographs were taken two sections of a tree trunk were used as counterweights. These weights have now been dispensed with by making the lower section of the mast out of solid 82mm steel rod.

Although I can build these structures single-handed the following are areas where some assistance would be of help.

- *Inserting the lower half of the mast into the base casing.* Two ropes are tied to the top of the lower section, using the holes drilled for the pivot bolt. The section can then be placed with the lower end over the base casing and the top supported on a pair of stepladders. The section can be raised using these ropes; at the same time the lower end is guided into the casing with a section of angle iron.

- *Placing the clevis at the top of the mast to enable the bolt to be fitted and inserting*

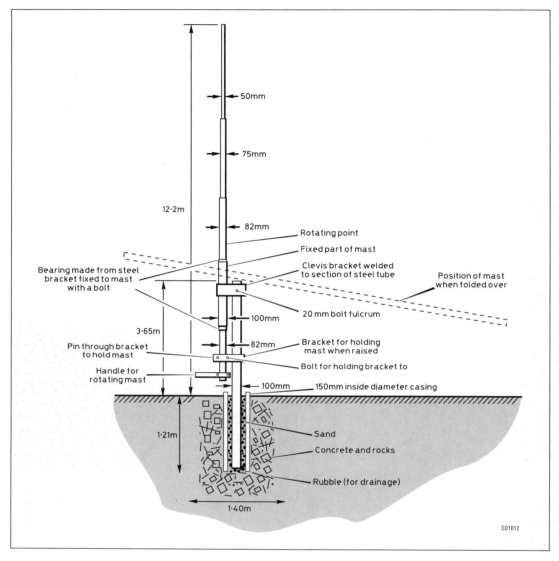

Fig 8.15. Counter-weighted fold-over rotatable 12m mast, constructional details

the mast into the oversize piping used as the tiltable thrust bearing. These tasks can be eased by using a gin pole with a pulley and rope. The gin pole can be constructed from steel angle iron and clamped to the mast with additional angle iron pieces or steel straps.

Other fold-over masts

Wooden masts

In the early days of amateur radio wood was a very popular material for constructing masts and even beam antennas. These days this material is less popular because of the cost of quality seasoned timber and the lack of sensible fold-over designs that can carry the payload of a medium-size beam antenna to a height of 10 to 15m. One design in a recent publication shows a fold-over mast with the fulcrum point 5 or 6m high. In the construction of a fold-over mast the folding section has to be carried up a ladder to the fulcrum point. If you are considering such a structure, use a design with a lower fulcrum point, say 3.5m, and make sure that the base pole is thickest and strongest at the point of maximum stress, ie where it emerges from the ground.

The selection of timber and weather treatment requires specialist knowledge which is beyond the scope of this book.

Commercial masts

Many radio amateurs use commercially designed masts. Most of these masts have a lattice structure, with sections of the fold-over lattice mast telescoping into each other. This design enables a fairly large mast to be erected into a relatively small garden.

A commercial mast has the advantage of having well-defined data regarding heights and wind loading, although they have a fairly high visual impact which may be a problem in some locations.

There is a range of commercial masts available, suppliers of which are listed in the Appendix.

Trees as antenna supports

If you have a tall tree in your garden then you may have a very good support for a wire antenna that does not require planning permission. As antenna supports, trees are unstable in windy conditions, except in the case of very large trees where the antenna support is well down from the top branches.

Fig 8.16. 12m (40ft) version of the mast in upright position, supporting a 14MHz metal quad antenna

Tree-supported antennas must be constructed much more sturdily than is necessary with stable supports. To this end the preferred method is to use a halyard and pulley shown in Fig 8.18.

The use of a halyard with a mast is shown in Fig 8.18(a). Here the halyard end can be lashed to a bracket.

When a tree is used as the support a weight is used, see Fig 8.18(b), to take up the movement of the tree. The endless loop shown in Fig 8.18 is to allow greater control of when raising and lowering the antenna.

Fixing the halyard pulley

If the point where the pulley is to be attached can be reached using a ladder then fixing it to a branch, pole or building is the easy bit. If you cannot reach the pulley fixing point then a line has to be thrown or propelled over the anchor point.

Fig 8.17. 12m (40ft) mast and quad folded over

My favourite missile projector is the catapult as shown in Fig 8.19. A missile or weight must be used that will not cause damage or injury if things go wrong. The best object for this purpose is a squash ball or, as used in Fig 8.19, a plastic practice golf ball filled with wood filler.

The best sort of pilot line is strimmer cord. This comes in several thicknesses, the heaviest for heavy-duty petrol-driven strimmers and the lightest weight for electric strimmers; the latter being the most suitable for the purpose. Strimmer line is very strong and resists kinking.

The line can be stretching out straight on the ground or, better still, zigzagged left and right on the ground. If snarling of the line is a problem (due, say, to garden plants and bushes), try making a stationary reel by driving eight nails, arranged in a circle, through 20mm board. After winding the line around the circle formed by the nails, the line should reel off readily at lift-off. The board should be tilted at approximately right-angles to the path of the shot.

If it is necessary to retrieve the line and start over again, the line should be drawn back very slowly; otherwise the swinging weight may wrap the line around a small branch, making retrieval impossible.

This system can also be used to place an antenna support over a roof.

The pilot line can be used to pull a heavier line over the tree or roof. This line is then used to haul a pulley up into the tree after the antenna halyard has been threaded through the pulley.

The line that holds the pulley must be capable of withstanding considerable chafing.

A metal ring, around 70 to 100mm (3 to 4in) in diameter can be used instead of a pulley. The antenna support wire is just looped through the ring. This has more friction than a pulley but it will not jam.

WIND LOADING

The saying that "if you haven't had an antenna fall down then you don't build big enough antennas" might sound very smart but it is hardly good engineering practice. Bridge building engineers would hardly get away with it.

Most antennas are brought down by very strong winds so it is important to consider the effect of wind loading of your antenna installation. While there are a couple of excellent articles on the subject [6, 7] a few suggestions are given here so that you can get some idea of the forces involved.

G3SEK says [8] that the round figures that stick in his mind are that at 100mph every square foot of exposed area suffers a sideways pressure of 25lb; or that at 45–50m/s the wind force is about 150kgf/m² (kilograms force per square metre). So how do you know how many square metres or feet your antenna installation is? To avoid any aerodynamics the best way is to simplify the parts of the elements to a 'flat slab' area. So a pole 3m long and 50mm (0.05m) diameter is a flat slab of 0.15m².

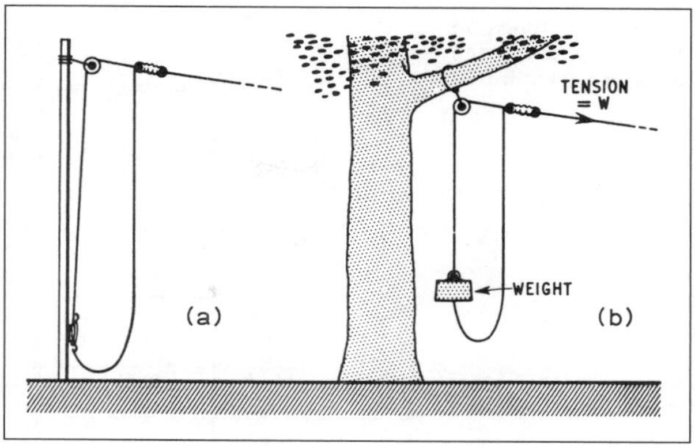

Fig 8.18. Halyard connections to (a) a pole and (b) a tree. The weight is equal to the required antenna wire tension

Assessing the exposed areas

The calculations are relatively simple. Take, for example, the small HF beam mounted on the roof of my house (shown on the front cover). The two elements are 4.49m long and 25mm in diameter. The flat slab area of the elements is 4.49 × 0.025 × 2 = 0.2245m².

The boom is 2.1m long and 0.035m diameter = 2.1 × 0.035 = 0.08m².

The loading coils and spokes at the ends of the elements are complicated so I have modelled them as four cylindrical objects 0.3m long by 0.06m in diameter. This gives an area of 0.3 × 0.06 × 4 = 0.072m².

The mast fixed to the chimney is around 1m long and 0.05mm diameter = 0.05m².

For the rotator I have allowed 0.15m × 0.13m = 0.02m².

Adding this lot up gives 0.225 + 0.072 + 0.05 + 0.02 = 0.367m², or for rough calculation, 0.4m².

You will notice I didn't include the boom, which would be end on to the wind if the beam were facing into wind.

If the beam were to be rotated 90° to the wind then the area facing the wind would be:

0.08 + 0.06 + 0.05 + 0.02 = 0.21 or say 0.2m².

Calculating the wind pressure

To work out the force acting on the antenna structure by the wind, see Fig 8.20.

Taking my antenna, with a total area of 0.4m, the sideways

Fig 8.19. The Mk2 G3LDO antenna support catapult launch pad. The catapult is held nearly upside down so that the line does not get caught up with anything when fired. It is advisable to gain proficiency with few practice runs in an open space before using it to secure an antenna support

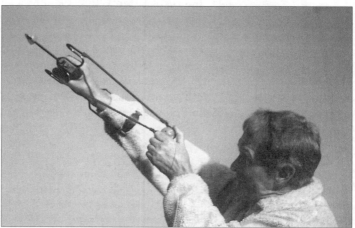

Fig 8.20. Conversion between wind speed and force per unit area

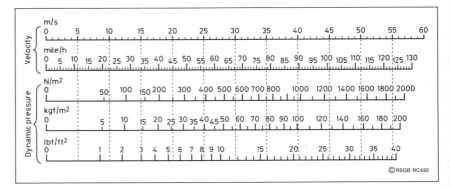

force on this with a 45m/s (100mph) wind, according to Fig 8.20, is 128kgf/m² × 0.4 = 51kg. By turning the antenna so that the elements are sideways to the wind, the area facing the wind is reduced to 0.2m² and the sideways force reduced to 10.3kg.

There are leverage forces that need to be taken into consideration with unsupported masts that extend above the supporting structure, such as a wall bracket, chimney bracket or guys on a mast. That is why an antenna should be fixed as close support or rotator as possible. If you have a 'Christmas tree' of antennas turned by one rotator then a rotator cage is a must.

Of course, these calculations are a simplification of the real world. The wind comes in gusts and there is a lot of turbulence over the roof. Nevertheless, the method of estimating wind forces by G3SEK does give some idea of the forces that will be encountered and enables you to engineer the structure accordingly. To sleep soundly when it's blowing a gale, you need some reassurance that the mast and its fixings are strong enough.

REFERENCES

[1] 'Eurotek', Erwin David, G4LQI, *RadCom* November 1999.

[2] *Protection against atmospheric corrosion*, Karel Barton, John Wiley, 1976.

[3] 'In Practice', Ian White, G3SEK, *Radio Communication* March 1995.

[4] 'In Practice', Ian White, G3SEK, *RadCom* November 1998.

[5] 'The Paul Buyan Whip', Alfred W Hubbard, K0OHM, *QST* March 1963.

[6] 'Wind loading', D J Reynolds, G3ZPF, *Radio Communication* April and May 1988 (reprinted in *The HF Antenna Collection*, RSGB).

[7] 'Ropes and rigging for amateurs – a professional approach', J M Gale, G3JMG, *Radio Communication* March 1970 (reprinted in *HF Antenna Collection* and in the *RSGB Microwave Handbook*, Volume 1).

[8] 'In Practice', Ian White, G3SEK, *Radio Communication* January 1995.

9 Transmission lines and baluns

THE PURPOSE OF TRANSMISSION LINE

The need to install an antenna in a clear space, as high as possible, has been emphasised in the preceding chapters. On the other hand, the transmitter that generates the RF power for driving the antenna is usually located in the shack, some distance from the antenna terminals. The connecting link between the two is the RF transmission line or feeder. Its sole purpose is to carry RF power from one place to another as efficiently as possible.

At radio frequencies every conductor that has appreciable length compared with the wavelength in use will radiate power; in other words it becomes an antenna. The transmission line must be designed so that RF power being carried to the antenna does not radiate.

Radiation loss from transmission lines can be prevented by using two conductors so arranged and operated that the electromagnetic field from one is balanced everywhere by an equal and opposite field from the other. In such a case the resultant field is zero; in other words, there is no radiation. This is illustrated in Fig 9.1.

CHARACTERISTIC IMPEDANCE

Transmission line with its two conductors in close proximity can be thought of as a series of small inductors and capacitors distributed along its whole

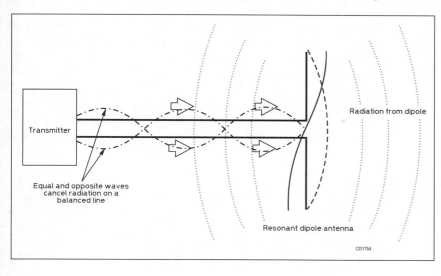

Fig 9.1. RF energy on a transmission line connected to an antenna. No radiation occurs on the line provided the RF energy on each of the lines is equal and opposite. Once the energy reaches the antenna there is no opposition to radiation

145

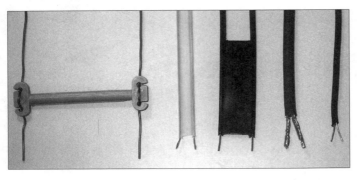

length. Each inductance limits the rate at which each immediately following capacitor can be charged when a pulse of electrical power is fed to one end of an infinitely long transmission line. The effect of the LC chain is to establish a definite relationship between current and the voltage of the pulse. Thus the line has an apparent resistance called its *characteristic impedance* or *surge impedance*, the conventional symbol of which is Z_0. Transmission line characteristic impedance is unaffected by the line length, but more about this later.

Fig 9.2. Five examples of twin-wire transmission line. *Left to right:* **Open-wire line constructed using 1mm diameter copper wire and spacers; 300Ω twin line with polyethylene insulation; 450Ω 'window' twin line; 75Ω heavy duty twin line; 75Ω lightweight twin line**

TRANSMISSION-LINE CONSTRUCTION

Two types of transmission line have been used to construct antenna systems described in this book. These are twin-line feeder (Fig 9.2) and coaxial cable.

Twin-line feeder

Twin-line feeders can be constructed from two copper wires supported at a fixed distance apart using insulated spacers. This type of construction is often known as *open-wire feeder*. Spacers may be made from insulating material, such as Plexiglas, polyethylene or plastic. The spacers shown in Fig 9.2 are specifically made for the job although their source is unknown. The characteristic impedance of such a line can be calculated with the formula:

$$Z_0 = \frac{267 \log 2S}{d}$$

The construction uses 1.5mm diameter copper wire and spacers hold the wires around 75mm apart. Using the formula this gives a Z_0 of 550Ω. If I had used 1mm diameter wire the Z_0 would have been 600Ω.

The 300Ω twin line (the light coloured line shown in Fig 9.2) is constructed by moulding the conductors along the edges of a ribbon of polyethylene insulation and for this reason is sometimes known as *ribbon line*. This type of feeder is convenient to use but moisture and dirt tend to change the characteristic of the line.

A further variation of commercial twin-line feeder is *window-line*, which has 'windows' cut in the polythene insulation at regular intervals. This reduces the weight of the line and breaks up the surface area where dirt and moisture can accumulate.

Coaxial cable

In most amateur installations coaxial cable transmission line is used. The two conductors of the transmission line are arranged coaxially, with the inner conductor supported within the tubular outer by means of a semi-solid, low-loss dielectric, normally polyethylene. The outer conductor is made from an outer copper wire braid and covered with a protective vinyl sheath, which makes it impervious to weather. Various types of coaxial cable are shown in Fig 9.3.

Coaxial cable has advantages that make it very practical for efficient operation in the HF and VHF bands. It is a shielded line and has a minimum of radiation loss. Since the line has little radiation loss, nearby metallic objects have minimum effect on the line because the outer conductor serves as a shield for the inner conductor.

The characteristic impedance of most coaxial cable used in amateur radio installations is usually 50Ω. Other impedance cable is used for impedance transformers and baluns (described later), but other cables are available in an impedance of 75Ω. The impedance of coaxial cable is often printed on the protective vinyl sheath; this is also described later.

In order to preserve the characteristics of the flexible, coaxial line, special coaxial fittings are available. These, and methods of fixing them, are described later.

Fig 9.3. Four examples of coaxial cable. From left to right, 50Ω RG213U, 50Ω RG58C/U, 75Ω television cable, 75Ω satellite cable

REFLECTIONS AND SWR

For the transmission line to operate at its highest efficiency its impedance should be the same as the output impedance of the transmitter and the feed impedance of the antenna. This is achieved by standardising the design of the transmitters/transceivers and coaxial cable so that their impedances are 50Ω. With these items standardised it only remains to do the same at the antenna. In practice this is not possible because the impedance of all antennas varies with frequency, causing some mismatch at some frequency.

When a wave travelling along a transmission line from the transmitter to the antenna (incident wave) encounters impedance that is not the same as Z_0 then some of the wave is reflected (reflected wave). Whenever two sinusoidal waves propagate in opposite directions along the same transmission line, as occurs in any system exhibiting reflections, a static interference pattern (SWR) is formed along the line, as illustrated in Fig 9.4.

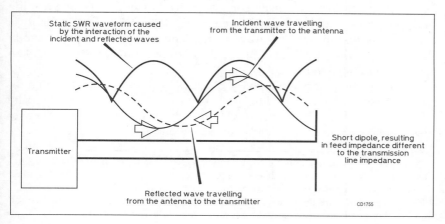

Static SWR waveform caused by the interaction of the incident and reflected waves

Incident wave travelling from the transmitter to the antenna

Transmitter

Short dipole, resulting in feed impedance different to the transmission line impedance

Reflected wave travelling from the antenna to the transmitter

CD1755

Fig 9.4. How a standing wave is created on a transmission line

For the purposes of quantifying reflection magnitude, however, we are interested in the amplitude of the potential nodes and nulls. Standing wave ratio (SWR) is defined as the ratio of the voltage or current maximum to the voltage or current minimum along a transmission line, as follows:

$$SWR = \frac{V_{max}}{V_{min}} = \frac{I_{max}}{I_{min}}$$

The traditional method of measuring SWR is to use a voltage detector. In the antenna laboratory at the RAF Radio School at Yatesbury (many years ago) a 400MHz transmitter energised an 800Ω open-wire transmission line, the length of the room. With a mismatch applied to the other end of this line the instructor would walk up and down the line with a fluorescence tube, which filled up or down with light like a thermometer tube, at high and low voltage points*.

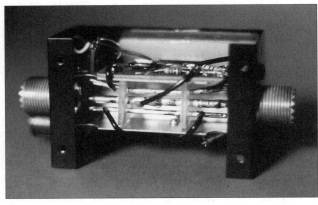

Note that the potential maximum must always be greater than the minimum; thus SWR is always greater than or equal to one. If no reflections exist, no standing wave pattern exists along the line, and the voltage values measured at all points along the transmission line are equal.

Fig 9.5. Example of SWR meter construction

In this case the impedance match is perfect, the numerator and denominator of the equation are equal, and SWR equals unity.

The various parameters for expressing impedance mismatch and the attendant reflective losses in a transmission line system include standing wave ratio (SWR); reflection coefficient; return loss and mismatch loss. Since these various parameters all describe the same phenomenon, they are all mathematically interrelated. Because most instruments available to radio amateurs for measuring antenna mismatch are SWR meters (and it is the parameter that most of you are probably most familiar with) I have standardised on SWR.

The usual in-line SWR meter comprises two power meters, one reading incident power and the other reflected power. Power detector directivity is possible because the incident wave voltage and current are in phase and in the reflected wave, 180° out of phase. An example of the construction of an SWR meter is shown in Fig 9.5.

It is often thought that a high SWR causes the transmission line to radiate. This is not true provided the power on each line is equal and opposite as shown in Fig 9.1. The balanced ATU by G0LMJ (see Chapter 4) is the only design that ensures the power in the feeder conductors is balanced.

---

* A fluorescence or neon tube is energised by the electrostatic component of an electromagnetic wave. When used to detect standing waves it can 'see' the voltage standing wave ratio (VSWR) as it is moved along the transmission line. The conventional in-line SWR meter reads ratios of incident and reflected current and voltage from which SWR is implied. For this reason I have used SWR rather than VSWR in this book.

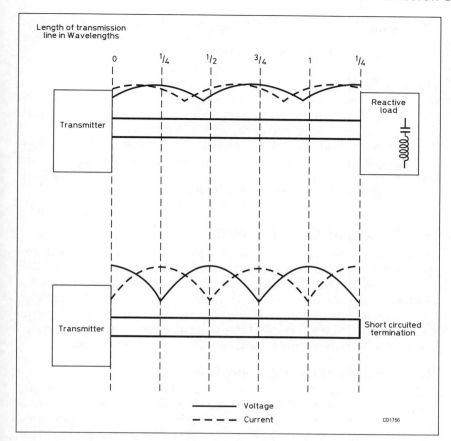

Length of transmission
line in Wavelengths

Fig 9.6. Transmission line (a) terminated with a reactive load and (b) terminated with a short. Note the points where values of the same impedance (and opposite impedance) reoccur

Voltage
Current
CD1756

THE TRANSMISSION LINE AS AN IMPEDANCE TRANSFORMER

When a transmission line is terminated with a small mismatch, such as an off-resonant antenna, a static interference pattern (SWR) is formed along the line, as illustrated in Fig 9.4. In fact there are two patterns, one voltage, the other current as shown in Fig 9.6(a). The phase difference between the voltage and current will depend on the reactance of the load and will be 90° for a resistive load.

Impedance can be defined by the ratio of current and voltage. This will be familiar to you when looking at the current and voltage distribution of the standing wave on a dipole antenna as shown in Fig 9.1. The voltage is high and the current zero at the end of the dipole (high impedance) while at the centre of the dipole the voltage is low and the current high (low impedance). The centre is obviously the best place to feed the antenna when using low-impedance coaxial cable.

If the transmission line is terminated with a short, as shown in Fig 9.6(b), the impedance at that point will be very low. You can see that the voltage is zero and the current very high. The standing wave pattern shows that this very low impedance is repeated at every half-wave point down the line. On the other hand the impedance will be very high a quarter of a wavelength down the line. This characteristic of transmission lines is often used as an

149

impedance transformer and is used with the G5RV antenna described in Chapter 2. It can also be used to measure the electrical length of the transmission line, described at the end of this chapter.

Velocity factor

With open-wire air-spaced lines the velocity of an electromagnetic wave is very close to that of light. In the presence of dielectrics other than air the velocity is reduced, since electromagnetic waves travel more slowly in dielectrics than they do in a vacuum. Because of this the wavelength as measured along the line will depend on the velocity factor that applies in the case of the particular type of line in use. The wavelength in a practical line is always shorter than the wavelength in free space.

LOSSES IN TRANSMISSION LINE

Practical transmission line has losses due to the resistance of the conductor and the dielectric between the conductors. As in the case of a two-wire line, power lost in a properly terminated coaxial line is the sum of the effective resistance loss along the length of the cable and the dielectric loss between the two conductors. Of the two losses, the resistance loss is the greater; since it is largely due to the skin effect this loss (all other conditions remaining the same) will increase directly as the square root of the frequency.

Measurement of coaxial cable loss

The classic method of measuring coaxial cable loss is to terminate the cable with a dummy load that is equal to the Z_0 of the line. Then use a power meter, first at the transmitter end and then the load end ensuring that the transmitter power is maintained at a constant level during the test. Then calculate the loss from the difference in power readings using the formula:

$$\text{dB loss} = 10 \log (P_1/P_2)$$

where P_1 is the power at the transmitter end and P_2 is the power at the dummy load.

Losses due to SWR

As described above, transmission line has losses due to the resistance of the conductor and the dialectic between the conductors. This is shown in Fig 9.7, which shows approximate losses for 450Ω twin line and RG213 coaxial cable. Additional losses occur due to antenna/transmission line mismatch (SWR), also shown in Fig 9.7. These losses are for a transmission line over 30m (100ft) long. SWR losses on the HF bands are not as great as is often thought, although at VHF and UHF it is a different matter. As you can see from Fig 9.7, even with an SWR of 5:1 on a 30m length of RG213 coaxial cable at 28MHz, the attenuation is only just over 1dB over the perfectly terminated loss. If the graph in Fig 9.7 is extrapolated to the VHF bands the losses are more significant.

   If you have an SWR due to a mismatch, an SWR reading at the transmitter will be lower than if the measurement were taken at the load end. The reason is that the losses on the line attenuate the reflected wave. This means

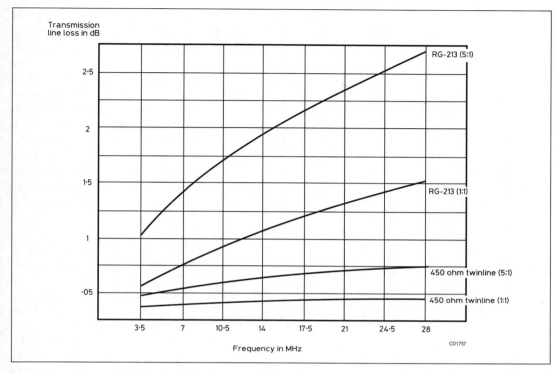

Transmission line loss in dB

RG-213 (5:1)

RG-213 (1:1)

450 ohm twinline (5:1)

450 ohm twinline (1:1)

Frequency in MHz

CD1757

you can use an SWR meter to measure transmission line loss, using the power meter method (only use a load that creates a mismatch, say 100Ω) described above. Measure the SWR at the transmitter and at then at the antenna. Use the graph in Fig 9.8 to determine the cable loss.

Fig 9.7. Graph showing losses on a 10m (100ft) of 450Ω twin line and RG213 coaxial cable at an SWR of 1:1 and 5:1

FITTING COAXIAL CONNECTORS

Fitting coaxial connectors to cable is something we all have to do, whether you are a home-brew equipment fanatic or someone who only rarely uses a soldering iron. If you have had trouble in the past fitting connectors, you should find the methods [1] described here by Roger Blackwell, G4PMK, very helpful. Although specific styles of connector and cable are mentioned, the methods are applicable to many others.

Cables and connectors

The main secret of success is using the right cable with the right connector. If you're buying connectors, it is important to be able to recognise good and bad types, and know what cables the good ones are for. Using the wrong connector and cable combination is sure to lead to problems. Any information you can get, such as old catalogues, is likely to prove useful, especially if you can get the cable cutting dimensions and equivalents lists. Two further sources of dimensions and techniques are references [2] and [3].

Cables commonly are of one of two families, the American 'RG' (Radio-Guide MIL specification) types and the English 'UR' (UniRadio) series. URM67 is equivalent to RG213, is 10.5mm in diameter and is the most

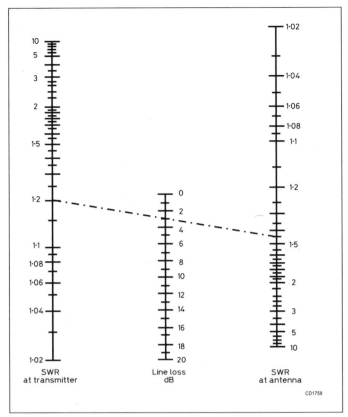

10
5
3
2
1·5
1·2
1·1
1·08
1·06
1·04
1·02

SWR
at transmitter

0
2
4
6
8
10
12
14
16
18
20

Line loss
dB

1·02
1·04
1·06
1·08
1·1
1·2
1·5
2
3
5
10

SWR
at antenna

CD1758

Fig 9.8. Nomograph for calculating transmission line loss using an SWR meter. Measure the SWR at the transmitter, then at the antenna. Place a straight edge over the two SWR readings and read off the line loss

common cable used with type N and PL259 connectors. URM43 (5mm OD) is one usually used with BNC connectors, although these also fit RG58 cable since both have similar dimensions. If there is any doubt about the quality of the cable, have a look at the braid. It should cover the inner completely. If it doesn't it is unlikely to be worth buying. There are a lot of so-called 'RG8' cables about these days, intended for the cheap end of the CB market, that are anything but good. Avoid them like the plague – *RG8 is an obsolete designation* – the modern equivalent is RG213 or URM67.

Having obtained your cable, the easy bit is over. Now select the connector. The three most popular connector types are the UHF, BNC and N ranges. These will be covered in some detail, a few others mentioned later. If you can, buy connectors from a reputable manufacturer (see Appendix). There are some good surplus bargains about, so a trawl through the boxes at the local rally may prove worthwhile.

It cannot be too widely known that the iniquitous UHF connector is no good much beyond 200MHz, because the impedance through the plug-socket junction is not 50Ω. The suitability of N and BNC connectors for use at UHF and beyond is due to their maintaining the system impedance (50Ω) through the connector. PL259 plugs, like the RG8 cable they were intended for, have a lot of nasty imitations. Beware of any that don't have PTFE insulation. They might be OK, but many cheap types are lossy and badly made. OK for receiving, maybe, but you put 400W PEP of 144MHz through that sort only once! The plating should be good quality (silver solders best, although some proprietary plated finishes are just about as good), and there should be two or more solder holes in the body for soldering to the braid. There should be two small tangs on the outer mating edge of the plug which locate in the serrated ring of the socket and stop the body rotating. If you are going to use small-diameter cable with these plugs, get the correct reducer. Often two types are available, one being for 75Ω cable. The 50Ω type is often called 'UG17S'. Using the wrong one is certain disaster. It is advisable to buy the reducers at the same time, because some manufacturers use different reducer threads.

With BNC, TNC (like the BNC but threaded) N and C (like N but bayonet) types, life can be more complicated. All these connectors are available in 50 and 75Ω versions. Be sure you get the right one!

To help those of you who like hunting for bargains at rallies, Table 9.1 shows some common manufacturers' designations. All of these connectors have evolved over the years, and consequently you will meet a number of different types. The variations are mostly to do with the cable clamping and centre-pin securing method. The original cable clamp type is usually called *unimproved MIL*, the later modification the *improved*, and the best for most uses is the *pressure-sleeve* type. If you are buying new connectors, then for normal use go for the pressure-sleeve type. It is *much* easier to fit.

If you are fortunate enough to have some of the double-braided PTFE dielectric cable such as RG142, you may find it easier to use the older clamp types, although the pressure-sleeve type will fit properly with care.

All original clamp types use a free centre pin that is held in place by its solder joint onto the inner conductor. Captive-contact types have a two-part centre insulator between which fits the shoulder on the centre pin. Improved MIL clamp types may have either free or captive contacts. Pressure-sleeve types have a captive centre pin. As an aid to identification, Fig 9.9 shows these types. Pressure clamp captive-pin types are easy to spot; they have a ferrule or 'top hat' that assists in terminating the braid, a two-piece insulator and a centre pin with a shoulder. Unimproved clamp types have a washer, a plain gasket, a cone-ended braid clamp and a single insulator, often fixing inside the body. Improved types have a washer, a thin ring gasket with a V-groove and usually a conical braid clamp with more of a shoulder. There are variations, so if you can get the catalogue description it helps!

Tools for the job

To tackle this successfully, you really need a few special tools; while they may not be absolutely essential, they certainly help. Most of them you probably have them

Table 9.1. Some common connectors and equivalents

	Pin	Clamp	Fits cable	MIL No
BNC types				
Plug	C	P	URM43	UG88D/U
Plug	F	I	URM43	UG88C/U
Plug	F	O	URM43	UG88
Angle plug	C	P	URM43	
Line socket	C	P	URM43	UG88C/U
N types				
Plug	C	P	URM43	UG536B/U
Plug	C	P	URM67	
Plug	F	I	URM67	UG21B/U
Angle plug	C	P	URM67	UG594U
Line socket	C	P	URM67	UG23D/U

Pin types are: C, captive, and F, free.
Clamp types are: P, pressure sleeve, I, improved, and 0, original.

Fig 9.9. Types of BNC/ N cable clamps

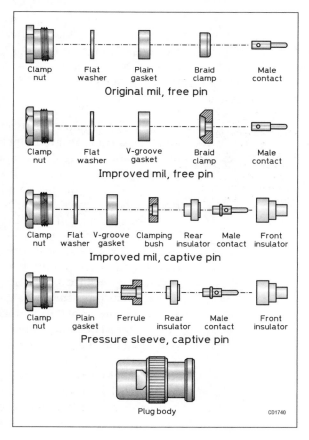

Clamp nut — Flat washer — Plain gasket — Braid clamp — Male contact
Original mil, free pin

Clamp nut — Flat washer — V-groove gasket — Braid clamp — Male contact
Improved mil, free pin

Clamp nut — Flat washer — V-groove gasket — Clamping bush — Rear insulator — Male contact — Front insulator
Improved mil, captive pin

Clamp nut — Plain gasket — Ferrule — Rear insulator — Male contact — Front insulator
Pressure sleeve, captive pin

Plug body

CD1740

anyway, so it's just a matter of sorting through the toolbox. First and foremost is a good soldering iron. If you never intend to use a PL259, then a small instrument type iron is sufficient. If you use PL259s, or intend to use some of the 'dirty tricks' described later, something with a lot more heat output is required. Ideally a thermostatically-controlled iron is best; as with most tools a little extra spent repays itself handsomely in the future.

A *sharp* knife is another must. A Stanley-type is essential for larger cables, provided that the blade is sharp. For smaller cables, you can use a craft knife or a very sharp penknife. G4PMK uses a scalpel, but notes that a word or two of warning is in order. Scalpels excel at the job they were designed for – cutting flesh. Make sure it isn't yours! Use sharp blades, cut away from you, and keep the object you're cutting on the bench, *not in your hand*. Although sharp, the steel blades are brittle and will shatter if you apply excessive force or bend them, with bits of sharp blade shooting all over the place. Dispose of used blades in a box or plastic jar. Model shops have a good range of craft knives, which will also do an excellent job.

A pair of sharp small scissors (not the XYL's nail scissors!) is needed for cutting braids, and a blunt darning needle (mount it in a handle made from a piece of wood dowelling) is useful for unweaving the braid. A scriber is also useful for this job. You will find a small vice a great help as well. For BNC, TNC and N type connectors, some spanners are essential to tighten the gland nuts. The BNC/TNC spanners should be thin $^7/_{16}$in AF. Those for type N need to be $^{11}/_{16} \times ^5/_8$ AF. A junior hacksaw is needed to cut larger cables such as URM67. Finally, if you intend to put heatshrink sleeves over the ends of plugs for outdoor use, some form of heat gun helps, although the shaft of a soldering iron may work. (A hot-air paint stripper can be used for this purpose – with care).

Preparing cables

Fitting a plug requires you to remove various bits of outer sheath, braid and inner dielectric. The important knack to acquire is that of removing one at a time, without damaging what lies underneath. To remove the outer sheath, use a sharp knife or scalpel. Place the knife across the cable and rotate the cable while applying gentle pressure. The object of doing this is to score right round the cable sheath. Now score a line from the ring you just made up to the cable end. If you have cut it just enough, it should be possible to peel away the outer sheath, leaving braid intact underneath. If this is not something you've tried before, practise on a piece of cable first. For some connectors, it is important that this edge of the sheath is a smooth edge at right-angles to the cable, so it really is worth getting right.

Braid removal usually just requires a bit of combing out and a pair of scissors. Removal of the inner dielectric is most difficult with large-diameter cables with laid multi-strand inner conductors like URM67. Again, it is important that the end is a clean, smooth cut at right-angles to the cable. This is best achieved by removing the bulk of the dielectric first, if necessary in several stages. Finally the dielectric is trimmed to length. There is a limit to how much dielectric you can remove at one go; 1–2cm is about as much as can be attempted with the larger sizes without damaging the lay of the inner. For the larger cables, it is worthwhile to pare down the bulk of the unwanted material before trying to pull the remainder off the inner. If you can, fit one plug on short cables before you cut the cable to length (or off the reel if you are so lucky). This will help to prevent the inner sliding about when you are stripping the inner dielectric.

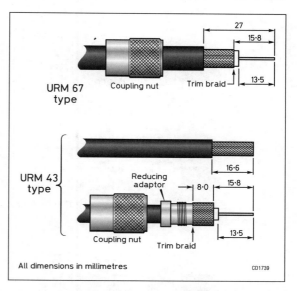

Fig 9.10. PL259 plug assembly

Fitting PL259 plugs

Without reducer, URM67-type cable

First, make a clean end. For this large cable, the only satisfactory way is to use a junior hacksaw. Chopping with cutters or a knife just spoils the whole thing. Having got a clean end, refer to Fig 9.10 for the stripping dimensions. First, remove the sheath braid and dielectric, revealing the length of inner conductor required. Do this by cutting right through the sheath and braid, scoring the dielectric, then removing the dielectric afterwards. Next carefully remove the sheath back to the dimension indicated, *without disturbing the braid*. Examine the braid; it should be shiny and smooth. If you have disturbed it or it looks tarnished, start again a little further down.

Now the tricky bit. With a hot iron, tin the braid carefully. The idea is to do it with as little solder as possible; a trace of a non-corrosive flux such as Fluxite helps. Lightly tin the inner conductor also at this stage. Take a breather while the cable cools.

Now slide the coupling piece onto the cable (threaded end towards the free end). Examine the plug body. If it isn't silver-plated and you think it might not solder easily, apply a file around and through the solder holes. Now screw the body onto the cable, hard. When you've finished, the sheath should have gone into the threaded end of the connector, the inner should be poking out through the hollow pin, and the end of the exposed dielectric should be hard up against the inside shoulder off the plug. Look at the braid through the solder holes. It should not have broken up into a mass of strands; that's why it was tinned. If it has, then it is best to start again.

If all is well, lightly clamp the cable in the vice and then apply the iron to the solder holes. Heat it up and then apply solder. It should flow into the holes; if it stays there as a sullen blob, the body isn't hot enough. Now leave it undisturbed to cool before soldering the inner by heating the pin and feeding solder down the inner. Finally, when it's all cool, cut any excess protruding inner conductor and file flush with the pin, then screw down the coupling ring. Merely as a confidence check, of course, test for continuity on both inner and outer from one end of the cable to the other, and check that the inner isn't shortened to the braid.

With reducer, URM43 type cable

First, slide the outer coupler and the reducer on to the cable. Next, referring to Fig 9.10, remove the outer sheath without nicking the braid. Now, using a blunt needle, gently unweave the braid a bit at a time until it is all straight

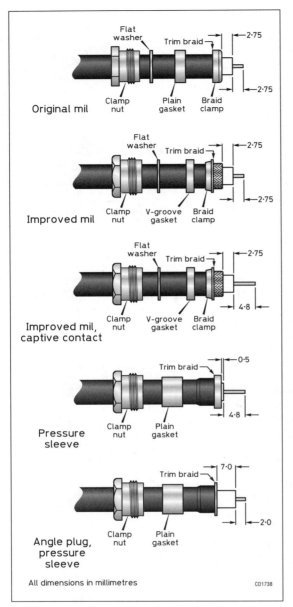

Flat washer
Trim braid
2·75
2·75
Clamp nut
Plain gasket
Braid clamp

Original mil

Flat washer
Trim braid
2·75
2·75
Clamp nut
V-groove gasket
Braid clamp

Improved mil

Flat washer
Trim braid
2·75
4·8
Clamp nut
V-groove gasket
Braid clamp

Improved mil, captive contact

Trim braid
0·5
4·8
Clamp nut
Plain gasket

Pressure sleeve

Trim braid
7·0
2·0
Clamp nut
Plain gasket

Angle plug, pressure sleeve

All dimensions in millimetres   CD1738

Fig 9.11. BNC dimensions, plugs and line sockets

and sticking out like a ruff around the cable. Remove the inner dielectric, without nicking the inner conductor, so as to leave the specified amount of dielectric. Tin the inner conductor. Bring up the reducer until the end of the reducer is flush with the end of the outer sheath. Fold the braid back so it lies evenly over the shank of the reducer, then cut off the excess braid with scissors so that it is not in danger of getting trapped in the threads. Smooth it down once more, then offer up the plug body and, while holding the reducer and cable still, screw on the plug body until it is fully home. The only really good way of doing this is with two pairs of pliers. Now hold the assembly in the vice and ready the soldering iron.

There has been a spirited discussion from time to time about the advisability of soldering the braid through the holes; the best information available is that you should. If you don't, the cable will sooner or later fail. So with a big iron, solder the braid through the holes. See the section above for advice. Finally, solder and trim the inner conductor and test the assembly as described earlier.

Fitting BNC and type N plugs

These are 'constant impedance' connectors; that is, when correctly made up, the system impedance of 50Ω is maintained right through the connector. It is vital that the cable fits the connector correctly; therefore check that each part fits the cable properly after you prepare it. Refer to Fig 9.11 for BNC dimensions and Fig 9.12 for N types.

Original or unmodified clamp types

Slide the nut, washer and gasket onto the cable in that order. With the sharp knife, score through the outer sheath by holding the knife and rotating the cable, without nicking the braid. Run the knife along the cable from the score to the end, and then peel off the outer sheath.

Using a blunt needle, for example, start to unweave the braid enough to enable the correct length of dielectric to be removed. Now slip the braid clamp on, pushing it firmly down to the end of the outer sheath. Finish unweaving the braid, comb it smooth then trim it with scissors so that it just comes back to the end of the conical section of the clamp. Be sure that the braid wires aren't twisted.

Now fit the inner pin and make sure that the open end of the pin will fit up against the dielectric. Take the pin off and lightly tin the exposed inner conductor. Re-fit the pin and solder it in place by placing the soldering iron bit (tinned but with the solder wiped off) on the side of the pin opposite the solder hole. Feed a small quantity of solder (22SWG or so works best) into the hole.

Allow the connector to cool and then examine it. If you've been careful enough, the dielectric should not have melted. Usually it does, and swells up, so with the sharp knife trim it back to size. This is essential, as otherwise the plug will not assemble properly. Remove any excess solder from around the pin with a fine file.

Now push the gasket and washer up against the clamp nut, check the braid dressing on the clamp, and then push the assembly into the plug body. Gently firm home the gasket with a small screwdriver or rod and then start the clamp nut by hand. Tighten the clamp nut by a spanner, using a second spanner to hold the plug body still; *it must not rotate*. Finally, check the completed job with the shack ohmmeter, sit back and relax!

Modified or improved clamp types

In general, this is similar to the technique for unmodified clamp types described above. There are some important differences, however. The gasket has a V-shaped groove in it, which must face the cable clamp. The clamp has a corresponding V-shaped profile on one side; the other side may be conical or straight sided, depending on the manufacturer. If the clamp end has straight sides, then the braid is fanned out and cut to the edge of the clamp only, not pushed down the sides. Some types have a small PTFE insulator, which is fitted before the pin is put on (common on plugs for the small RG174 cable). You now appreciate why having the assembly instructions for your particular flavour of plug is a good idea! Still, by using these instructions as a guide, it shouldn't be too difficult to get it right, even if it does not fit the first time.

One important point – if the plug has been assembled correctly and tightened up properly, the clamp will have (intentionally) cut the gasket, which

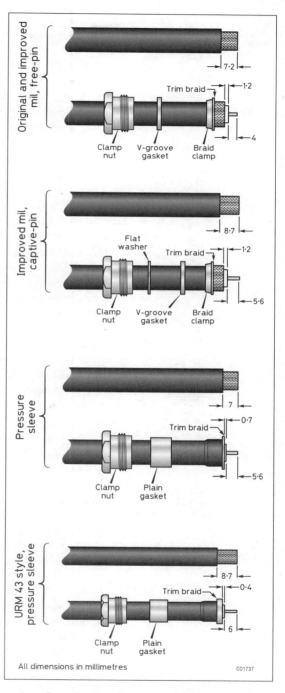

Fig 9.12. N-type dimensions, plugs, angle plugs and line sockets

is then rather difficult to re-use. This thin gasket will not stand a second attempt. The thicker gasket types will often allow careful re-use.

Captive contact types

These have a small shoulder on the pin, and a rear insulator which fits between the pin and the cable. Most types use a thick gasket and a ferrule, although some use a V-grooved braid clamp and thin gasket. The ferrule type is described first because these are the most commonly available, and the easiest to fit.

First, slip the nut and gasket on to the cable.

Refer to Fig 9.11 or 9.12 for cutting dimensions, then strip off the correct amount of outer sheath by rotating the cable, producing a neat scored circle. Score back to the end of the cable and peel off the unwanted sheath. Comb out the braid, and with it fanned out evenly around the cable, slide the ferrule (small end first) on to the dielectric-covered inner conductor. Push it home so that the narrow portion of the ferrule slides *under* the outer sheath, and the end of the outer sheath rests against the ferrule shoulder. Trim the braid with scissors to the edge of the ferrule. Slide up the gasket so that it rests gently against the ferrule shoulder, which will prevent the braid from being disturbed. Using the sharp knife, trim the dielectric back to the indicated dimension without nicking the inner conductor. Fit the rear insulator, which will have a recess on one side to accommodate the protruding dielectric. Incidentally, if you don't have the size for your particular plug, trim the dielectric until it fits; but don't overdo it!

Now trim the exposed inner conductor to length and check by fitting the pin, whose shoulder should rest on the rear insulator unless the inner has been cut too long. Tin the inner lightly, then fit the pin and solder it by applying the iron tip (cleaned of excess solder) to the side of the pin opposite from the solder hole and feed a small amount of solder into the hole.

Allow to cool, and then remove the excess solder with a fine file. Now fit the front insulator (usually separate from the body) and push the whole assembly into the body. Push down the gasket gently into the plug body with a small rod or screwdriver. Start the nut by hand, and then tighten fully with one spanner, using the other to prevent the body from rotating. Check with the ohmmeter, then start on the other end – remember to put the nut and gasket on first!

Variations

Angle plugs generally follow a similar pattern to the straight types, except that connection to the inner is via a slotted pin, accessed via a removable cap screw. Tighten the connector nut before soldering the inner. Line sockets are fitted in the same way as plugs.

Dirty tricks

We would like to use new connectors every time but often a pressure-sleeve type can be reused if the gasket is not too deformed. Get all the solder you can out of the pin and then carefully ream out the rest with a small drill, held in a pin chuck. The sizes to use are 1mm for URM43-style pins, and 2.6mm for URM67 ones.

Tarnished silver-plated connectors can be made to shine by dipping the metal parts in Goddards 'Silver Dip' silver cleaner or a solution of photographic fixer. Rinse carefully afterwards, then bake in a slow oven.

BNC connectors for URM67 cable can be rather hard to find. A standard captive contact BNC plug can be fitted to URM67 in the following way. First, discard the nut, gasket and ferrule, and prepare the rear insulator by removing the ridge from it with a sharp knife. Now prepare the cable by cutting with a knife, right through the jacket, braid and insulator about 5mm back from the end. Cut sufficiently deep so that you notch the inner conductor strands, and remove the remains. Carefully bend the six individual outer strands of the inner so they break off flush with the end of the dielectric, leaving one straight inner strand. Now remove sufficient outer jacket (about 2cm) such that when the body is pushed on the cable, some braid is still visible. Tin the braid and inner conductor lightly, then fit the rear insulator, pin and front insulator and push home the assembly into the plug body. With the big iron, heat the plug body and feed solder down the joint with the braid. After it has cooled, put some heatshrink adhesive lined sleeving over the plug and cable join to protect it. This arrangement is almost as good as the real plug, and certainly better than an adapter; it will happily stand 100W of 1296MHz.

An N plug can be *carefully* pushed on to a BNC socket; OK for quick test equipment lash-ups, but don't do it too often or too hard as you will eventually damage the socket. In a similar vein, the pin of a PL259 is about the same diameter as a 4mm wander plug; after all, what is a PL259 but a screened wander plug?

To make a PL259-to-BNC adapter, solder a length of copper wire to the back of a BNC single-hole socket. Drop it (without the nut) on to the top of a PL259 so that the wire pokes through the pin of the plug. With a big iron or a careful blowtorch, solder the body of the socket and plug together. After it has cooled, solder the inner wire to the pin. Not exactly a precision job, but good enough for a PL259!

Finally, to waterproof a connector-cable joint and to provide added strength where flexing of the cable will occur, heatshrink a piece of adhesive lined heatshrink sleeving over the plug body and cable. For N connectors, a 19mm diameter variety (that shrinks to a minimum of 6mm) can be slid on to the cable and connector after assembly.

Conclusions

With a little practice, care and patience, the fitting of connectors can be less of an uncertain business. Practice on some short leads (there is no such thing as too many spare short coaxial leads in any shack) and remember that the best time to put new connectors on the feeder is not two minutes before the start of the contest!

Note

Greenpar connectors are numbered systematically in a way that should enable quick identification of connectors and to check through those rally 'bargains'. The part number is 'GE' followed by a five-digit number, a letter, another number and lastly some more letters. The first digit is the connector

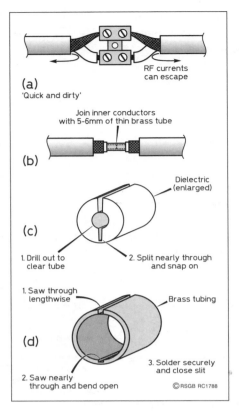

(a)
'Quick and dirty'

RF currents
can escape

Join inner conductors
with 5-6mm of thin brass tube

(b)

Dielectric
(enlarged)

(c)

1. Drill out to
clear tube

2. Split nearly through
and snap on

1. Saw through
lengthwise

Brass tubing

(d)

2. Saw nearly
through and bend open

3. Solder securely
and close slit

©RSGB RC1788

Fig 9.13. Methods of splicing coaxial cable

series (N, BNC etc) which is already apparent from looking at the connector. The second digit is vital – it is 'S' for 50Ω connectors, and '7' for 70 or 75Ω types. The next three numbers are the connector style. The letter refers to the cable clamp method – it is 'C' for pressure sleeve types, 'A' for modified MIL clamp with captive contact, 'D' for crimp types and '-' for MIL clamps with non-captive pins. The next group of numbers is the cable series. Useful ones are '1' for URM67 and RG213, '4' for RG214 *and* URM67 and RG213, '10' for URM43, URM76, RGS8 and 142, and '22' for URM9S and RG174. There are many others for less-common cables. The final group of one or more letters refers to the panel mounting holes and optional finish (if any). So a connector numbered GE3507C22 is a BNC plug suitable for RG174 or URM95 50Ω cable with a pressure-sleeve clamp.

SPLICING COAXIAL CABLE

The radio engineer's method of joining two lengths of coaxial cable together is to use coaxial connectors. However, in the description of coaxial cable splicing by G3SEK [4] that follows, you will see that a splice can be made entirely without connectors. A splice in coaxial cable needs to be as close as possible to an uninterrupted run of cable. In practice this requires four things:

1. Constant impedance through the splice.
2. As short an electrical length as possible, if it is not possible to make the impedance quite constant.
3. Continuous shield coverage.
4. Good mechanical properties: strong and waterproof.

At low frequencies coaxial cable can be spliced with a two-pole connector block as shown in Fig 9.13(a). Tape over the joint and it's done. Even though this creates a non-constant impedance, the electrical length of the splice is so short that it's most unlikely to have any significant effect. The main drawback is that the break in the shield cover provides an opportunity for RF currents to flow out from the inside of the shield and onto the outer surface (the skin effect makes RF currents flow only on surfaces). This may undo all your good efforts to keep RF currents off the feedline, using baluns or feedline chokes.

For a truly coaxial splice you need to join and insulate the inner conductor, and then replace the outer shield. Avoid making a big blob of twisted inner conductors and solder if you can, because that will create an impedance bump – a short section of line with a different impedance from the coaxial cable itself.

The neatest and electrically the best way to join the inner conductors is to use a 5–6mm (¼in) sleeve of thin brass tubing – see Fig 9.13(b). This is available from good hobby shops in sizes from $1/16$ in (1.6mm) outside diameter up to $1/2$ in (12.7mm), in steps of $1/32$ in (0.8mm); these sizes telescope together, by the way. To replace the dielectric, take a piece of the original insulation, drill out the centre to fit over the sleeve, and split it lengthways so that it snaps over the top – see Fig 9.13(c). To complete the shield on braided coaxial cable, one good way is to push the braid away from each end while you join the inner conductor, and then pull it back over the splice. Solder the braid quickly and carefully to avoid melting the dielectric underneath. For mechanical strength you can tape a rigid 'splint' alongside the joint as you waterproof it.

Alternatively the splice can be made using a very short length of air-insulated line of the same characteristic impedance. The inner conductor is joined using tubing as already described in Fig 9.13(b). The outer is made from a short length of brass or copper tubing.

The outer tube is 'hinged' to fit over the joint as shown in Fig 9.13(d) which shows how to then solder the whole thing up solidly. This method makes a very strong splice with excellent RF properties.

For 50Ω air-spaced coaxial cable, the ratio of the inner to outer conductor diameters is 0.43, so all you need to do is to choose the right diameters of tubing for the inner and outer conductors. Remember that the relevant dimensions are the outside diameter of the inner conductor and the inside diameter of the outer conductor. It so happens that airspaced line needs a larger inner diameter than solid-dielectric, semi-air spaced or foamed line, which conveniently accommodates the wall thickness of the inner sleeve. For UR67, RG213 and RG214, the best available choices are $5/16$ in (8mm) and $5/32$ in (4mm) outside diameters.

These coaxial splices will be at least as good as a splice using coaxial connectors.

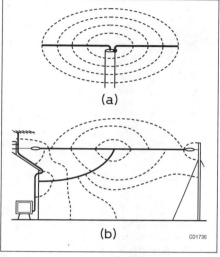

Fig 9.14. (a) Idealised picture of electric fields around a coaxial dipole. (b) The typical reality

BALANCED-TO-UNBALANCED TRANSFORMERS (BALUNS)

I used to be rather dismissive about the use of baluns but after reading an article on the subject by Ian White, G3SEK, I have become a convert. What follows is a slightly edited version of his article [5].

Real-life antennas are nothing like the textbook pictures. The textbooks show us a simple dipole; fed in the centre, with electric field lines neatly connecting the opposite halves, and lines of magnetic flux looping around the wires. Fig 9.14(a) is a typical version of this pretty picture, showing only the electric field lines for clarity. Everything is symmetrical, and the system is said to be 'balanced' with respect to ground.

The reality of a typical installation is very different. As Fig 9.14(b) shows, the electric field lines connect not only with the opposite half of the dipole, but also with the feedline, the ground, and any other objects nearby. The magnetic field may be less disturbed, but the overall picture is in no way symmetrical! Although the electromagnetic coupling between the opposite

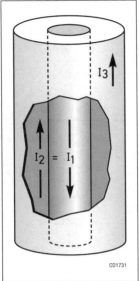

Fig 9.15. Currents on the inside of a coaxial cable (I_1 and I_2) are always equal and in antiphase. The skin effect allows a separate current I_3 to flow on the outside

Fig 9.16. If the antenna currents on either side of the feed point are unequal, the difference $I_3 = I_1 - I_2$ will flow down the outside of the cable

halves of a horizontal dipole makes the antenna 'want' to be balanced, the coupling has to compete with the distorting effects of the asymmetrical surroundings. As a result, practical antennas can be very susceptible to the way they are installed, and are hardly ever well balanced.

Contrast the messy environment of the antenna with the tidy situation inside a coaxial cable shown in Fig 9.15. The currents on the centre core (I_1) and the inside of the shield (I_2) are equal and opposite, ie 180° out of phase. The two conductors are closely coupled along their entire length, so the equal and antiphase current relationship is strongly enforced.

Also, what goes on inside the cable is totally independent of the situation outside. Thanks to the skin effect, which causes HF currents to flow only close to the surfaces of conductors, the inner and outer surfaces of the coaxial shield behave as two entirely independent conductors. You can hang the cable in the air, tape it to a tower or even bury it, yet the voltages and currents inside the cable remain exactly the same.

About the only things you can do wrong with coaxial cable are to let water inside or bend it so sharply that it kinks. That's why coaxial cable is popular – it is so easy to use.

The problems arise when you connect a coaxial cable to an antenna. If the antenna is in any way unbalanced – which it will be in any practical situation – a difference will appear between the currents flowing in the antenna at either side of the feed point.

This difference current is shown in Fig 9.16 as I_3, and is equal to ($I_1 - I_2$). The current I_3 has to flow somewhere. It cannot flow down the inside of the cable because I_1 and I_2 must be equal, so instead it flows down the outside of the outer sheath. As a result, the feed line becomes part of the radiating antenna. This causes distortion of the radiation pattern, RF currents on metal masts and Yagi booms, and problems with 'RF in the shack'. Even worse can be RF currents flowing in the mains and on TV cables, leading to all manner of EMC problems.

By using an appropriate type of balun at the antenna feed point, you can effectively prevent stray surface currents on the feed line. As a result, the current distribution on the antenna will adjust itself to become more symmetrical, so the antenna will work better and many of your EMC problems may also disappear.

Baluns

The word 'balun' is short for 'balanced to unbalanced'. A balun is a device which somehow connects a balanced load to an unbalanced coaxial line. There are two ways of approaching this task, so there are two distinct types of balun. The *choke balun* aims to prevent I_3 from flowing by placing a large series impedance on the outside of the feed line. As a result, the antenna

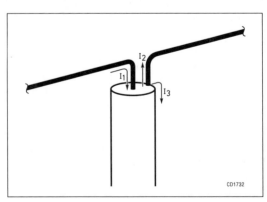

currents can only flow on the inside of the feed line, and the properties of the coaxial cable force the antenna currents at either side of the feed point to be equal and in antiphase, ie balanced. The *transformer balun* aims to force the voltages and currents at either side of the feed point to be equal and in antiphase. As a result, no difference current I_3 remains to flow on the outside of the feed line.

Antenna balance and feed-line surface currents are inter-related, and choke and transformer baluns are merely tackling the same problem from its two opposite ends. Choke off the difference current, and the antenna currents must adjust themselves to become more symmetrical. Alternatively, try to make the antenna currents equal, and the difference current will tend to disappear. Given these opposite approaches to the same problem, you can see how a variety of quite different looking devices come to be called 'baluns'. And since the same kind of balun can work well in one situation but not in another, it's small wonder that many people find the subject confusing.

Further confusion arises because baluns can be used for different purposes. To give just two examples, a balun can be used to cure TVI by suppressing feed-line radiation; or it can be used to force a more symmetrical current distribution upon an antenna which is basically unbalanced with respect to ground (eg a low-mounted vertical dipole). In these two examples you are expecting quite different things from the balun, so you might well choose a different type for either task.

To clarify matters, let's look at some well-known baluns and see how they work – and when they might not.

Choke baluns

The simplest baluns are the ones that prevent surface currents from flowing by forming the coaxial cable into an RF choke at the antenna feed point. (The currents flowing inside the cable are quite unaware that the cable has been coiled up.) At its very simplest, a choke balun can be just a few turns of cable in a loop of diameter 300 to 600mm (6 to 12in), see Fig 9.17(a), and in some circumstances this may be all you need.

Alternatives are to wind the cable around a toroid or a ferrite rod – see Fig 9.17(b) and (c). Yet another alternative, popularised by W2DU, is to feed the cable through ferrite tubes or beads to form a sleeve as shown in Fig 9.17(d); this is generally lighter and more compact than a coiled choke but somewhat more expensive. Ideally the cable should be a close fit inside the

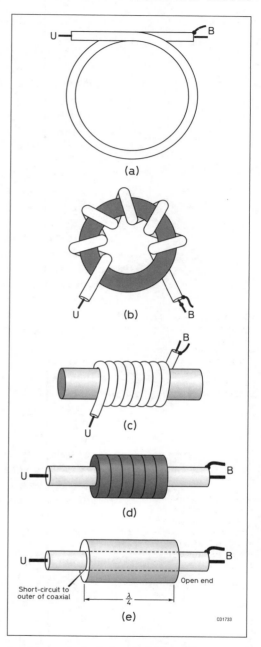

Fig 9.17. Five varieties of choke-type balun. (a) Coil of coaxial cable (typically 6–10 turns – only one turn shown). (b) Coaxial cable on toroid. (c) Coaxial cable on ferrite rod. (d) Ferrite sleeve. (e) Quarter-wave sleeve or 'bazooka'

ferrite sleeve, and this may not be easy to achieve with readily available materials.

The VHF or UHF equivalent of the choke balun is the quarter-wave sleeve or 'bazooka' – see Fig 9.17(e). The sleeve forms an additional section of co-axial line over the outside of the cable, and this outer line is short-circuited a quarter-wavelength away from the feed point. At the feed point, a quarter-wave distant, this short-circuit appears as a high impedance against currents flowing onto the outer surface of the coaxial cable. At its resonant frequency, the bazooka thus acts as an RF choke on the outer surface of the feeder.

The power rating of any choke balun is essentially that of the cable itself. Even if magnetic material is involved, the main feeder currents cancel inside the cable, leaving only the small residual surface current to magnetise the core.

Although choke baluns will prevent surface currents from flowing at the feed point itself, electromagnetic coupling between the antenna and points further down the feed line may induce surface currents which the balun cannot prevent. This will happen if the installation is asymmetrical.

Induced currents become much greater if the feed-line length is resonant, producing greater RF voltages on the line and on the equipment in the shack. The resonant length has to be measured from the feed point, down the co-axial cable, through the equipment in the shack, and away to down to RF ground via various lengths and loops of wire and metal plumbing. There can be many additional loading effects which alter the resonant length from its free-space value, so it can be very difficult to identify the exact causes of feed-line resonance. This can lead to mysterious complaints such as "Ever since I put in this new coaxial cable, I've had RF in the shack! Should I send the cable back?"

So if a choke-type balun fails to suppress feed-line currents, the solution is to *leave the balun there,* but also place further RF chokes, see Figs 9.17 (a), (b) and (c), at intervals down the feed line to interrupt any resonant current distributions. A suitable interval would be a quarter-wavelength, or in a multi-band system you could use pairs of chokes 2.5–3m apart, avoiding half-wave separations at any frequency in use.

Transformer baluns

A balanced-antenna feed point will present an equal impedance from each side to ground. The accusation levelled at choke baluns is that they treat the symptom (the surface current I_3) without attempting to correct the imbalance that causes it. A transformer balun, on the other hand, does create equal and opposite RF voltages at its output terminals, relative to the grounded side of its input. This works fine in the laboratory but, up in the air where the balun is located, what exactly do we mean by 'grounded'?

Transformer baluns may or may not involve a deliberate impedance transformation. You are probably familiar with the basic 1:1 and 4:1 baluns. Fig 9.18 shows a wire-wound 1:1 balun, and both wire-wound and coaxial-cable versions of the 4:1 type. These all have the common property of forcing balance at their output terminals by means of closely coupled windings within the transformer itself. The 4:1 balun in Fig 9.18(b) is the easiest to understand. Typically, it transforms 50Ω unbalanced to $4 \times 50 = 200$Ω balanced. This is achieved simply by a phase inversion. An applied voltage v at one side of the feed point is converted by the transformer action into a voltage $-v$ at the other side. These two voltages 160° out of phase represent the balance we are seeking to achieve. The 4:1 impedance transformation arises as follows. If the original voltage on the feed line was v, the voltage difference between opposite sides of the feedpoint is now $2v$. Since impedance is proportional to voltage squared, and $(2v)^2 = 4v^2$, the impedance is stepped up by a factor of 4.

In the wire-wound 4:1 balun shown in Fig 9.18(b), the 160° phase inversion is achieved by the connection of the windings, while the coaxial equivalent in Fig 9.18(c) does it by introducing an electrical half-wavelength of cable between opposite sides of the feed point. Strong coupling between the windings and inside the coaxial cable forces the whole system into balance.

Or does it? If you treat any balun as a 'black box' and look at the currents flowing in and out, you will find that any current difference between the two sides of the antenna has nowhere else to flow but down the outside of the coaxial cable [6]. But that does not mean that the balun is no better than a direct connection; when you insert the balun, it forces the currents in the antenna to readjust and become more symmetrical. To make a meaningful evaluation of the effects of a balun, you therefore need to include the entire antenna and its surroundings in your analysis.

Any unbalanced antenna/feed line system will always 'push back' against an attempt to force it into symmetry. So although the transformer balun may do a good job, it still may not achieve total equality between the currents on opposite sides of the feed point. That may leave a residual difference current I_3 to flow down the outside of the coaxial cable, as noted above. Unfortunately, having made its effort to minimise that difference current, the transformer balun does nothing to prevent it from flowing onto the coaxial cable. And there is still the possibility of additional currents being induced further down the surface of the feed line. This implies that a transformer-type balun may require additional RF chokes at the balun itself and possibly further back down the line.

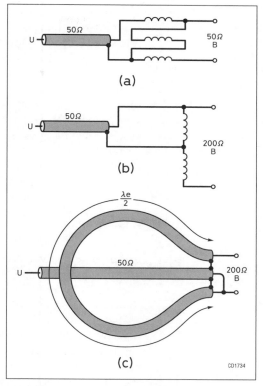

Fig 9.18. Transformer-type baluns. Windings shown separately are bifilar or trifliar wound, possibly on a ferrite rod or core. (a) Wire-wound 1:1 (trifilar). (b) Wire-wound 4:1 (bifilar). (c) Coaxial 4:1. The half-wavelength must allow for the velocity factor of the cable

Problems with baluns

Some people swear by baluns, while others swear at them because they allegedly cause mismatches, get hot, generate harmonics and spread despondency. Many of these problems are not the fault of the balun itself.

A 'pure' choke balun acts only on the outside of the feed line, and cannot introduce any impedance mismatch on the inside. However, introducing an innocent choke balun can in fact change the SWR. You may even find that the SWR changes when you insert an extra length of coaxial cable, which is totally contrary to the theory of standing waves! The SWR measured anywhere along the feed line should always be the same, says the theory – but only if the load impedance hasn't changed.

And that is the clue to the puzzle. Recall that if the system is unbalanced, the outside of the coaxial cable becomes part of the antenna itself. So when you change the feeder length, you are in fact altering the whole antenna system and changing the distribution of RF currents upon it. The change in currents at the feed point will indeed change the load impedance, so that changes the SWR.

Yet another complication is that some SWR meters are not RF-tight, and permit a crossover of currents between the inside and outside of the coaxial line. Such meters will react to changes in out-surface currents, with a constant SWR.

The sensitivity of the SWR to the length of feed line can be a very good test of the effectiveness of a balun in your particular situation. Simply add an extra quarter-wave of feed line, using well-matched coaxial connectors, and see if the SWR varies. The variations with a balun in place should be markedly less than without one.

We can now deal with another well-worn question. Can you avoid the need for a balun by providing a perfect resonant match? The answer is 'NO'. Impedance matching, as measured by the SWR, occurs entirely inside the coaxial cable, where as antenna balance and feed-line radiation happen in the world outside. So SWR and balance are totally separate issues unless they interact at the antenna feed point, the only place where the inside and outside are joined. To stop that interaction, you always need a balun.

Having sorted out those misconceptions about impedance mismatches, which are not really the fault of the balun, what about the genuine mismatch problems caused by the balun itself? Many papers and articles have been written about this, and especially about wire-wound transformer baluns [7–11].

The fact most overlooked by amateur constructors is that the windings of the balun form an extra section of transmission line between the coaxial cable and the antenna. In order to match 50Ω cable to a balanced 50Ω load, the transformer windings must themselves be 50Ω lines.

Now it so happens that two pieces of enamelled wire twisted together, or laid close together and parallel, will make a transmission line with a characteristic impedance of about 50Ω – but not exactly, so some impedance mismatch can arise. Distributed capacitance between the turns of the transformer can cause unwanted resonances, which create impedance mismatches and throw off the balance, and so too can the leakage inductance due to carelessly loose coupling between windings.

We can examine these problems further by looking at a few practical types of balun.

Practical HF transformer baluns

This simplest balun that you will find is a pair of wires wound onto a toroid core, and sometime found as a 1:1 balun in some commercial T tuner ATUs.

If a load which is already well balanced needs to be connected to an unbalanced source, this type of balun will let it happen; but it won't contribute much positive help.

The performance of the 1:1 balun is improved dramatically by adding a third winding as shown earlier in Fig 9.18(a). This provides a necessary current path from end to end of the choke without upsetting the desired voltage and phase relationships. The third (tertiary) winding must have close magnetic coupling with the other two. This is usually achieved by winding all three wires together, either laid parallel or twisted, in a trifilar winding.

G6XN gives some good advice about techniques for wire-wound baluns [10]. Instead of twisting the wires, you could wrap three straight wires together with plumber's PTFE tape as suggested by GM4GSJ, and then wind all three onto the former or core; the tape makes the wires lay down flat and parallel.

A successful alternative to the three-wire 1:1 balun is to for the two main wires to be coaxial, and lay the tertiary winding close alongside as shown in Fig 9.19(a) [7]. This has the advantage of avoiding impedance discontinuities in the main line. The constructional technique, suggested in the original article, was to strip the outer insulation from thin coaxial cable, and to bind the enamelled tertiary wire closely to the coaxial cable using heatshrink sleeving. PTFE tape would work equally well but would require additional waterproofing.

The fact that one wire is inside a coaxial cable, one is outside and the third 'wire' is tubular has no effect on the magnetic coupling between all three. This type of construction is reported to give excellent performance with a particularly good impedance match.

The simple choke balun of Fig 9.16(a) can be improved in a similar way by adding an extra tertiary wire to the coil of coaxial cable. This converts the choke balun into an air-cored version of Fig 9.19(a) [11], which should be suitable for the 14–30MHz range.

Broad-banding and magnetic cores

Most types of HF balun are designed for good broadband performance, typically for use with 3.5–30MHz multi-band dipoles or 14–30MHz beams. The limits on performance are usually expressed in terms of accuracy of amplitude balance from side to side, accuracy of phase angle and SWR. Balance within 1dB, a phase angle of 180±10° and a SWR of less than 1.5 into a balanced load are generally regarded as adequate performance at

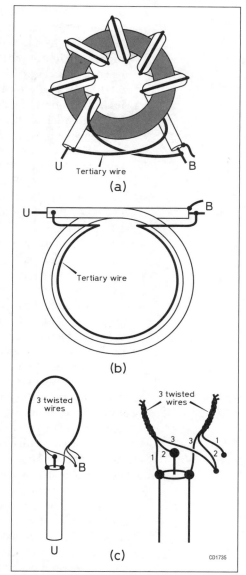

Fig 9.19. (a)Toroidal trifilar balun using coaxial cable plus a tertiary wire. (b) The coaxial choke balun of Fig 9.16 can be improved by adding a tertiary wire. For 14–30MHz make a two-turn coil using 600mm of cable and the same length of wire, plus small additional lengths for connections. (c) Air-cored trifilar 1:1 balun for 14–70MHz by G3KJC. The 50Ω trifilar transmission line is made from three lengths of 1.6mm enamelled copper wire twisted together and formed into a two-turn loop

the edges of the operating band. In fact all of these characteristics tend to be related.

The high-frequency limit of performance is approached when the distributed capacitance of the transmission line becomes series resonant with its leakage inductance [10]. At the series-resonant frequency, somewhere around 50–100MHz for typical HF construction, the balun becomes completely useless, and in practice it should not be used above half that frequency [7]. The lower frequency limit on performance is set by the requirement that the reactance of the inductive winding must be several times the circuit impedance. If we require the reactance to be eight to 10 times 50Ω at 3.5MHz, the inductance of the winding should be 20–25µH. Since a large number of turns would spoil the HF response, a magnetic core is generally used to extend the broad-band performance on the LF side.

Conventional toroidal baluns are generally made with either 10–12 trifilar turns on a 'number 2' iron-dust core of permeability 10, about six turns on a nickel-zinc ferrite core (ρ = 120), or 3–4 turns on a high-permeability ferrite core. With proper construction, all of these baluns can have excellent performance down through 3.5MHz, and may still be going strong at 1.6MHz. However, their performance at 28MHz may deteriorate if either the leakage inductance or the electrical length of poorly matched twisted-wire line are becoming significant; these are potentially more serious problems for the baluns which use greater numbers of turns on a lower-permeability core.

G6XN has pointed out that it is not necessary to use a toroid; six or seven trifilar turns on a medium-wave broadcast type of ferrite rod will work perfectly well and at far less cost [10]. Such a balun has rather less series inductance than the normal toroidal balun, so it shifts the whole performance band upward in frequency. The performance of G6XN's type of balun is excellent, especially on the higher HF bands. G3SEK has built several using six trifilar turns on pieces of scrap ferrite rod. Although originally intended for 14–30MHz, with careful construction they are usable at 50MHz upwards and cost next to nothing.

Poorly matched loads can ruin the performance of a balun, particularly at the HF end of its range where the length of the coiled transmission line may approach an electrical quarter-wave. The resulting high SWR and increased circulating currents can cause saturation of high-permeability ferrites. This in turn can lead to overheating and either temporary or permanent loss of magnetic properties. The solution is to avoid mismatches in the first place – which implies that the output side of an ATU is often not a good place for a balun with a magnetic core – and also to use larger sections of magnetic materials, which are less prone to saturation. A balun wound on a straight ferrite rod is much less prone to saturation than a toroid, because most of its magnetic circuit is 'air gap' rather than ferrite.

The high-frequency balun designed by Roy Church, G3KJC, uses no magnetic core at all. The balun shown in Fig 9.17(c) works from 14MHz to at least 70MHz and is wound on fresh air! A coil of trifilar twisted wire provides plenty of series inductance for these frequencies. The secrets lie in getting the right number of twists per inch to make a good 50Ω transmission line, coiling up the wire to create the necessary series inductance, and making short VHF-type connections between the various windings. The wires are twisted together by holding one end bundle in a vice and the other end in a hand-drill. The wires are then stretched straight and parallel and then the drill then turned to make 20 regularly spaced twists along the 500mm length.

It is virtually impossible to overload or damage this balun by either raw power or high SWR. Having no core, there is nothing to saturate, and the voltage breakdown is limited only by the quality of the enamel – the proto-type survived 3kV DC between adjacent wires! As with any balun, it should be mounted reasonably far from metal objects, particularly those made of magnetic materials.

Testing HF baluns

Low-power tests on HF baluns can be made using a balanced dummy load consisting of two resistors in series. You don't need a professional vector impedance meter or network analyser to tell the difference between a good balun and a poor one. You can measure the SWR of the balun on all the amateur bands in the normal way. Frequency-swept measurements using a general-coverage receiver and a noise bridge can be even more revealing, especially if you can extend them up to about 100MHz, where most HF baluns look extremely sick! By grounding the centre-tap between the two load resistors, you can also measure amplitude balance using a high-impedance RF voltmeter or oscilloscope.

The main high-power test is of insertion loss. Since a high-power bal-anced dummy load may be difficult to arrange, the best way to carry out this test is to make two identical baluns and connect them back-to-back be-tween the transmitter and a normal coaxial dummy load [10]. With the aid of an RF wattmeter you can estimate the power loss in the pair of baluns, though a simpler test is to feel their temperature after a few minutes carry-ing full power. The balun might reasonably become warm to the touch; if it gets really hot, it is either underrated, badly designed or badly constructed.

Which HF balun is best?

The question of choke versus transformer baluns has generated fervent de-bate for years (especially among people who believe that every issue can be resolved by confrontation). So don't expect it to be resolved in a few para-graphs! The underlying question is whether antenna imbalance should be tackled by eliminating feed-line currents or vice versa. Since each follows from the other, like the proverbial chicken and the egg, both answers are equally right – or wrong.

More to the point, W7EL has made some direct comparative tests between choke and transformer baluns in something approximating a real situation. The baluns were inserted between a horizontal 28MHz dipole and a half-wavelength of coaxial feeder [6]. Since the transmitter end of the feeder was well grounded, this feeder length presents a particularly low impedance to surface currents at the feed point and places great demands on the balun. W7EL measured the currents in the dipole at both sides of the feed point, and also the imbalance current on the surface of the coaxial cable. He found that even minor physical asymmetry in the installation resulted in marked electrical asymmetry; and that both types of baluns produced improvements.

Many amateurs have found this for themselves. Whichever type of balun cures your particular problems (such as RF in the shack or EMC), it's good enough. However, in W7EL's experiments the choke balun produced consistently better improvements in balance than the transformer type. This is consistent with the lack of direct effort in the transformer balun to suppress feed-line surface currents. On the other hand, we hear plenty of stories of choke baluns that failed to work too.

The verdict is that either type of balun at the feed point will have a positive effect, but that the 'best HF balun' depends entirely on your particular circumstances and the problem you wish it to cure. Whichever balun you use, you may also need to wind the coaxial cable into additional RF chokes to remove the last traces of outer-surface currents.

VHF and UHF baluns

At VHF and UHF there are generally fewer difficulties with imbalance created by the antenna's surroundings. The problem is usually the difficulty of making a symmetrical junction at the feed point, because the lengths of connecting wires and the necessary gap at the centre of a dipole become significant fractions of the wavelength.

For all its popularity the gamma match is not a balun. It does nothing to create balance between the two sides of a dipole; on the contrary, it relies entirely on electromagnetic coupling between the opposite sides of the dipole to correct the imbalance of the gamma match itself. When used with an all-metal Yagi, the direct connection of the coaxial cable shield to the centre of the dipole invites the resulting imbalance currents to travel along the boom as well as the outer surface of the feedline. G3SEK has used a gamma match successfully at 50 and 70MHz but would not recommend it for 144MHz or above.

The coaxial half-wave balun is definitely the 'best buy' for all VHF/UHF bands up to at least 432MHz – see Fig 9.18(c). It strongly enforces balance, yet it does not introduce an impedance mismatch unless the cable or its length is markedly different from a true electrical half-wavelength. The problem with using this balun is that the feed-point impedance of the antenna must be transformed up to 200Ω. Fortunately, this is often very simple. For example, the highly successful family of DL6WU long Yagis [13] (see Chapter 7) have a feed-point impedance which is close to 50Ω at the centre of the dipole driven element; this impedance can be raised to the necessary 200Ω simply by converting the driven element into a folded dipole. Other alternatives for creating a symmetrical 200Ω feed point impedance include the T match and the delta match [10].

The impedance of the coaxial cable used in a half-wave balun is not important, though characteristic impedance of one-half the load impedance (ie in most cases 100Ω) has been shown to give optimum broad-band balance [12]. Low-loss 100Ω coaxial cable is difficult to obtain, though, and it is perfectly adequate to use good-quality 50Ω cable, carefully cut to length with an allowance for the velocity factor.

THE PA0SE BALUN

This balun design [14], by Dick Rollema, PA0SE, was the solution for feeding an all-band (7MHz to 29MHz) antenna. The feed impedance of this antenna ranged from 33Ω on 7MHz to 560Ω on 29MHz and was highly reactive, although balanced. This ruled out direct single-coaxial cable feed and also the use of ferrite or powdered iron in the baluns. Units with a 4:1 impedance ratio promised a better match to my 17m of RG217/U to the shack than 1:1 baluns, especially on the highest frequencies, where the coaxial cable feeder losses due to mismatch were highest.

How it works

The balun is made from coaxial cable as shown in Fig 9.20(a). Two equal lengths are connected in parallel at their unbalanced left-hand ends and in series at the balanced right-hand ends. Let us assume that instantaneous HF voltage can be measured on the centre pin of the left-hand coaxial cable connector and that this voltage is +100V with respect to earth. The result is +100V on the top balanced terminal and −100V on the bottom balanced terminal, ie 200V between them, balanced with respect to earth.

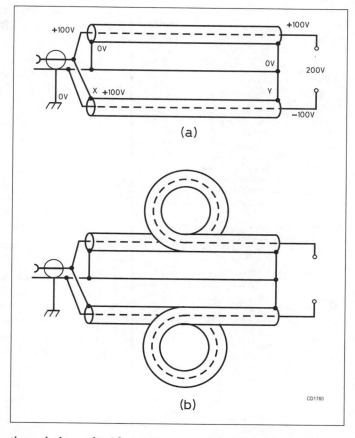

(a)

(b)

Fig 9.20. Principle of the 4:1 coaxial cable balun. Short-circuiting the voltage between X and Y in (a) is remedied by the self-inductance created by coiling the coaxial cable as in (b). The upper coaxial cable is coiled for neatness only

However, with straight lengths of coaxial cable there would be a short-circuit between the +100V at point X and 0V at Y.

This short is eliminated by coiling the lower cable as shown in Fig 9.19(b). Between X and Y there is now the reactance of that coil; if sufficiently high, point X no longer 'sees' point Y and there can be a voltage difference between them. For the top coaxial cable there is no such problem as both ends are at the same potential, but it is coiled for neatness.

This balun produces a 4:1 impedance transformation only if both cables are terminated in their characteristic impedance. PA0SE used 75Ω coaxial cable, so for 'flat' lines a purely resistive, balanced load of 2 × 75 = 150Ω would be required. Looking into the unbalanced end of the balun, an impedance of 75/2 = 37.5Ω would then be seen.

With most antennas the feed impedance is anything but 150Ω resistive. Unless the length of the cables in the balun is short with respect to the wavelength, the balun produces an additional impedance transformation which is largest when the cable lengths are near λ/4. This can add to or subtract from the 4:1 ratio. In the extreme, the impedance at the unbalanced end can even be higher than that of the balanced load! But that does no harm; the balancing action is valid over the whole intended frequency and impedance range.

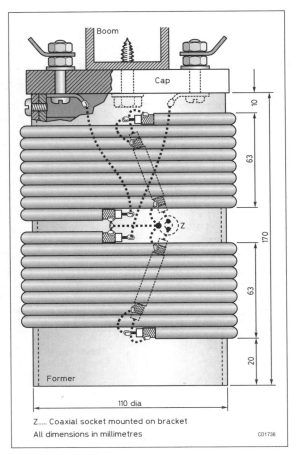

Z..... Coaxial socket mounted on bracket
All dimensions in millimetres   CD1736

Fig 9.21. Construction of a 4:1 balun of 75Ω coaxial cable on a PVC former. The dashed connections are inside the former

Construction

The balun assembly, with dimensions, is shown in Fig 9.21. None of these dimensions or the materials and cable types is critical. The former on the prototype was made of grey 110mm OD PVC waste pipe.

PA0SE used matching end caps for the balanced ends; these are not cemented on but made removable by securing them with three self-tapping stainless steel screws. An N socket (not shown) on a copper bracket is mounted inside the former for connection to the RG213/U coaxial cable feeder at point Z. N connectors are waterproof by design and additionally are sheltered by the former.

On the prototype off-cuts from a 75Ω cable TV installation, whose specification is similar to Uniradio M203, was used.

The balun is made from two equal lengths of cable wound into the two eight-turn coils (note the winding direction). They are held in place by the ends of the bare-wire jumpers, which protrude through snug-fit holes in the former.

At the balanced end of the coils the braids are joined and connected to the N socket outer, via a bare wire jumper. The centre conductors are connected to the balanced terminals using bare wire jumpers (shown with dotted lines). The unbalanced outer ends of the coaxial cable coils are connected by short lengths of coaxial cable inside the former to the N socket.

Note that the inside conductor of the coaxial cable link is connected to the top coil braid and the braid to the inner conductor (on the top coil only).

All coaxial cable ends, solder connections and feed-through holes were fixed and waterproofed with epoxy cement. Three coats of clear yacht varnish protect the completed assembly against ultra-violet light. After four years use, the baluns are as good as new.

MEASURING RESONANT LENGTHS OF COAXIAL CABLE

It is very useful to be able to measure the resonant length (electrical length) of a length of coaxial cable. Sometimes we wish to avoid resonant lengths of transmission line to reduce the effects of antenna currents on the line. On the other hand we need resonant lengths to make a coaxial balun or a phasing network for a directional array or for a circular polarised Yagi. The need for identical electrical lengths of coaxial cable also arises whenever you need to feed two or more antennas in phased arrays.

Usually you need a precise number of electrical half-wavelengths or quarter-wavelengths. The physical lengths of cable required can be anything from say 53m (an electrical half-wavelength on Top Band) down to 40mm, an electrical quarter-wave for 1.3GHz. The obvious method of using a ruler is often not practical. Even if you know the velocity factor of the cable in question, it's often difficult to measure an accurate length, especially if your steel tape is as flexible as the cable itself. You may also want to measure the electrical length of a section of cable that is already part of an antenna installation or a roll of cable on a drum.

All that is required to make the measurement is the station transceiver and SWR meter. Connect the cable to a T-adaptor between the SWR meter and a dummy load as shown in Fig 9.22. The SWR meter is fed from your transmitter, at sufficiently low power that strange load impedances won't damage the transmitter. One or two watts are usually plenty. Without the cable connected at the 'T', the SWR meter 'sees' the matched dummy load, so the indicated SWR should be very low. If you connect a random length of cable at the 'T', its reactance appears in shunt across the dummy load and the SWR will rise. The exception is when the shunt reactance at the end of the cable is very high, almost as high as if the cable were unplugged.

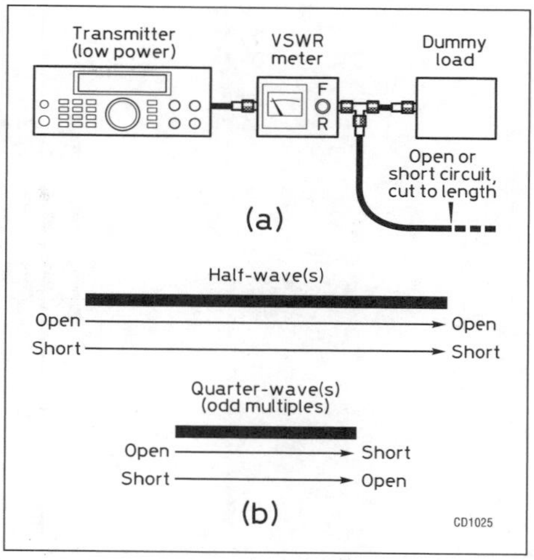

Fig 9.22. (a) Set-up for measuring coaxial cable length using an SWR meter. (b) An electrical half-wave (or any multiple) shows the same impedance at its far end. An electrical quarter-wave (or any odd multiple) shows the 'opposite' at its far end. Also see Fig 9.6

REFERENCES

[1] 'Fitting coaxial connections', Roger Blackwell, G4PMK, *Radio Communication* May 1988.

[2] *The Radio Amateur's Handbook* (any year), ARRL.

[3] *Microwave Measurements and Techniques,* T S Laverghetta, Artech, 1976. (Good advice on cable, connectors and how to fit them. Much useful practical advice on many subjects, not just for microwavers!)

[4] 'In Practice', Ian White, G3SEK, *RadCom* June 1998.

[5] 'Balanced to unbalanced transformers', Ian White, G3SEK, *Radio Communication* December 1989.

[6] 'Baluns: what they do and how they do it', Roy W Lewallen, W7EL, *ARRL Antenna Book*. (W7EL coined the term 'current balun' for the type described in this article as a choke balun, and 'voltage balun' for the transformer type.)

[7] 'High performance broadband balun', John J Nagle, K4KJ, *Ham Radio* February 1980.

[8] *The ARRL Handbook* (all editions), ARRL.

[9] *Transmission Line Transformers*, J Sevick, ARRL.

[10] *HF Antennas for All Locations*, Les Moxon, G6XN, RSGB.

[11] 'Ham radio techniques: a balun for 10 meters', Bill Orr, W6SAI, *Ham Radio* January 1989.

[12] 'The half-wave balun: theory and application', John J Nagle, K4KJ, *Ham Radio* September 1980.

[13] 'High performance long Yagis', Ian White, G3SEK, *Radio Communication* April 1987. See also Chapter 7.

[14] 'Eurotek', Erwin David, G4LQI, *Radio Communication* August 1992.

10 Estimating and measuring antenna performance

THERE are two aspects to this chapter. The first is ascertaining antenna performance from technical articles, manufacturer's information or computer programs. The second consideration is checking the performance of an antenna during or after installation.

ANTENNA TECHNICAL DATA
Impedance
The impedance presented at the feed point by an antenna is a complex function of the size and shape of the antenna, the frequency of operation and its environment. The impedance is affected by the proximity of other conducting objects, where the induction of RF currents alters the impedance through mutual coupling between the antenna and object. The elements of a Yagi antenna are mutually coupled together, and the driven element would present a very different impedance if measured in isolation from the rest of the structure. This is why a single dipole may have an impedance of around 50 to 70Ω and a Yagi driven element is only around 20Ω, requiring a matching arrangement when fed with 50Ω coaxial cable.

Input impedance comprises both resistive and reactive parts. The resistive part is composed of the radiation resistance, which can be thought of as dissipating power by radiating it as electromagnetic energy (desirable), and loss resistance, which dissipates power as heat (not desirable). The reactive part arises from the behaviour of antenna elements as resonators (tuned circuits), and it can change rapidly as the operating frequency is varied.

Impedance bandwidth
Technical data from antenna manufacturers often includes SWR plots with regard to frequency. Indirectly this is showing the variation in impedance of the antenna with frequency and this is known as *impedance bandwidth*. SWR is often quoted to show the 'goodness' of an antenna and, while it may provide valuable information, remember that a 50Ω resistor will give an excellent SWR.

The impedance bandwidth of an antenna is defined as the frequency range over which the antenna impedance results in a SWR less than some arbitrary limit. This may be typically 1.5:1 for amateur operation with solid-state transmitters, or higher values for other applications. Ideally, an antenna should be impedance matched to the feed line and thence to the transmitter or receiver. Although tuned feed arrangements are sometimes used at HF, where a high standing-wave ratio may be acceptable on the feed line, the losses in VHF feeders and tuning components usually preclude this approach at VHF and UHF.

Electrically small antennas for HF with loading inductors tend to give narrow impedance bandwidths, ie the SWR varies sharply with frequency. This does not mean that the antenna performance is poor. A narrow impedance bandwidth means that the Q of the antenna is high but you will have to use an ATU if you want to cover all the band.

With VHF and UHF antennas a low SWR is important because transmission line losses are much greater at these frequencies compared with the HF bands.

Radiation patterns

You will have noticed that many of the antennas in this book have radiation patterns shown in a polar format. Polar plots present the relative field strength or power levels a radial distance from the centre of the graph at the relevant angle. These diagrams were obtained by computer modelling. The following is a description of the use and limitations of radiation patterns.

If you are trying to assess the performance of a commercial antenna from the polar plot produced by the manufacturers then some knowledge of how the latter is produced is useful.

A polar diagram of an antenna can be obtained by *measurement*. This is done by energising the antenna with a known level of RF power and then performing a number of field-strength measurements. These measurements are made at a constant distance in the far field at different angles relative to the antenna under test (AUT). A large number of these measurements would produce a large amount of field-strength measurement data, which could then be plotted into a three-dimensional polar diagram or space pattern. The antenna performance is then determined by comparing it with some reference antenna.

Polar diagrams can also be obtained by *calculation*. Although most of the diagrams you see these days are done using a computer the technique of producing polar diagrams mathematically has been around a long time [1].

Reference antennas

Radiation from a practical antenna never has the same intensity in all directions. For this reason a hypothetical point source antenna has been devised as a reference. This reference antenna, which radiates equally in all directions, is known as an *isotropic radiator*. Because the field strength is the same in all directions it follows that the three-dimensional polar diagram or space pattern of an isotropic radiator is a sphere as shown in Fig 10.1(a). The isotropic radiator is very useful with antenna mathematical modelling, and when used as a reference is given the symbol 'dBi', (dB isotropic).

For practical comparisons a single half-wave dipole is often used as a reference because it is the simplest practical form of radiator. The radiation pattern of a dipole is not uniform and has a power gain of 2.15dBi in the plane of maximum radiation – see Fig 10.1(b). Gain measurement figures,

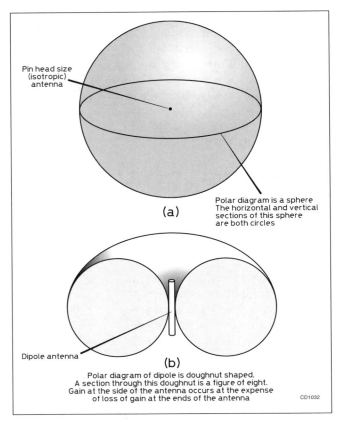

Pin head size
(isotropic)
antenna

Polar diagram is a sphere
The horizontal and vertical
sections of this sphere
are both circles

(a)

Dipole antenna

(b)

Polar diagram of dipole is doughnut shaped.
A section through this doughnut is a figure of eight.
Gain at the side of the antenna occurs at the expense
of loss of gain at the ends of the antenna

CD1032

Fig 10.1. Three-dimensional free-space polar diagrams for an isotropic radiator (a) and a dipole (b)

using the dipole radiator as a reference, are symbolised 'dBd' (dB dipole).

Gain, front-to-back ratio and beamwidth

In practice a full three-dimensional description is usually unnecessary and a section through the three-dimensional space pattern will provide enough information. A useful analogy is the contour line of equal height on a map of a hill, which shows the general shape of the hill.

In the case of a polar diagram the contour line is one of equal signal strength but, like a map contour line, the shape can change depending where the section through the three-dimensional polar diagram is made. In practice two sets of measurements, one vertical (elevation) and the other horizontal (azimuth) are made. When diagrams are produced by calculation they are drawn in space, so that there are no RF obstacles to influence the diagram. A diagram produced this way is called a *free-space diagram*. Like the isotropic antenna, the free-space model is theoretical and only used in antenna mathematical models. A computer-derived free-space azimuth polar diagram of a beam antenna is shown in Fig 10.2.

The *gain* of an antenna in a given direction is the ratio of the radiation intensity in that direction compared with an isotropic source or a dipole. The gain (line A in Fig 10.2) is given as dBi as described above. The *front-to-back ratio* (F/B) is the ratio of forward radiation to radiation from the rear of the beam in dBs; see lines A and B in Fig 10.2.

The *beamwidth* is the width in degrees of the major lobe between the two directions (lines C) at which the relative radiated power is equal to one half its value at the peak of the lobe (half power = 3dB).

Other parameters given in the text of Fig 10.2 will be described later.

Polar diagram plotting scales

The linear scale

This scale was used in most antenna literature, including the *ARRL Antenna Book*, prior to 1982. This scale can only show features from maximum signal strength down about 15 to 20dB or so. The linear plot gives a very optimistic picture of directivity and suppresses the back lobes. Polar diagrams of a dipole and of an array comprising four 19-element Yagis using a linear scale are shown in Fig 10.3.

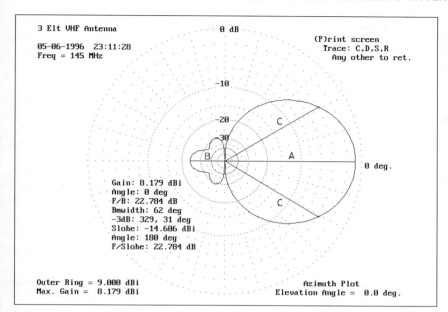

Fig 10.2. Polar diagram showing gain (A), front-to-back ratio (A/B) and 3dB down beamwidth (C)

The linear log scale

If, on the other hand, either of these antennas were connected to a receiver, and a plot were to be made using the receiver S-meter readings, then the plots would probably look more like those shown in Fig 10.4.

Each of these plots has strengths and weaknesses. The linear scale has the advantage of being very sensitive in to changes in level in the region of maximum signal strength and is useful for making gain comparisons between different antennas.

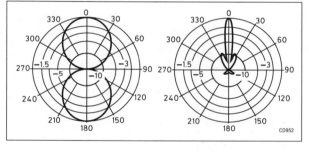

Fig 10.3. Azimuth antenna polar diagrams using a linear voltage plot

A polar diagram plotted on a logarithmic (linear dB) grid, on the other hand, displays a signal level range of at least 80dB. This grid gives a much more accurate picture of how the antenna will perform when connected to the station receiver, and explains why the directivity of a given antenna is often not as good as its published polar diagram might suggest.

The log-periodic polar plot

The ARRL has devised a polar diagram having a log-periodic grid – see Fig 10.5.

Instead of the graduations varying linearly with the log of the field intensity, as shown in Fig 10.4, they vary periodically. The constant of this periodicity is 0.89 for 2dB intervals. This represents a compromise between the extremes of linear and linear decibel grids so far described. It possesses

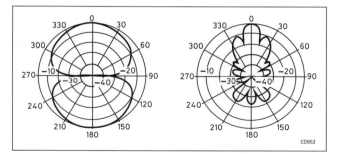

Fig 10.4. Azimuth antenna polar diagrams using a linear-log plot

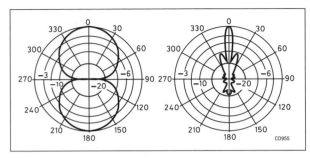

Fig 10.5. Azimuth antenna polar diagrams using the ARRL log-periodic plot

good sensitivity to small changes in maximum signal while at the same time it is able to display the minor lobes.

The effect of ground

Real antennas are always some finite distance from the ground so its effects should be understood. In Chapter 1 the effects of placing a dipole at different heights above ground were considered.

The ground under the antenna acts as a reflector. Electromagnetic waves from the antenna radiate in all directions and some of these waves are reflected by ground.

If the reflected wave is in phase, or partially in phase, with a direct wave it enhances radiation and increases gain at a particular angle. Other combinations of reflected and direct waves, whose phases tend to cancel, reduce gain at other angles.

In Fig 10.6 waves A and C enhance gain while B and C tend to cancel and reduce the gain. This is the cause of the familiar elevation antenna patterns. This aspect is most important and has implications as regards the shape of any azimuth polar diagram of a practical antenna.

Consider the three-dimensional polar diagram of a three-element beam in Fig 10.7(a). If we take a vertical or elevation cross-section of this diagram it produces the familiar vertical diagram shown in Fig 10.7(b).

It is important to consider the height above ground because of the ground effect. If the antenna is over half a wavelength high, several lobes can be produced, so where do we draw a section to make the azimuth diagram? We can't draw it through the true horizontal because of the effect of ground. In fact if you ask an antenna modelling computer program to plot a polar diagram of an antenna above real ground at an elevation angle of zero degrees it will come up with an error message saying that there is no field to plot at zero degrees.

Normally, what is done in practice is to plot the azimuth diagram at the angle of maximum radiation of the main lobe. This section is a cone whose side angle, relative to ground, is that of the angle of maximum radiation. The effect of plotting or calculating the azimuth polar diagram at different angles is shown in Fig 10.8.

It is often thought that a VHF antenna elevation plot is unaffected by ground when placed at its normal operating height. Nothing could be further from the truth as shown in Fig 10.9.

Fig 10.6. A diagram illustrating the effect of ground reflection on directly radiated waves

Manufacturers' data

All manufacturers give some data on their beam antennas. It usually comprises a gain figure and a front-to-back ratio, and perhaps an SWR plot with respect to frequency. Very few match the detailed information produced by Tonna, manufacturers of VHF and UHF beams. I have quoted

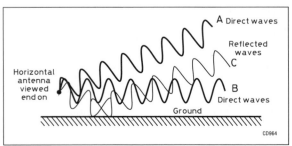

from their catalogue to give the quality of their technical information justice.

I have included an illustration, see Fig 10.10, from a description of their 50MHz beam. It shows free-space E-plane (azimuth) and H-plane (elevation) polar diagrams. It gives the usual SWR curve and, unusually, an impedance plot with frequency plotted on a restricted-range Smith Chart. The text accompanying this and all the other beam data in the catalogue is as follows:

"All the radiation patterns plotted in this catalogue have been generated by computer. They are very close to patterns experimentally recorded on a test range. There are only slight differences in diffuse lobes and rear lobes. Quite often, for a given antenna, the experimental pattern has lower side lobes than the computer generated pattern.

Patterns are plotted on a logarithmic scale having a 40dB dynamic range, whereas in competitors' catalogues, scales are usually 'power linear' or 'voltage linear' (square law), with a maximum dynamic range of 20dB. On a 40dB scale, it is possible to visualise all the diffuse lobes that lie below 20dB from the maximum, and the first side lobe set is greatly magnified: the main lobe looks very broad and is easy to interpret. It must also be pointed out that all minor lobes below 23dB have practically no influence on the efficiency of the antenna.

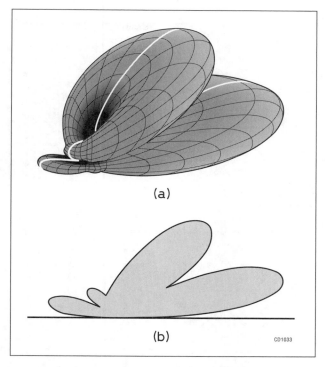

(a)

(b)

CD1033

Fig 10.7. (a) Three-dimensional polar diagram of a three-element beam, showing an elevation section. (b) Elevation diagram resulting from this section

Gains given for each antenna have been computed using numeric integration of the computed E & H radiation patterns. Integration of experimental pattern may yield slightly different values (±0.2 to ±0.5dB); this is mainly due to the fact that experimental side lobes may be differently distributed than computed side lobes. The given gain figures are truly the upper limits of the effective gain of an antenna. On most of the antennas in this catalogue, the efficiency is close to unity below 1GHz, and lies around 0.9 at 1.3GHz.

In the case of the Yagi-Uda antenna fed on a single element, the gain bandwidth is always much broader than the impedance bandwidth; the only data given in this catalogue are the bandwidth limits at the −1dB points. Above the −1dB points, the bandpass is usually very flat, without any practical ripple.

All the listed gains are referred to the isotropic radiator.

SWR plots are experimental recordings. SWR values up to 1.4:1 scarcely affect the overall efficiency of the antenna-and-transmission-line system. All SWR values listed in this catalogue are much lower than this value. This provides a safety margin which 'buffers' random mismatches caused when

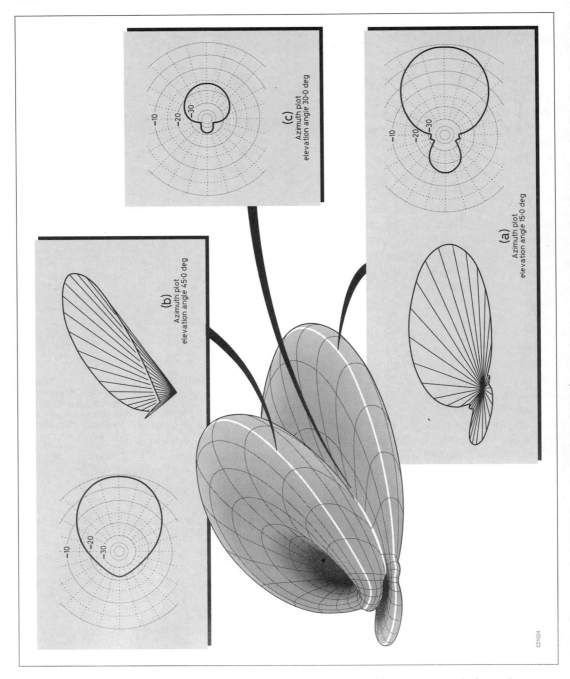

Fig 10.8. (a) Three-dimensional polar diagram of a three-element beam showing a horizontal conical section at the angle of maximum radiation. (b) Diagram at the angle of maximum radiation. (c) Diagram at an angle other than that of maximum radiation

a connector set or a sharp bend is encountered along the transmission line."

It is interesting to note the polar diagram plotting scale, and the reason for this choice of scale, which is very similar to the ARRL scale described above. Technical information of this quality gives one confidence in the product.

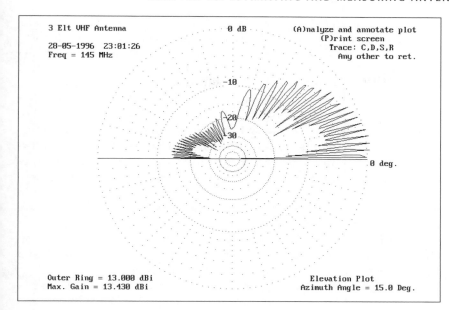

Fig 10.9. Computed elevation plot of a 145MHz three-element beam, 10m high

CHECKING THE PERFORMANCE OF YOUR ANTENNA

On-air tests

The real test of any antenna is just using it. We will assume that you have sorted out all the initial problems of tuning and matching.

If you already have an existing antenna whose performance you are already familiar with, then this is very useful. Initial tests can be done on receive. A coaxial switch is beneficial in this situation, allowing you to switch quickly between antennas and be ahead of propagation fading. It is always useful to have a notebook where all these notes of the comparisons between antennas can be jotted down. Don't use scraps of paper – they soon get lost. If you are operating from a new location with a new antenna then it will take time to know how your antenna is performing.

Ground-wave tests with another station

One of the most frequently used and reliable methods of testing an antenna is with another station some distance away, say 2 to 3km (1 to 2 miles). There are some pitfalls; if the other station is using a

Fig 10.10. Graphic data on the four-element 50MHz antenna from Tonna

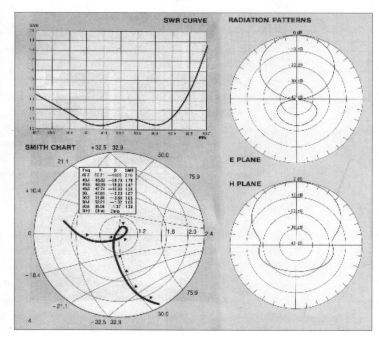

vertical antenna and you are making comparisons with a horizontal and a vertical antenna then the vertical antenna will result in greater signal reports.

Ground-wave tests are particularly useful for obtaining beam antenna gain comparison and directivity data. I noted earlier that if you asked a computer program to plot a polar diagram of an antenna above real ground, at an elevation angle of zero degrees, it will come up with an error message saying that there is no field to plot at zero degrees. A nearby station, a couple of kilometres away, would have an almost zero elevation angle and accordingly would not receive any signal. This is where mathematical modelling and practice do not agree. The real reason why the other station receives a signal (and a strong signal at that) is because the actual situation with respect to ground is far more complex than the simplified model. In practice, when you are testing a beam antenna with a local station, it is easy to get a good indication of the directivity.

Tests can be done at a closer range using low transmitter power or with an attenuator fitted into the antenna feeder of the receiver. The receiver RF gain must be set at maximum for the S-meter to function correctly.

Tests can be conducted at greater distances but it normally requires a higher-gain antenna at the opposite end of the link. Generally, at these greater distances, the S-meter readings are much lower but still provide valuable data if carried out at night when interference via ionospheric propagation is very low.

Tests can also be performed using a HF mobile as the other station. The main advantage of using a mobile is that it can be sited at a distance that is more compatible with transmitter power and AUT gain. It is also easier to select a path free of power and telephone lines, which may disturb the radiation pattern.

The importance of beam antenna optimisation

I have included a few sentences on the adjustment of beam antennas. This is included because it answers one of the most frequently asked questions when I have given lectures at radio clubs.

All installations benefit from some tuning and most well-known DX operators have spent a considerable amount of time adjusting the antenna for maximum efficiency, particularly when a new antenna is constructed. It is almost impossible to get complete reproducibility of any design. All installations are located in different environments, made of slightly different materials and situated at different heights. For example, if you use bare copper wire instead of plastic insulated wire for wire elements it will be necessary to multiply the wire dimension figures, given in the design data on any wire antenna, by 1.04. (Plastic-covered wire appears to have a velocity factor of about 0.96. Try measuring the resonance of two identical lengths of wire, one with insulation and the other without, to check this.) Wire element resonances can also be dependent on types of insulator and methods of connecting the wire to the insulator.

If the performance of an antenna is not optimised, a promising new design can be prematurely abandoned because of an unwarranted inferior performance. Ideally, the antenna should be adjusted in situ. In the case of a VHF antenna it may be adjusted at a height of two or three wavelengths without any difficulty – there will be very little change when it is raised to 10 wavelengths. Adjusting an HF antenna in situ is only possible if the antenna is mounted on top of a flat roof or on a fixed tower with a working platform at the top of it, with the antenna element lengths and feeder matching adjustments easily accessible.

Before an antenna is adjusted ensure that the dimensions of the elements and spacings are correct, by checking the lengths with available design data. If you are working with a new design adjust the driven element to the resonant frequency, the reflector to 5% lower than resonance and directors 5% higher as a starting point.

When measuring the driven element resonance disconnect the feeder and short the feed point. When the feeder cable is connected it may cause many very deep false resonances if the feeder is not terminated correctly.

Metal elements

Elements made of different-diameter telescoped tubes clamped with hose clamps are easy to adjust. Just loosen the clamp and slide the tube to the required length. It is a good idea to make a mark on one of the tubes to provide a reference in case you find it necessary to return to this point during the adjustments.

Wire elements

Often design data does not include the extra length of wire that may be needed to fix it to the insulator. I find the best way of making adjustments is to make the element too long and to fold the excess wire down along the element. In this way the elements can be made adjustable. Tape the excess wire back along the element away from the insulator so it can be cut off when the adjustments are completed as shown in Fig 2.4.

Adjusting an antenna in situ

Adjusting an antenna in situ is relatively simple:

1. Adjust the matching of the antenna to the feeder. If the feeder is connected directly to the element this adjustment is achieved by altering the length of the driven element. If a matching device is used, such as a gamma match, then this should be adjusted. Optimise the matching by aiming for the lowest standing wave ratio using an SWR bridge.
2. Adjust the parasitic elements for maximum front-to-back ratio or maximum gain.
3. Readjust the driven element for the best match to the feeder.

Adjusting an HF antenna on a fold-over mast

It is not possible to adjust an HF antenna on the ground, then install it on top of a mast and hope that it will give optimum performance. In practice, the antenna is adjusted, hauled up into position, then the performance is checked. The antenna is then brought down again for further adjustment. The whole process can be very laborious unless you have a fold-over mast; this is the reason I have detailed the construction of these in Chapter 8.

1. Fold the mast over so that the antenna reflector element is nearest the ground, with the beam pointing upwards. The driven-element matching

system (gamma match) or length adjustment should then be accessible using stepladders.

2. Adjust the driven element as described above in step (1) of 'Adjusting an antenna in situ'.
3. Raise the antenna and check the performance already described.
4. Repeat these adjustments as often as is necessary to optimise the antenna.
5. If the antenna has director element(s), lower the mast so that these elements are nearest the ground. Adjust the length(s), raise the antenna and check the performance. When the parasitic element adjustments are complete, readjust the driven-element feeder matching.
6. All stages of antenna adjustment should be documented, including element lengths and performance. This is essential to follow the trends in change of performance, and to be able to go back to the previous settings if a different set of adjustments is to be tried. Once the antenna is adjusted for optimum performance, record all antenna dimensions, element resonances and performance figures. This information is very important because it is your reference for further work.

TEST EQUIPMENT

Only the bare minimum of test equipment is used in this book. If you are interested in antenna experimenting and using antenna test equipment then read *The Antenna Experimenter's Guide* [2].

The SWR meter

The most basic of all items of antenna test equipment is the SWR meter. As this instrument is to be found in every radio shack there seems little point in describing it here. You can obtain these instruments very cheaply and even CB SWR meters work quite well in the amateur bands. You can check the calibration quite easily. Terminate the antenna connector with a 50Ω non-inductive resistor and the SWR should read 1:1. Repeat with a 25 and a 100Ω resistor and the reading should be 2:1 for both these resistors. You can check the SWR meter with any value resistor between 10 and 250Ω. If the test resistor value is below 50Ω, just divide its value into 50 to get the SWR reading. If the test resistor is above 50Ω just divide its value by 50.

All this assumes that the SWR meter is designed for 50Ω.

These measurements should be done using a transmitter or transceiver with a variable power output control. Use only enough power to make the measurements. Use test resistors that are capable of taking the power, although you can get away with low-power resistors if you make very-short-duration transmissions. If the resistors get hot then the resistance value may change, upsetting the calibration check.

RF current meter

An RF current meter is a fundamental item of antenna equipment. It can be used to measure relative currents in antenna elements and radials. It can also be used to see if there are RF currents flowing on the outside of coaxial cable or other conductors where current should not be flowing.

The design [3] by Dennis Walker, G3OLM, which follows describes how to make an instrument calibrated for 1A FSD and the information given will enable you to construct a meter with any current range.

A system for measuring current should present a low resistance so as to ensure minimum disturbance to the circuit conditions. Low resistance is of course a relative term and in the context of measuring current on antenna wires and transmission lines it is the effective characteristic impedance which determines what is an acceptable value. This characteristic impedance will normally lie in the range 50 to 1000Ω. As long as the current measuring system has an input resistance of not more than 0.5Ω there should be little problem in disturbing the conditions by introducing the system.

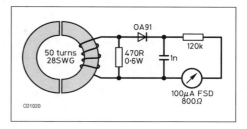

Fig 10.11. Circuit of an RF clamp-on current meter with a FSD of 1A

With the wide availability of small ferrite rings it is possible to take a small current sample in a precise proportion. Rectifying the sample and applying the output to a moving-coil meter provides a predictable and reliable method of current indication which will tolerate large overloads, is linear scaled and will respond quickly. The following is the design of an RF current meter with a full-scale indication of 1A when using a 100µA moving-coil meter.

The essential property of a current transformer is that the ampere-turns on the primary are precisely balanced by the ampere-turns on the secondary. With a single turn on the primary side and 50 turns on the secondary 20mA will be available to circulate in the secondary for each amp of primary current. In dealing with toroid ring cores a 'turn' simply means a pass through the central hole – it does not need to be complete.

The other necessary condition is that the secondary load must be low enough to allow the current to circulate, otherwise the instrument is not a current transformer! A value of 470Ω is suitable as this will reflect into the primary an equivalent resistance of 470/2500 or 0.18Ω which is low enough to meet the conditions outlined above. (Resistance is transformed according to the square of the turns ratio.)

With 20mA circulating in 470Ω gives 9.4V RMS available for rectification corresponding to 13.2V peak. Approximately 0.5V will be lost at the detector diode, leaving a DC voltage of 12.7 to drive the moving-coil meter. To obtain full-scale deflection of 100µA with 12.7V requires a total resistance of 127kΩ. The meter itself will contribute about 800Ω and the nearest standard value is 120kΩ, which will fit the bill with negligible error. A range of different value meter series resistors (or even a multi-meter to replace the resistor and meter) could be used to extend the current range of this instrument.

Finally the effective resistance of the detector circuit will be much greater than the 470Ω so there will be negligible error due to loading here. A circuit of the current meter is shown in Fig 10.11.

REFERENCES

[1] *Radio Engineering*, Terman, 2nd edn, 1937.
[2] *The Antenna Experimenter's Guide*, 2nd edn, Peter Dodd, G3LDO, RSGB, 1996.
[3] 'Current transformers', Dennis Walker, G3OLM, Technical Update, *Radio Communication* November 1995.

Glossary of terms

THIS glossary provides a list of terms used frequently in amateur radio conversation and literature about antennas, and a list of common abbreviations. It is based on the glossary in the *ARRL Antenna Book* and is given here with the ARRL's permission.

With each item is a brief definition of the term. Some of the terms given here are discussed more thoroughly in the text of this book, and may be located by using the contents list or the index.

A index A measure of the geomagnetic disturbance caused by the Sun on a scale 0 to 400.

Actual ground The point within the Earth's surface where effective ground conductivity exists. The depth for this point varies with frequency and the condition of the soil.

Antenna An electrical conductor or array of conductors that radiates signal energy (transmitting) or collects signal energy (receiving).

ATU (antenna tuning unit) A device containing variable reactances (and perhaps a balun). It is connected between the transmitter and the feed point of an antenna system, and adjusted to 'tune' or resonate the system to the operating frequency. Also known as an 'ASTU' (antenna system tuning unit). In the USA an ATU is normally referred to as a 'transmatch'.

Aperture, effective An area enclosing an antenna, on which it is convenient to make calculations of field strength and antenna gain. Sometimes referred to as the 'capture area'.

Apex The feed-point region of a V type of antenna.

Apex angle The included angle between the wires of a V, an inverted-V dipole, and similar antennas, or the included angle between the two imaginary lines touching the element tips of a log-periodic array.

Array A group of radiating elements spaced some distance apart, with the current in each element having a particular amplitude and phase to increase the gain.

Balanced line A symmetrical two-conductor feed line that has uniform voltage and current distribution along its length.

Balun A device for feeding a balanced load with an unbalanced line, or vice versa. May be a form of choke, or a transformer that provides a specific impedance transformation (including 1:1). Often used in antenna systems to interface a coaxial transmission line to the feed point of a balanced antenna, such as a dipole.

Bandwidth The current taken by a resonant antenna, and hence the radiation, falls off as the frequency is varied away from resonance. There will be two frequencies, one above and one below resonance, at which the power will be reduced by half. The difference between these frequencies is termed the 'bandwidth' of the antenna.

Base loading A lumped reactance that is inserted at the base (ground end) of a vertical antenna to resonate the antenna.

Bazooka A transmission line balancer. It is a quarter-wave conductive sleeve (tubing or flexible shielding) placed at the feed point of a centre-fed element and grounded to the shield braid of the coaxial feed line at the end of the sleeve farthest from the feed point. It permits the use of an unbalanced feed line with balanced-feed antennas.

Beamwidth Related to directive antennas. The width, in degrees, of the major lobe between the two directions at which the relative radiated power is equal to one half its value at the peak of the lobe (half power = −3dB).

Broadside array A broadside source has maximum radiation normal to its axis. A representative broadside array is a collinear array of horizontal array dipoles.

Bridge A circuit with two or more ports that is used in measurements of impedance, resistance or standing waves in an antenna system. When the bridge is adjusted for a balanced condition, the unknown factor can be determined by reading its value on a calibrated scale or meter.

Capacitance hat A conductor of large surface area that is connected at the high-impedance end of an antenna to effectively increase the electrical length. It is sometimes mounted directly above a loading coil to reduce the required inductance for establishing resonance. It usually takes the form of a series of wheel spokes or a solid circular disc.

Capture area See 'aperture'.

Centre fed Transmission-line connection at the electrical centre of an antenna radiator.

Centre loading A scheme for inserting inductive reactance (coil) at or near the centre of an antenna element for the purpose of lowering its resonant frequency. Used with elements that are less than a quarter wavelength at the operating frequency.

Characteristic impedance The relationship of current and voltage on a transmission line caused by the distributed inductance and capacitance. Most coaxial cable has a characteristic impedance of 50Ω.

Coax See 'coaxial cable'.

Coaxial cable Any of the coaxial transmission lines that have the outer shield (solid or braided) on the same axis as the inner or centre conductor. The insulating material can be air, helium or solid-dielectric compounds.

Collinear array A linear array of radiating elements (usually dipoles) with their axes arranged in a straight line. Popular at VHF and above.

Common mode signal Signal of similar amplitude and phase on both wires of a transmission line or input to an amplifier (as opposed to the normal anti-phase signal)

Conductor A metal body such as tubing, rod or wire that permits current to travel continuously along its length.

Counterpoise A wire or group of wires mounted close to ground, but insulated from ground, to form a low-impedance, high-capacitance path to ground. Used at MF and HF to provide an RF ground for an antenna. Also see 'ground plane'.

Current loop A point of current maxima (antinode) on an antenna.

Current node A point of current minima on an antenna.

D layer The lowest of the ionised layers of the ionosphere.

Decibel A logarithmic power ratio, abbreviated to 'dB'. May also represent a voltage or current ratio if the voltages or currents are measured across (or through) identical impedances. Suffixes to the abbreviation indicate references: dBi, isotropic radiator; dBd, dipole; dBm, milliwatt; dBW, watt.

Delta loop A full-wave loop shaped like a triangle or delta.

Delta match Centre-feed technique used with radiators that are not split at the centre. The feed line is fanned near the radiator centre and connected to the radiator symmetrically. The fanned area is delta shaped.

Dielectrics Various insulating materials used in antenna systems, such as found in insulators and transmission lines.

Differential capacitor Similar to split-stator capacitor but arranged so that the capacitance on one side increases and the other side decreases as the moving vanes are rotated.

Dipole An antenna that is split at the exact centre for connection to a feed line. A resonant dipole is usually a half-wavelength long. A multi-band dipole is usually fed with tuned feeders.

Directivity The property of an antenna that concentrates the radiated energy to form one or more major lobes.

Director A conductor placed in front of a driven element to cause directivity. Frequently used singly or in multiples with Yagi or cubical-quad beam antennas.

Doublet A dipole.

Driven array An array of antenna elements, which are all driven or excited by means of a transmission line, usually to achieve directivity.

Driven element An element connected to the transmitter/receiver via a transmission line.

Driven element A radiator element of an antenna system to which the transmission line is connected.

Dummy load A resistor used to provide a non-radiating substitute for an antenna for testing transmitters or transmission line test equipment.

E layer The ionospheric layer nearest the Earth from which radio signals can be reflected to a distant point, generally a maximum of 2000km (1250 miles).

E plane Related to a linearly polarised antenna, the plane containing the electric field vector of the antenna and its direction of maximum radiation. For terrestrial antenna systems, the direction of the E plane is also taken as the polarisation of the antenna. The E plane is at right-angles to the H plane.

Effective radiated power (ERP) For a lossy low-frequency antenna the power dissipated in the radiation resistance when other losses have been taken into consideration. For omnidirectional vertical antennas the more common term is 'ERMP' (effective radiated monopole radiated power). For HF, and particularly VHF/UHF, the power supplied to the antenna multiplied by the relative gain of the antenna in the direction of maximum radiation. The term 'EIRP' (effective isotropic radiated power) is also used, taking the gain of the antenna into account as referenced to an isotropic antenna.

Efficiency The ratio of useful output power to input power, determined in antenna systems by losses in the system, including in nearby objects.

Elements The conductive parts of an antenna system that determine the antenna characteristics. For example, the reflector, driven element and directors of a Yagi antenna.

End effect A condition caused by capacitance at the ends of an antenna element. Insulators and related support wires contribute to this capacitance and lower the resonant frequency of the antenna. The effect increases with conductor diameter and must be considered when cutting an antenna element to length.

Endfed An end-fed antenna is one to which power is applied at one end, rather than at some point between the ends.

Endfire antenna An endfire source has maximum radiation along the linear axis; a representative endfire array is the Yagi antenna.

EZNEC Computer program for calculating the performance of an antenna, see Appendix.

F layer The ionospheric layer that lies above the E layer. Radio waves can be refracted from it to provide communications distances of several thousand miles by means of single- or double-hop skip.

Feed line See 'feeders'.

Feed point The point where the feeder is connected to the antenna element

Feed impedance The impedance of an antenna at the point where it is connected to the feeder.

Feeders Transmission lines of assorted types that are used to route RF power from a transmitter to an antenna, or from an antenna to a receiver.

Field strength The intensity of a radio wave as measured at a point some distance from the antenna. This measurement is usually made in microvolts per metre.

Free space A term used where antenna performance calculations are simplified by ignoring the effect of ground.

Front to back The ratio of the radiated power off the front and back of a directive antenna. For example, a dipole would have a ratio of 1, which is equivalent to 0dB.

Front to side The ratio of radiated power between the major lobe and that 90° off the front of a directive antenna.

Gain The increase in effective radiated power in the desired direction of the major lobe compared with a reference, such as a dipole or an isotropic source.

Gamma match A matching system used with driven antenna elements to effect a match between the transmission line and the feed point of the antenna. It consists of a series capacitor and an arm that is mounted close to the driven element and in parallel with it near the feed point.

Grid dip oscillator Grid (or gate) dip oscillator, an instrument for measuring element resonance.

Ground plane A system of conductors placed beneath an elevated antenna to serve as an earth ground. Also see 'counterpoise'.

Ground screen A wire mesh counterpoise.

Ground wave Radio waves that travel along the Earth's surface.

H plane Related to a linearly polarised antenna. The plane containing the magnetic field vector of an antenna and its direction of maximum radiation. The H plane is at right-angles to the E plane.

Hairpin match A U-shaped conductor that is connected to the two inner ends of a split dipole for the purpose of creating an impedance match to a balanced feeder.

Harmonic antenna An antenna that will operate on its fundamental frequency and the harmonics of the fundamental frequency for which it is designed. A 7MHz dipole operating on 21MHz is an example.

Helical A helically wound antenna, one that consists of a spiral conductor. If it has a very large winding length to diameter, it provides broadside radiation. If the length-to-diameter ratio is small, it will operate in the axial mode and radiate off the end opposite the feed point. The polarisation will be circular for the axial mode, with left or right circularity, depending on whether the helix is wound clockwise or counterclockwise.

Impedance The ohmic value of an antenna feed point, matching section or transmission line. An impedance almost always contains reactance, and is normally expressed as $R \pm jX$, which means resistance and either + reactance (inductive) or – reactance (capacitive).

Inverted V Any antenna erected in the form of an upside-down V; normally with the feed point at the apex.

Isotropic An imaginary or hypothetical point-source antenna that radiates equal power in all directions. It is used as a reference for the directive characteristics of actual antennas.

K index A measure of the geomagnetic disturbance caused by the Sun on a scale 0 to 9.

Lambda Greek symbol λ used to represent a wavelength with reference to electrical dimensions.

Line loss The power lost in a transmission line, usually expressed in decibels.

Line of sight Transmission path of a wave that travels directly from the transmitting antenna to the receiving antenna.

Litz wire Stranded wire with individual strands insulated from each other. Used to reduce RF losses in lower-frequency inductors.

Load The electrical entity to which power is delivered. The antenna system is a load for the transmitter.

Loading The process of a transferring power from its source to a load. The effect a load has on a power source.

Lobe A defined field of energy that radiates from a directive antenna.

Log periodic antenna A broad-band directive antenna that has a structural format causing its impedance and radiation characteristics to repeat periodically as the logarithm of frequency.

Long wire A wire antenna that is one wavelength or greater in electrical length. When two or more wavelengths long it provides gain and a multi-lobe radiation pattern. When terminated at one end it becomes essentially unidirectional off that end.

Marconi antenna A shunt-fed monopole operated against ground or a radial system.

Matching The process of effecting an impedance match between two electrical circuits of unlike impedance. One example is matching a transmission line to the feed point of an antenna. Maximum power transfer to the load (antenna system) will occur when a matched condition exists.

Monopole Literally, one pole, such as a vertical radiator operated against the earth or a counterpoise.

Null A condition during which an electrical unit is at a minimum. The null in an antenna radiation pattern is that point in the 360° pattern where a minima in field intensity is observed. An impedance bridge is said to be 'nulled' when it has been brought into balance, with a null in the current flowing through the bridge arm.

Open-wire line A type of transmission line that resembles a ladder, sometimes called 'ladder line'. Consists of parallel, symmetrical wires with insulating spacers at regular intervals to maintain the line spacing. The dielectric is principally air, making it a low-loss type of line.

Parasitic element An element which is not connected directly to the transmitter/receiver via a transmission line, but which receives its energy by the coupling due to the proximity of other elements.

Parasitic array A directive antenna that has a driven element and at least one independent parasitic element (director or reflector), or a combination of both. A Yagi antenna is one example of a parasitic array.

Phasing lines Sections of transmission line that are used to ensure the correct phase relationship between the elements of a driven array or between bays of an array of antennas. Also used to effect impedance transformations while maintaining the desired phase.

Polarisation The sense of the wave radiated by an antenna, by convention is aligned with the E field of an electromagnetic wave. This can be horizontal, vertical, elliptical or circular (left- or right-hand circularity), depending on the design and application.

Q section Term used in reference to transmission-line matching transformers and phasing lines.

Quad A parasitic array using rectangular or diamond shaped full-wave wire loop elements. Often called the 'cubical quad'.

Radiation pattern The radiation characteristics of an antenna as a function of space co-ordinates. Normally, the pattern is measured in the far-field region and is represented graphically.

Radiation resistance The ratio of the power radiated by an antenna to the square of the RMS antenna current, referred to a specific point and assuming no losses. The effective resistance at the antenna feed point.

Radiator A discrete conductor that radiates RF energy in an antenna system.

Random wire A random length of wire used as an antenna and fed at one end and resonated by means of an ATU.

Reflector A parasitic antenna element or a metal assembly that is located behind the driven element to enhance forward directivity. Hillsides and large man-made structures such as buildings and towers may act as reflectors.

Refraction Process by which a radio wave is bent and returned to earth from an ionospheric layer or other medium after striking the medium.

Resonator In antenna terminology, a loading assembly consisting of a coil and a short radiator section. Used to lower the resonant frequency of an antenna, usually a vertical or a mobile whip.

Radiation pattern The radiation characteristics of an antenna as a function of space co-ordinates. Normally, the pattern is measured in the far-field region and is represented graphically.

Shunt feed A method of feeding an antenna driven element with a parallel conductor mounted adjacent to a low impedance point on the radiator. Frequently used with grounded quarter-wave vertical antennas to provide an impedance match to the feeder. Series feed is used when the base of the vertical is insulated from ground.

Solar flux A measure of solar activity, on a scale 66 to 300, obtained by measuring the noise from the Sun on 2800MHz.

Split-stator capacitor Variable capacitor with two sets of fixed plates and one variable set. Often used for tuning small loop antennas.

Stacking The process of placing similar directive antennas atop or beside one another, forming a 'stacked array'. Stacking provides more gain or directivity than a single antenna.

Stub A section of transmission line used to tune an antenna element to resonance or to aid in obtaining an impedance match.

Surge impedance See 'Characteristic impedance'.

SWR Standing-wave ratio on a transmission line caused by the line being mismatched. When the line is perfectly matched the SWR is 1:1. Where only the voltage component of the reflected wave is measured (ie when using a neon indicator) it is called 'VSWR' (voltage standing-wave ratio).

SWR analyser Self-contained instrument for measuring SWR. Later models are also able to measure impedance.

Tank circuit A parallel-tuned circuit in a power amplifier or ATU.

T match Method for matching a transmission-line to an unbroken driven element. Attached at the electrical centre of the driven element in a T-shaped manner. In effect it is a double gamma match.

Top loading Addition of a reactance (usually a capacitance hat) at the end of an antenna element opposite the feed point to increase the electrical length of the radiator.

Transmatch See ATU.

Trap Parallel L-C network inserted in an antenna element to provide multi-band operation with a single conductor.

Tuned feeder A transmission line that provides a designed degree of impedance transformation, in addition to its primary purpose of conveying RF energy with minimal radiation.

Valve Thermionic amplifying device, known as a 'tube' in the USA.

Velocity factor The ratio of the velocity of radio wave propagation in a dielectric medium to that in free space. When cutting a transmission line to a specific electrical length, the velocity factor of the particular line must be taken into account.

VSWR Voltage standing-wave ratio. See 'SWR'.

WARC bands Frequency bands 10.100–10.150MHz, 18.068–18.168MHz and 24.890–24.990MHz.

Wave A disturbance or variation that is a function of time or space, or both, transferring energy progressively from point to point. A radio wave, for example.

Wave angle The angle above the horizon of a radio wave as it is launched from or received by an antenna.

Wavefront A surface that is a locus of all the points having the same phase at a given instant in time.

Yagi A directive, gain type of antenna that utilises a number of parasitic directors and a reflector. Named after one of the two Japanese inventors (Yagi and Uda).

Z match A multi-band ATU derived from the link-coupled PA tank circuit.

Zepp antenna A half-wave wire antenna that operates on its fundamental and harmonics. It is fed at one end by means of open-wire feeders. The name evolved from its popularity as an antenna on Zeppelins.

Abbreviations

A	ampere	dBi	decibels referenced to isotropic
AC	alternating current	dBm	decibels referenced to one
AM	amplitude modulation		milliwatt
ARRL	American Radio Relay League	dBW	decibels referenced to one watt
AWG	American wire gauge	DC	direct current
Az-el	azimuth-elevation	deg	degree
Balun	balanced to unbalanced	DF	direction finding
BC	broadcast	DPDT	double pole, double throw
BCI	broadcast interference	DPST	double pole, single throw
BW	bandwidth	DVM	digital voltmeter
cm	centimetre	DX	long-distance communication
Coax	coaxial cable	E	ionospheric layer, electric field
CT	centre tap	EIRP	effective isotropic radiated
CW	continuous wave		power
dB	decibel	ELF	extremely low frequency
dBd	decibels referenced to a dipole	EMC	electromagnetic compatibility

EME	Earth-Moon-Earth		NO	normally open
EMF	electromotive force		OD	outside diameter
ERP	effective radiated power		P-P	peak to peak
F	farad		PC	printed circuit
F	frequency		PEP	peak envelope power
F	ionospheric layer,		pF	picofarad
F/B	front to back (ratio)		Q	tuned circuit figure of merit
FM	frequency modulation		R	resistance, resistor
ft	foot or feet (unit of length)		RF	radio frequency
F1	ionospheric layer		RFC	radio frequency choke
F2	ionospheric layer		RFI	radio frequency interference
GDO	grid- or gate-dip oscillator		RHCP	right-hand circular polarisation
GHz	gigahertz		RLC	resistance-inductance-
GND	ground			capacitance
H	henry		PMR	private mobile radio
H	magnetic field		RMS	root mean square
HF	high frequency (3–30MHz)		RSGB	Radio Society of Great Britain
Hz	hertz (unit of frequency)		s	second
I	current		S	siemen
ID	inside diameter		S/NR	signal-to-noise ratio
IEEE	Institute of Electrical and		SINAD	signal-to-noise and distortion
	Electronic Engineers		SPDT	single pole, double throw
IEE	Institution of Electrical		SPST	single pole, single throw
	Engineers		SWR	standing wave ratio
in	inch		TPI	turns per inch
j	vector notation		TR	transmit-receive
kHz	kilohertz		TVI	television interference
km	kilometre		UHF	ultra high frequency (300–
kW	kilowatt			3000MHz)
kΩ	kilohm		UTC	Universal Time, Coordinated
L	inductance		V	volt
lb	pound (unit of mass)		VF	velocity factor
LF	low frequency (30–300kHz)		VHF	very high frequency (30–
LHCP	left-hand circular polarisation			300MHz)
In	natural logarithm		VLF	very low frequency (3–30kHz)
log	common logarithm		VOM	volt-ohm meter
LP	log periodic		VSWR	voltage standing-wave ratio
LPDA	log periodic dipole array		VTVM	vacuum-tube voltmeter
LPVA	log periodic V array		W	watt
LUF	lowest usable frequency		WARC	World Administrative Radio
m	metre (unit of length)			Conference
mA	milliampere		WPM	words per minute
max	maximum		X	reactance
MDF	medium-density fibreboard		Z	impedance
MF	medium frequency (0.3–3MHz)			
mH	millihenry			

Other symbols and Greek letters

MHz	megahertz		°	degree
min	minimum		λ	wavelength
mm	millimetre		μ	permeability
ms	millisecond		μF	microfarad
mS	millisiemen		μH	microhenry
MUF	maximum usable frequency		μV	microvolt
mW	milliwatt		Ω	ohm
MΩ	megohm		π	3.14159
NBS	National Bureau of Standards		pF	picofarad
NC	no connection, normally closed		mH	millihenry
NiCd	nickel cadmium		nF	nanofarad

Appendix

RESONANT DIPOLE LENGTHS

Table A.1 gives the equivalent wavelengths and half-wavelengths for given frequencies in metric and imperial units. Half-wavelengths for centre-fed dipole or vertical antennas, described in Chapter 2, are also given in metric and imperial units and are calculated using EZNEC.

Most antenna books use the formula $143/f$ (MHz) = L (metres) or $468/f$ (MHz) = L (feet). This gives a close enough approximation on the higher-frequency bands but may be a bit short for the lower bands. For example the formula gives a dipole length of 40.6m for 3.52MHz while EZNEC calculates a length of 41.42m for the same frequency.

Remember these lengths are total lengths – the wire has to be cut in half at the centre to connect the coaxial cable and that the gap in the centre is part of the whole dipole length. You also need to be aware around 160mm (6in) at each end of each half of the dipole elements is required to connect them to the centre insulator and the end insulator.

When a larger-diameter conductor is used for the antenna element then the length has to be reduced by an amount known as the *K factor* (based on the length-to-diameter ratio). For example, the calculated length for a

Freq (MHz)	λ (m)	λ (ft/in)	λ/2 (m)	λ/2 (ft/in)	Dipole (m*)	Dipole (ft/in*)	Dipole (m#)	Dipole (ft/in#)
1.83	163.82	537'6"	81.91	268'9"	80	262'	–	–
1.9	157.78	517'8"	78.89	259'10"	77	260'7"	–	–
3.52	85.17	279'5"	42.58	139'8"	41.56	135'10"	–	–
3.65	82.13	269'6"	41.07	134'9"	40.08	131'6"	–	–
7.02	42.7	140'1"	21.35	70'0"	20.76	68'2"	–	–
10.125	29.61	97'2"	14.8	48'7"	14.4	47'2"	14.2	46'7"
14.05	21.34	70'0"	10.67	35'0"	10.35	33'11"	10.20	33'5"
14.20	21.11	69'3"	10.55	34'10"	10.24	33'7"	10.09	33'1"
18.1	16.56	54'4"	8.28	27'2"	8.03	26'4"	7.88	25'10"
21.05	14.24	46'9"	7.12	23'5"	6.9	22'8"	6.78	22'3"
21.2	14.14	46'5"	7.07	23'3"	6.86	22'6"	6.73	22'1"
24.94	12.62	39'6"	6.31	19'9"	5.82	19'1"	5.70	18'8"
28.05	10.69	35'0"	5.34	17'6"	5.18	17'0"	5.05	16'7"
28.4	10.56	34'8"	5.28	17'4"	5.1	16'8"	4.99	16'4"
29.5	10.16	33'4"	5.08	16'9"	4.9	16'1"	4.80	15'9"

Table A.1. Wavelengths and half–wavelengths, together with resonant lengths for dipoles relative to frequency for the HF bands

' = ft, " = in. The dipole lengths * are calculated for a wire diameter of 2mm. The dipole lengths # are calculated for a tube diameter of 25mm.

Table A.2. Half-wavelengths and resonant lengths for dipoles relative to frequency for the VHF/UHF bands

Freq (MHz)	λ/2 (mm)	λ/2 (in)	Dipole (mm*)	Dipole (in*)	Dipole (m#)	Dipole (in#)
50.5	2968	116.9	2878	113.3	2842	111.9
51.5	2911	114.6	2822	111.1	2803	110.4
70.25	2133	84	2062	81.2	2031	79.96
144.5	1037	81.70	1000	39.37	980	38.54
145.5	1033	81.34	997	39.24	972	38.27
431	347.8	13.7	331.5	13.05	321	12.62
433	346.2	13.69	330	12.99	319	12.57
435	344.6	13.56	328	12.93	317	12.50

Dipole lengths * are calculated for a wire diameter of 1mm. Dipole lengths # are calculated for a tube diameter of 6mm.

dipole for 21.2MHz is 6.86m, or 22ft 6in. If the conductor diameter is increased from 2mm to 25mm (1in) then the total length should be reduced to 6.73m (22ft 1in).

This can influence the design when making a vertical antenna with the top element of 25mm diameter tube and the lower element(s) of wire. You should use the appropriate column for determining the length. Remember that these figures are for a half-wave antenna. For a ground-plane antenna on 21.2MHz the top quarter-wave 25mm-diameter section should be 6.73/2 = 3.36m. The lower wire radials are 6.86/2 = 3.43m.

In practice tubular elements are best constructed using different diameter telescopic sections. This makes it easy to adjust the length on test for minimum SWR.

VHF/UHF dipole lengths are shown in Table A.2 for 1mm wire or 6mm tube.

METRIC/IMPERIAL UNIT CONVERSION FACTORS

Table A.3. Length and weight conversions

Metric unit	Factor	Imperial unit
mm	25.4	in
cm	2.54	in
cm	30.48	ft
m	0.3048	ft
m	0.9144	yard
km	1.609	mile
g	28.349	oz
kg	0.45359	lb

Metric unit = Factor *multiplied* by imperial unit. Metric unit *multiplied* by Factor = imperial unit

POWER AND VOLTAGE RATIOS IN DECIBELS

Power and voltage ratios are normally expressed in decibels where:

$$N \text{ (dB)} = 10 \log 10 \, (P_2/P_1) \text{ or } N \text{ (dB)} = 20 \log 10 \, (V_2/V_1)$$

Table A.4. Power and voltage ratios

Voltage ratio (equal Z)	Power ratio	Voltage ratio (equal Z)	Power ratio	+ or − dB
1.000	1.000	1.000	1.000	0
0.989	0.977	1.012	1.023	0.1
0.977	0.995	1.023	1.047	0.2
0.966	0.933	1.035	1.072	0.3
0.955	0.912	1.047	1.096	0.4
0.944	0.891	1.059	1.122	0.5
0.933	0.871	1.072	1.148	0.6
0.923	0.851	1.084	1.175	0.7
0.912	0.832	1.098	1.202	0.8
0.902	0.813	1.109	1.230	0.9
0.891	0.794	1.122	1.259	1.0
0.841	0.708	1.189	1.413	1.5
0.794	0.631	1.259	1.585	2.0
0.750	0.562	1.334	1.778	2.5
0.708	0.501	1.413	1.995	3.0
0.668	0.447	1.496	2.239	3.5
0.631	0.398	1.585	2.512	4.0
0.596	0.335	1.679	2.818	4.5
0.562	0.316	1.778	3.162	5.0
0.531	0.282	1.884	3.548	5.5
0.501	0.251	1.995	3.981	6.0
0.473	0.224	2.113	4.467	6.5
0.447	0.200	2.239	5.012	7.0
0.422	0.178	2.371	5.623	7.5
0.398	0.158	2.512	6.310	8.0
0.376	0.141	2.661	7.079	8.5
0.355	0.126	2.818	7.943	9.0
0.335	0.112	2.985	8.913	9.5
0.316	0.100	3.162	10.00	10
0.282	0.0794	3.550	12.6	11
0.251	0.0631	3.980	15.9	12
0.224	0.0501	4.47	20.0	13
0.200	0.0398	5.01	25.1	14
0.178	0.0316	5.62	31.6	15
0.159	0.0251	6.31	39.8	16
0.141	0.0200	7.08	50.1	17
0.126	0.0159	7.94	63.1	18
0.112	0.0126	8.91	79.4	19
0.100	0.0100	10.0	100.0	20
3.16×10^{-2}	10^{-3}	31.6	10^3	30
10^{-2}	10^{-4}	100	10^4	40
3.16×10^{-3}	10^{-5}	316	10^5	50

P_2 and P_1 are power ratios being compared. V_2 and V_1 are voltage ratios being compared; a constant impedance is assumed.

A value in decibels only has absolute meaning if the reference level is stated. The expressions dBm and dBw are frequently used for ratios with respect to 1mW and 1W respectively. A power level of 1mW into 50 or 600Ω has become the standard for comparative purposes and has been given the datum 0dBm. Signal levels above and below this datum are expressed in +dBm and −dBm respectively; they correspond to finite voltage or current levels – not ratios.

0dBm into 600Ω resistance corresponds to 0.775V while 0dBm into 50Ω resistance corresponds to 0.225V.

WIRE GAUGES

Table A.5. Wire gauge table				
	SWG		AWG	
Wire No	(in)	(mm)	(in)	(mm)
0000	0.40	10.16	0.460	11.68
000	0.372	9.45	0.409	10.41
00	0.348	8.84	0.365	9.27
0	0.324	8.23	0.325	8.25
1	0.300	7.62	0.289	7.35
2	7.276	7.01	0.258	6.54
3	0.252	6.40	0.229	5.83
4	0.232	5.89	0.204	5.19
5	0.212	5.38	0.182	4.62
6	0.192	4.88	0.162	4.11
7	0.176	4.47	0.144	3.66
8	0.160	4.06	0.128	3.26
9	0.144	3.66	0.144	2.90
10	0.128	3.25	0.102	2.59
11	0.116	2.95	0.091	2.30
12	0.104	2.64	0.081	2.05
13	0.092	2.34	0.072	1.83
14	0.081	2.03	0.064	1.63
15	0.072	1.83	0.057	1.45
16	0.064	1.63	0.051	1.29
17	0.056	1.42	0.045	1.15
18	0.048	1.22	0.040	1.02
19	0.040	1.02	0.036	0.91
20	0.036	0.92	0.032	0.81
21	0.032	0.81	0.028	0.72
22	0.028	0.71	0.025	0.64
23	0.024	0.61	0.023	0.57
24	0.023	0.56	0.020	0.51
25	0.020	0.51	0.018	0.45
26	0.018	0.46	0.016	0.40
27	0.016	0.41	0.014	0.36
28	0.014	0.38	0.013	0.32
29	0.013	0.35	0.011	0.29
30	0.012	0.305	0.010	0.25
31	0.011	0.29	0.009	0.23
32	0.0106	0.27	0.008	0.20
33	0.010	0.254	0.007	0.18
34	0.009	0.229	0.0063	0.16
35	0.008	0.203	0.0056	0.14
36	0.007	0.178	0.0050	0.13
37	0.0067	0.17	0.0044	0.11
38	0.006	0.15	0.0040	0.10
39	0.005	0.127	0.0035	0.08

SWG = Standard Wire Gauge, AWG = American Wire Gauge

COIL WINDING DATA

Most inductors for tuning in the HF bands are single-layer coils and they are designed as follows. The inductance of a single-layer coil is given by:

$$L \text{ (μH)} = \frac{D^2 \times T^2}{457.2 \times D + 1016 \times L}$$

where D is the diameter of the coil (millimetres), T is the number of turns and L is the length (millimetres). Alternatively:

$$L \ (\mu H) = \frac{R^2 \times T^2}{9 \times R + 10 \times L}$$

where R is the radius of the coil (inches), T is the number of turns and L is the length (inches).

Note that when a ferrite or iron dust core is used, the inductance will be increased by up to twice the value without the core. The choice of which to use depends on frequency. Generally, ferrite cores are used at the lower HF bands and iron dust cores at the higher. At VHF, the iron dust cores are usually coloured purple. Cores need to be moveable for tuning but fixed thereafter and this can be done with a variety of fixatives. A strip of flexible polyurethane foam will do.

Designing inductors with ferrite pot cores

This is a simple matter of taking the 'factor' given by the makers and multi-plying it by the square of the number of turns.

Example

A RM6-S pot core in 3H1 grade ferrite has a 'factor' of 1900 nanohenrys for one turn. Therefore 100 turns will give an inductance of:

$$100^2 \times 1900nH = 10000 \times 1900nH = 19mH$$

There are a large number of different grades of ferrite; for example, the same pot as above is also available in grade 3E4 with a 'factor' of 3300. Manufac-turers' literature should be consulted to find these 'factors'.

ANTENNA MODELLING PROGRAMS

EZNEC, described in Chapter 8, can be obtained from Roy Lewallen, W7EL, PO Box 6658, Beaverton, Oregon 97007, USA. At the time of writing (early 2000) the price is $89. Add $3 outside US/Canada. VISA and MASTERCARD accepted.

ANTENNA ANALYSERS

In the UK the MFJ-259B and MFJ-259MkII is available from: Waters and Stanton, 22 Main Road, Hockley, Essex, SS5 4QS. Tel: 01702 206835.

The MFJ-259MkII is also available from: Haydon Communications, 132 High Street, Edgware, Middlesex, HA8 7EL.

The Autek RF1 (1.2–35MHz), Autek VA2 (which also measures impedance) and the Autek RF5 (35–530MHz) RF antenna analysers are available from: Eastern Communications, Cavendish House, Happisburgh, Norfolk, NR12 0RU. Tel: 01692 650077.

ANTENNAS, ANTENNA MATERIALS AND TUNERS

A comprehensive range of coaxial cable, 300 and 450Ω balanced twin feed-ers, antenna wire, insulators, dipole centre boxes and coaxial plugs, sockets and adapters are obtainable from: W H Westlake, West Park, Clawton, Holdsworthy, Devon, EX22 6QN. Tel: 01409 253758.

The Texas Bugcatcher HF mobile antenna, described in Chapter 3, and the MFJ VersaTuner V, described in Chapter 4, are available from: Waters and Stanton, 22 Main Road, Hockley, Essex, SS5 4QS. Tel: 01702 206835.

A selection of VHF/UHF antennas, and antenna mounting hardware (see Chapter 8) are available from Waters and Stanton (address above) and: Moonraker (UK) Ltd, Unit 12, Cranfield Road, Woburn Sands, Bucks, MK17 8UR. Tel: 01908 281705.

A selection of VHF/UHF antennas, antenna wire and antenna mounting hardware are available from: Haydon Communications, Unit 1, Thorrock Commercial Park, Purfleet Industrial Eastate, London Road, Aveley, Essex, RM15 4YD. Tel: 01708 826524.

COMPONENTS
The following UK distributors supply various components, such as high-power variable capacitors, meters, switches and plugs.

Maplin MPS, PO Box 777, Raleigh, Essex, SS68LU. Tel: 01702 556001.

Nevada, 189 London Road, North End, Portsmouth, Hants, PO2 9AE. Tel: 01705 662145.

Circuit Distribution Ltd, Park Lane, Broxbourne, Herts, EN10 7NQ (produce a catalogue). Tel: 01992 441306.

A high-power variable capacitor kit, dummy load kit and HF-VHF SWR/RF wattmeter kit is available from: Waters and Stanton, 22 Main Road, Hockley, Essex, SS5 4QS. Tel: 01702 206835.

ANTENNA MASTS
Lightweight wall-mounting telescopic mast and free-standing masts: Tennamast Scotland Ltd, 81 Mains Road, Beith, Ayrshire, KA15 2HT. Tel: 01505 503824. Web: www.tennamast.com.

Heavier-duty lattice masts: Strumech Versatower, Portland House, Coppice Side, Brownhills, Walsall, West Midlands, WS8 7EX. Tel: 01543 452321.

IONOSPHERIC PROPAGATION INFORMATION
The Sunspot Index Data Centre in Brussels now prepares the numbers from information supplied by a number of observatories. They appear in DX propagation information available from a wide variety of sources, including the RSGB.

The GB2RS weekly news broadcasts give details of the solar flux, A and K indices described in Chapter 1. These broadcasts are made on a variety of frequencies on a Sunday, details of which can be found in the *RSGB Yearbook*. This propagation information is also available on website http://www.rsgb.org. More immediate daily information can be found on http://dx.qsl.net.propagation.

Index

MORE BOOKS FROM THE RSGB

HF Antenna Collection

Edited by Erwin David, G4LQI

An invaluable collection of the outstanding articles and short pieces that were published in the Radcom magazine during the period 1968-89. Includes ingenious designs for single element, beam and miniature antennas, as well providing comprehensive information about feeders, tuners, baluns, testing, modelling, and how to erect your antenna safely.

1st Edn, 1992, RSGB, paperback, 184 by 245 mm, 233 pages, ISBN: 1-872309-08-9.

Price: £9.99

The Antenna File - NEW

The Radio Society of Great Britain produces some of the best works on antennas and this is a collection of that work from the last ten years. This book contains 288 pages of articles drawn from the Radcom magazine and includes: · 50 HF antennas, 14 VHF/UHF/SHF antennas, 3 receiving antennas, · 6 articles on masts and supports, · 9 articles on tuning and measuring. · 4 on antenna construction. · 5 on design and theory · And 9 Peter Hart antenna reviews. · Every band from 73kHz to 2.3GHz · Beams, wire antennas, verticals, loops, mobile whips and the G2AJV Toroid. In fact everything you need to know about antennas and how to get the best out of them.

1st Edn, 2001, RSGB, paperback, 297 by 210 mm, 288 pages, ISBN: 1-872309-72-0.

Price: £18.99

HF Antennas for all Locations

By Les Moxon, G6XN

This is a thought-provoking book, which has been a major contribution to the state of the art from an acknowledged expert. It explains the 'why' as well as the 'how' of HF antennas, and takes a critical look at existing designs in the light of the latest developments. This second edition has been completely revised and greatly expanded. There are more novel antenna designs, including beams which cover more bands with fewer problems, no trap losses and better rejection of interference. A new chapter presents a comprehensive review of ways to make antennas smaller, with particular emphasis on small transmitting loops. An essential reference for the experimenter and enthusiast.

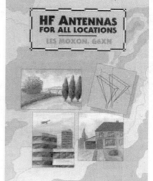

2nd Edn, 1993, RSGB, paperback, 187 by 245 mm, 322 pages, ISBN: 1-872309-15-1.

Price: £7.99

www.rsgb.org/shop Tel: 0870 904 7373

RSGB ORDER FORM

ORDERED BY

ORDER NO.   DATE

DELIVER TO

Code	Description	Price	Qty	Total
1-872309-54-2	Backyard Antennas	£18.99		
1-872309-08-9	HF Antenna Collection	£9.99		
1-872309-72-0	The Antenna File NEW	£18.99		
1-872309-15-1	HF Antennas for all Locations	£7.99		
1-872309-11-9	Practical Antennas for Novices	£7.99		
1-872309-36-4	The Antenna Experimenter's Guide	£17.99		
1-872309-74-7	RSGB Yearbook 2002 NEW (available Sept)	£15.99		
1-872309-53-8	Radio Communication Handbook	£29.99		
1-872309-65-8	Low Frequency Experimenter's Handbook NEW	£18.99		
1-872309-40-2	PMR Conversion Handbook	£16.99		
1-872309-30-5.	Radio Data Reference Book	£14.99		
1-872309-35-6	Practical Receivers for Beginners	£14.99		
1-872309-21-6	Practical Transmitters for Novices	£16.99		
1-872309-23-2	Test Equipment for the Radio Amateur	£12.99		
1-872309-61-3	Technical Topics Scrapbook 1995-99	£14.99		
1-872309-51-8	Technical Topics Scrapbook 1990-94	£13.99		
1-872309-20-8	Technical Topics Scrapbook 1985-89	£9.99		
1-872309-71-2	The RSGB Technical Compendium NEW	£17.99		
0-705652-1-44	Radio & Electronics Cookbook NEW	£16.99		
1-872309-73-9	Low Power Scrapbook NEW	£12.99		
1-872309-00-3	G-QRP Circuit Handbook	£9.99		
0-900612-89-4	Microwave Handbook **Volume 1**	£11.99		
1-872309-01-1	Microwave Handbook **Volume 2**	£18.99		
1-872309-12-7	Microwave Handbook **Volume 3**	£18.99		
1-872309-48-8	The RSGB Guide to EMC	£19.99		
1-872309-58-5	Guide to VHF/UHF Amateur Radio NEW	£8.99		
1-872309-42-9	The VHF/UHF Handbook	£19.99		
1-872309-63-1	Amateur Radio Operating Manual NEW	£24.99		
N/A	Prefix Guide (fifth edition, 1999)	£8.99		
1-872309-43-7	Your First Amateur Station	£7.99		
1-872309-62-3	The RSGB IOTA Directory	£ 9.99		
1-872309-31-3	Packet Radio Primer	£9.99		
1-872309-38-0	Your First Packet Station	£7.99		
1-872309-49-6	Your Guide to Propagation	£9.99		
1-872309-60-7	Radio Today – Ultimate Scanning Guide	£19.99		
1-872309-27-5	Novice Licence - Student's Notebook	£4.99		
1-872309-28-3	Novice Licence - Manual For Instructors	£9.99		
1-872309-45-3	Radio Amateur's Examination Manual	£14.99		
1-872309-18-6	RAE Revision Notes	£5.00		
1-872309-19-4	Revision Questions for the Novice RAE	£5.99		
1-872309-26-7	Morse Code for Radio Amateurs	£4.99		
1-872309-50-0	Amateur Radio ~ the first 100 years	£49.99		
0-900612-09-6	World at Their Fingertips	£9.99		
Post & Packing		P&P		
UK only - £1.50 for 1 item £2.95 for 2 or more items		Discount		
Rest of World - £2.00 for 1 item 4.00 for 2 & £0.50 for each extra item		Total		

RSGB, Lambda House, Cranborne Road, Potters Bar, Herts EN6 3JE UK
Tel: 0870 904 7373 Fax: 0870 904 7374 E-mail sales@rsgb.org.uk